MICROECONOMICS

Microeconomics:
Concepts and Applications

J. HOLTON WILSON
Central Michigan University

HARPER & ROW, PUBLISHERS, New York
Cambridge, Hagerstown, Philadelphia, San Francisco,
London, Mexico City, São Paulo, Sydney

1817

Sponsoring Editor: John Greenman
Project Editors: Céline Keating/Jon Dash
Designer: Michel Craig
Production Manager: Willie Lane
Compositor: Bi-Comp, Incorporated
Printer and Binder: Halliday Lithograph Corporation
Art Studio: Vantage Art Inc.

Microeconomics:
Concepts and Applications

Library of Congress Cataloging in Publication Data

Wilson, J   Holton, 1942–
    Microeconomics—concepts and applications.

    Includes bibliographies and index.
    1. Microeconomics. I. Title.
HB172.W59   338.5   80-26517
ISBN 0-912-21213-6

To Beth

CONTENTS

PREFACE

This text is intended for use in the undergraduate intermediate microeconomics course, although I have used various drafts of this material in helping master's degree students in business administration and urban studies gain an appreciation for the usefulness of microeconomic reasoning. The text is written for students. The style and level is purposely less formal than many other intermediate microeconomics texts. The prerequisites for a successful learning experience using this text are few. Students will find it advantageous to have had an introductory economics course and some basic facility with algebraic and graphic relationships. No complex algebra or calculus is necessary.

The major objective of the text is to provide students with a solid foundation in microeconomic theory without using much mathematics or getting unnecessarily involved with many of the sophisticated subtleties of economic theory. My experience in teaching the course suggests that a concise and clear approach to the material is more beneficial at this level than attempting to transmit an overdose of microeconomic theory to students who often are not even economics majors. This text will help students learn the basics of microeconomics as well as to see how these concepts can be applied in meaningful ways.

ORGANIZATION

The text is divided into two parts. The first contains fourteen chapters that present the core of microeconomic theory. These chapters emphasize the development of the logic and methods that form the backbone of microeconomics, but they also include numerous examples of how these concepts relate to contemporary economic problems. To this extent, the degree of "applications" in this text is similar to other leading texts in the field.

However, in Part II of the text, extended applications of microeconomic theory to four topic areas provide students with an opportunity to see how a variety of microeconomic concepts can be brought to bear on particular issues. These topics include entire chapters on agriculture, tax policy and society, economics and the environment, and inflation and unemployment. Some professors will wish to have students read relevant sections from these final four chapters during their study of Chapters 1 through 14. Others will wait and cover these chapters at the end of the course. The author's preference is a mix of these alternatives: to assign some sections of Chapters 15 through 18 during the early part of the course, but to study the chapters in their entirety at the end of the term. For example, the following sections from Chapter 15 ("Agriculture") can be used with appropriate sections of the earlier chapters, as indicated.

FROM "AGRICULTURE," CHAPTER 15	ASSIGNED WITH
Market demand	Chapter 4 and/or Chapter 5
Production and cost	Chapter 7 and/or Chapter 8
Market structure	Chapter 9
Price fluctuations	Chapter 9
Agricultural policy	Chapter 2 and/or Chapter 5

Chapter 16 ("Tax Policy and Society") can be integrated with earlier study in a similar manner.

FROM "TAX POLICY AND SOCIETY," CHAPTER 16	ASSIGNED WITH
Principles of tax analysis	Chapter 1 and/or Chapter 2
The personal income tax	Chapter 4 and/or Chapter 13
Sales and excise taxes	Chapter 4 and/or Chapter 6
Corporate taxes	Chapter 7
Government expenditures	Chapter 2 and/or Chapter 6

While similar integration of material from Chapters 17 and 18 is also possible, my preference is to treat those as separate, self-contained, units. The topics discussed in all four of these final chapters can provide a focal point for class discussion and can be fruitfully used as a basis for student papers and/or group presentations.

ACKNOWLEDGMENTS

Many individuals have contributed to the evolution of this text. The students who provided constructive evaluation of various class handouts and of the pedagogical aspects of my intermediate microeconomics courses for more than a decade are too numerous to single out. Their contributions to the development of this text, however, cannot be overstated. Discussions with faculty colleagues at the four institutions where I have taught microeconomics have provided insights and examples which have, without doubt, enhanced the effectiveness of my approach to the microeconomics course. Professor Bernie Bowlen deserves special mention in this respect, as well as for his encouragement and support during much of the writing process.

Three reviewers provided extensive and very helpful comments on various portions of the manuscript. They are: Ann Fisher, Timothy P. Roth, and A. Ross Shepherd. Their attention to content, organization, and style has improved the text significantly. Professor Steve Shwiff has prepared an excellent instructor's manual, which includes complete answers to all of the chapter-end questions, as an accompaniment to the text.

I have been fortunate to have had the talents of Annette Cook and Bobbie Smith in transforming my thoughts and scrawlings into a cohesive manuscript which they typed, in various phases, with skill and patience. Virginia Gilmore, once more, provided outstanding research and editorial support, for which I am grateful. Despite the efforts of all these persons, I must accept responsibility for those errors of omission or commission that may remain.

J. Holton Wilson

PART 1
MICROECONOMIC CONCEPTS

CHAPTER 1
THE ROLE AND METHOD
OF MICROECONOMICS

WHAT IS MICROECONOMICS?

Before addressing this question directly, let us define economics in its broadest sense. There may be nearly as many specific definitions of economics as there are economics instructors. One definition having fairly universal acceptance is that economics is the branch of the social sciences that is concerned with the manner by which individuals in society choose to allocate relatively scarce resources among alternative uses in order to provide satisfaction to members of the society. Several important concepts are contained in this definition.

First we identify economics as a social science. Economics is an academic discipline that uses the objectivity of the "scientific method" to analyze a certain class of problems that are important to the human society. We can summarize the essence of the scientific method or approach to problem solving as follows:

1. Define or identify the problems or phenomena to be investigated in an explicit manner.
2. Hypothesize possible relationships between the most important factors relating to the phenomena.
3. From the tentative relationships hypothesized, establish predictions or conclusions about the phenomena using deductive reasoning.

3

4. Test the predictions based on the hypothesized relationships against actual observations of the phenomena and, where necessary, go back to step 2 to improve the predictive ability by adopting new or different hypotheses about the relationships involved.

Exactly how scientific economic analysis is depends, to a large degree, on how closely one follows this general outline of the scientific method. To be sure, there are many important economic questions for which it is quite difficult to hypothesize a reasonable set of relationships and make logical deductions from them to predict behavior. In these cases, economics may be more an art than a science. However, as more detailed socio-economic measures are being developed and made available, and as more sophisticated equipment becomes available to store, sort, and analyze this information, we become more capable of applying a scientific approach to a wider range of economic problems.

Our definition of economics contains the idea that resources are relatively scarce. By this we mean that they are scarce relative to our potential to use them to satisfy human needs and desires. For years students in primary and secondary schools were taught that many nations were blessed with an abundance of natural resources without much (if any) attention being directed to the other side of the coin: the fact that growing populations and expectations were placing rapidly increasing demands on those resources. Today we accept as a fact of life that most resources are available in relatively scarce supply. Perhaps nothing has been more dramatic in focusing public attention on this issue than the OPEC nations' oil embargo of the early 1970s.

Even if all of our resources were not scarce there would still be the economic problem of allocating those resources that are scarce among alternative and competing uses. The method of allocation depends largely on the type of economic system. In a totalitarian society, allocation may be achieved by the dictates of the ruling government body. In a more democratic society, the market economy, or price system, provides the primary structure through which resources are allocated. Most Western economies have some form of mixed capitalistic market system in which some resources are allocated through a private sector using the price system, while other resources are allocated through the public sector via the political process.

It has become traditional to divide the study of economics into two broad categories: macroeconomics and microeconomics. Macroeconomics is that branch of economics that addresses problems from the perspective of the entire national economy with particular emphasis on the determinants of the aggregate level of employment, the general or average level of prices, and the rate of economic growth for the entire economy. Microeconomics is more concerned with the allocation aspects of our definition of economics and the behavior of individual economic units.

In microeconomics we shall seek to develop a framework that helps us to draw conclusions about, and predict, how individual economic units behave given particular circumstances and objectives. We shall do so by building a set of models that provide insight into a wide spectrum of economic problems.

WHEN IS MICROECONOMIC ANALYSIS USEFUL?

As our world society becomes increasingly crowded and complex, economic problems come to be the focal point of attention with greater frequency and intensity. These problems cover a wide array of situations not only from an international perspective but for each nation; each state, commonwealth, or province; each county, township, city, or village; each corporation, partnership, or proprietorship; each hospital, school, library, volunteer organization, or other "not-for-profit" organization; and, each social club, household, or individual. All have economic problems for which solutions must be found. Within each of these levels the range of different problems is substantial, but a great many can be clarified by using microeconomic theory.

Let us consider just a small sample of the economic problems that are of most direct concern to many of us and/or are the subject of considerable public attention as we move through the last quarter of the twentieth century. At the individual or household level we are faced with several economic problems. How should we allocate our limited money income among various forms of consumption? Should we go to a concert or a movie? How much money should we allocate for clothing and how much for recreation? How much insurance should we buy? Should we save and, if so, how much and in what form? We are also faced with economic decisions regarding where to live and work. The choice to attend college has important economic costs and benefits.

Business firms engaged in the production of cars, calculators, food products, steel, clothing, beer, and so forth, are also faced with many microeconomic problems. They must attempt to forecast potential sales at the various alternative prices at which they might sell their products. They must select the best combination of resources or methods of production to use in producing their output. They must decide on the location at which to establish production facilities and determine the most efficient means for distributing the product to consumers.

Although we often neglect the not-for-profit sector of the economy, it is an important part of our economic community, and the managers of these operations must make decisions that are similar to those for the more traditional business firms. Hospital administrators must make decisions on the amount and types of equipment to purchase or whether to lease some facilities, the number and types of employees to hire, and the need for expansion and the best way to obtain the necessary funds. Administrators of colleges and universities make decisions on student fees, the number of sections of various classes to offer, the salary to pay each member of the faculty, whether to run their own book store or have it run by an outside firm, and whether or not to have a summer session, among other economic problems.

In the public sector the importance of microeconomic analysis is becoming increasingly evident. More federal agencies are being asked to justify their existence and programs on the basis of whether the benefits generated by their activities are sufficient to justify the costs involved. Government agencies must decide whether it is better to provide poor families having inadequate housing with a housing subsidy, with government-built housing, or with greater income so that they can obtain better housing in the private sector. The federal government has the responsibility for establishing programs to maintain price stability and a low level of unemployment. State governments are faced with the decision of whether it is better to raise revenue through a sales tax or by using an income tax. Local government must determine whether to provide water at a flat monthly rate or whether to use a metered water system. All these decisions, and many others, can be improved by using microeconomic analysis.

The examples given above barely scratch the surface of potential applications of microeconomic analysis. The decisions we have mentioned are in very different types of economic activity and are quite diverse in nature. Nevertheless, they all have certain common characteristics which bring them within the domain of microeconomics. They each involve the allocation of some limited resources to various alternative and competing uses, each of which would be desirable. Because of the relative scarcity of resources, however, obtaining more of one thing necessarily means having less of something else (unless there are unemployed or underemployed resources that can be mobilized for additional production).

Another commonality of each of the examples given above is that the objective of each decision is in some way tied to benefits that result from the decision. The benefit may be earnings for a business or individual, it may be increased crop yield for an agricultural service, and so on. The benefits resulting from some decision must be compared to the costs involved in the course of action implied by the decision. Although the identification and measurement of benefits and costs varies among the various problem areas, the comparison of them is an important aspect of microeconomic analysis.

MICROECONOMICS AND THE THREE
FUNDAMENTAL ECONOMIC QUESTIONS

In the process of allocating scarce resources among alternative uses, the economic system must answer the following three fundamental and interrelated questions:

1. *What* goods and services will be produced?
2. *How* should these be produced?
3. *For whom* should they be produced? Or, alternatively, *to whom* should the goods and services be distributed?

To a considerable degree the answers to these questions can be deduced from the essentials of microeconomic theory. Very briefly, the answers are (in order):

1. Those goods and services that will be produced are the ones that consumers are willing and able to purchase (and those intermediate goods that go into making the things consumers purchase).
2. These goods and services will be produced by using the production methods that enable producers to do so in as efficient a manner as possible relative to their own objective (some benefit to them).
3. The persons who ultimately obtain the goods and services are, for the most part, those people who are able to contribute in a meaningful way to the productive process.

We can expand on these simple and brief answers by referring to a diagram of the flow of resources, products, and money in our economy.

In the simple diagram of this flow illustrated in Figure 1.1, we see that consumers not only represent a market for the output of producers, but also provide the labor and other resources necessary for production. It is assumed that this diagram is representative of a market economy in which there is private ownership of all resources or factors or production. The way in which consumers are willing to allocate their dollars to various producers determines the composition of the upper loop representing the flow of goods and services. This answers the question of what will be produced. For example, since about 1970 consumers have allocated more and more dollars for the purchase of small electronic calculators, while spending fewer dollars on slide rules. The result has been a boom in the calculator industry but has greatly curtailed production of slide rules. Such microeconomic decisions of millions of individuals ultimately determines what goods and services are produced in the economy. Much of our early study in this course will involve hypothesizing

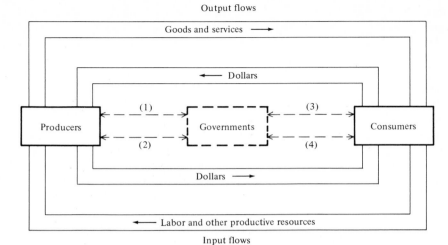

Figure 1.1 A Schematic Model of the Economy The flow of resources, products, and money in the economy can be represented using a schematic model such as this "circular flow" diagram. In order for the economy to continue to function smoothly, the flow into each sector must equal the flow out of that sector.

relationships that allow us to explain and predict how consumers will allocate their incomes among various goods and services. That is, we will develop an economic theory of consumer behavior.

Producers will determine the method of producing those products (that consumers will purchase) in such a manner as to achieve their own objective(s) as efficiently as possible. The producers will need to determine the best combination of various resources and types of labor that permits them to produce the desired level and type of output, given the existing state of technology and the cost of each input (resource). Thus the question of how goods and services will be produced is answered. After we have developed our economic model of consumer behavior, we shall turn our attention to hypothesizing the relationships that permit us to explain and predict how firms will allocate their expenditures among various resources for the purpose of producing goods and services. In doing so, we will develop an economic theory or model of production. Given this model of production, and the prices of resources, we can develop an understanding of how the cost of production varies as the level of output changes.

As we look at Figure 1.1, we see that there is a flow of money (income) to consumers in exchange for the resources, or factors of production,[1] those consumers provide. Persons that own relatively valuable re-sources (e.g., fertile farmland or land with rich mineral deposits) or have a labor skill that is highly valued by firms will obtain more dollars in exchange than less fortunate members of society. Thus, income is deter-mined by the amount of value of the resources persons have at their command. The amount of income individuals have, in turn, determines who can afford to purchase the goods and services available from the producing sector. We have now answered the question of for whom the output of the economy is produced. Once we have integrated our models of consumer and producer behavior, we will turn to the task of hypothesizing the relationships that will permit us to evaluate the re-turns to various factors of production.

Before leaving the discussion of Figure 1.1, let us consider the role of governments in the mixed capitalistic economy. There are four flows between government and producers or consumers identified in Figure 1.1, each of which has two dimensions. The flow labeled 1 represents the flow of goods and services from producing firms to the government. For example, the Keener Rubber Company of Alliance, Ohio, sells rubber bands to various government agencies, and General Motors sells cars and trucks to governmental organizations. The other dimension of this flow (number 1) is the money paid to the producing firm by the government. The second flow (labeled 2) represents services provided to the business community by various levels of government. These include the devel-opment and enforcement of a legal structure, the provision of highways, and other goods or services provided by the government that makes the smooth operation of the private sector possible. The opposite dimension of this flow is the payment of revenue by firms to governments in the form of taxes and various user charges such as license fees or highway tolls.

There are also important flows between consumers and the govern-ment. The flow labeled 3 in Figure 1.1 represents the labor and other resources that the private sector provides for the production of goods and services in the public or government sector. For example, in 1977 govern-ments (federal, state, and local) employed almost 16 million people. That represented about 16 percent of the total labor force including armed forces. The two largest categories of government employment in 1977 were education (6.5 million) and health and hospital employees (1.6 mil-lion). Other categories of employment include national defense, police

---

[1] Economists have historically classified factors of production as land, labor, capital, and entrepreneurship (risk taking and innovation). Each of these is composed of a large hetero-geneous mix of subcategories. For our purpose it is sufficient to consider this part of the flow simply as labor and other resources as long as we recognize the vastness and diversity of things that are included therein.

and fire protection, highways, natural resources, and so on.[2] The opposite direction of flow 3 is the payment to the private sector for the use of privately owned resources and labor.

Flow 4 represents the goods and services produced in the public sector that are used by the consuming sector of the economy. Examples are abundant and can, at least in part, be determined from the categories of employment given above. They include such things as education, health care, libraries, parks, and so forth. The reverse direction of flow 4 includes the various taxes we pay to governments, user charges such as tolls, fees for education at a state university, and other payments we make to federal, state, and local governments. In the chapters in the last section of this text we shall investigate applications of microeconomic theory to the analysis of these four flows between the government and private sectors of the economy.

MODELS IN MICROECONOMICS

In microeconomic studies various phenomena are investigated by using "models." A model is a representation of some real-world situation that incorporates only the most essential features or relationships necessary to explain or predict behavior. A model may be physical such as the double helix models of DNA molecules that are frequently used in biology courses to help explain the behavior of these important building blocks of life. A model may be schematic such as the simple model of the flows in the economy presented in Figure 1.1. Clearly, this model does not attempt to show all of the interactions between the producing, consuming, and government sectors in the economy. It does, however, capture essential relationships that simplify the reality of our complex economy in a meaningful way.

Models may also be expressed in algebraic or graphic forms. For example, in introductory economics the relationship between personal consumption expenditures and national income is usually depicted as a graphic model such as in Figure 1.2. In that figure we see that as national income increases (moving to the right on the horizontal axis), personal consumption expenditures also increase (as measured on the vertical axis). This graphic model shows the relationship between personal consumption expenditures C and national income Y. If we know that income is at some level, say Y^*, we can predict that consumption will be C^*. Certainly factors other than income affect consumption, but what this

---

[2] These data and further details can be found in the *Statistical Abstract of the United States,* published by the Bureau of the Census, or in *Facts and Figures on Government Finance,* published by the Tax Foundation, each year.

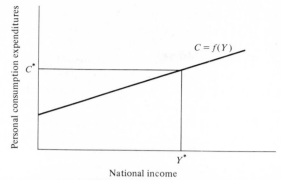

Figure 1.2 A Graphic Model of Consumption Expenditures This graphic model of personal consumption expenditures shows those expenditures to be a linear function of income. For any given level of income, we can determine the corresponding level of consumption from the graph. Thus, at income level Y^* consumption would be C^*.

model does is simplify the problem to allow us to examine only the most important determinant of consumption.

An algebraic model that most high school students learn (and soon forget) is the law of gravity, which expresses the distance d an object will fall in a given period of time t due to the force of gravity g. The model is:

$$d = \tfrac{1}{2} gt^2$$

Again, although this model does not include all variables that may influence the distance an object will fall, the essential factors are included; thus the model has been found to provide an excellent basis for prediction. The graphic model of personal consumption expenditures given in Figure 1.2 may also be expressed as an algebraic model in the form:

$$C = a + bY$$

where a is the intercept on the vertical axis and b is the slope of the function. The value of b tells us the rate at which consumption changes as income changes.

In constructing a model it is necessary to make assumptions about the relationships among many factors influencing the phenomena we wish to study. A frequent complaint by students is that the assumptions made in economic models do not approximate reality with sufficient precision. If we keep in mind that a model is an abstraction and simplification of reality that allows us to focus on only the most important factors necessary to explain or predict behavior, the reality of the assumptions becomes much less important. For example, we may assume that managers of business firms try to maximize profits. Whether or not they do so is not as important as whether the models based on this assumption allow us to predict how business managers behave in economic affairs.

The validity and usefulness of models depends upon their ability to produce sufficiently accurate predictions. A model is useful to the extent that it leads us to make predictions that are better than we could make using some other model.[3] It does not matter whether the subjects of our models understand the model or make any explicit attempt to follow the model as long as the model is useful for explaining their behavior and for predicting the consequences of certain events. Milton Friedman has made the observation that the mathematical models of physics could be used to determine the best way of executing a given billiards shot. Thus, using these models, one could predict the shots of an expert billiard player.[4] It is likely that most billiard players do not know much about these physical models, much less perform the calculations implied by the models before completing each shot. However, they perform *as if* they were following those models or else they would not, in fact, be expert billiard players.

SUMMARY

Economics is the branch of the social sciences that is concerned with the manner in which society's scarce resources are allocated among alternative uses to provide benefits to members of the society. Within this discipline, microeconomics is a subset that focuses specifically on the allocation problems in our society and on explaining how individual economic units interact to determine that allocation.

Applications of microeconomics can be found in many diverse segments of economic activity. The principles developed in this course are applicable to the firm's problem of determining the method of combining resources in the most efficient manner to produce their product as well as to individual consumer decisions on how to allocate limited income to the purchase of various goods and services. In addition to these traditional applications, microeconomic reasoning is applicable to the decisions that must be made by managers in not-for-profit organizations, such as schools or hospitals, and to decisions in the public sector at federal, state, and local levels.

Every economic society must answer three fundamental questions: What should be produced? How should it be produced? To whom should

[3] Even those people who claim to object most strenuously to the use of models use some form of model. They fail to formalize the model, and make "judgments" based on their own experience; but implicit in their judgments is some basic model with unspecified but existent assumptions.

[4] Milton Friedman, "The Methodology of Positive Economics," in *Essays in Positive Economics* (Chicago: University of Chicago Press, 1953).

the products be distributed? The answers to each of these questions can be deduced, at least in part, from the concepts developed in microeconomics. A microeconomic analysis of the circular flow of economic activity in the society helps to clarify answers to these questions by focusing on relationships between consumers, producers, and various levels of government.

The schematic representation of the economy in a circular flow diagram is one type of economic model. Other models may be physical, graphic, or mathematical. Throughout this text our emphasis will be on graphic and algebraic economic models. Models are, by definition, abstractions from reality. They provide a means by which very complex and interdependent economic phenomena can be studied without having to deal with the vast array of variables that may have some influence on the phenomena. Only those factors that are of primary importance are included in the economic models we will employ.

The usefulness of our economic models should be judged by their ability to help us predict or explain complex phenomena rather than on the exactness with which the assumptions of the model reflect reality. Even if individuals that make economic decisions do not themselves know or follow the models, the models are useful if they contribute to our ability to explain behavior patterns.

Selected Readings

Cohen, Kalman J., and Richard M. Cyert. "The Methodology of Model Building." In *The Theory of the Firm: Resource Allocation in a Market Economy.* Englewood Cliffs, N.J.: Prentice-Hall, 1965, chap. 2.

Friedman, Milton. "The Methodology of Positive Economics." In *Essays in Positive Economics.* Chicago: The University of Chicago Press, 1953.

Iwand, Thomas, and Henry Thomassen. "The Firm in the Industrial State." *Nebraska Journal of Economics and Business* (Autumn 1972), 135–144.

Koch, James V. "On 'A Critique of Positive Economics.'" *American Journal of Economics and Sociology* 31 (July 1972), 327–332.

Machlup, Fritz. "Theories of the Firm: Marginalist, Behavioral, Mangerial." *American Economic Review* (March 1976), 1–33.

QUESTIONS

1. Write a short explanation of the following terms or concepts that were used in this chapter:
   (a) circular flow of economic activity
   (b) microeconomics
   (c) models
   (d) resource scarcity
   (e) scientific method
   (f) what, how, and for whom (in allocating scarce resources)

2. Identify and explain how scarcity may relate to each of the following situations:
   (a) Increasing cost of gasoline and diesel fuel
   (b) The changing price of residential single-family dwellings
   (c) Determination of the number and types of courses to be offered at your university during the normal academic year as well as during the summer session
   (d) Your ability as a student to accomplish all your academic, employment, and social goals
3. Explain what we mean by a model. Why are models so useful in the physical, social, and behavioral sciences?
4. Consider courses you have studied outside of economics and explain examples of models that have been used in those courses. Try to include some that are simply descriptive, some that are graphical, some that are physical, and some that are mathematical.
5. For two of the models you identified in Question 4 explain how you would evaluate the usefulness and adequacy of each model.
6. Briefly explain some economic problems that relate to each of the following: individuals, households, durable goods manufacturers, fast-food restaurants, nursing homes, a public transit authority, the department of tourism in your state, and the United States Air Force.

CHAPTER 2
THE MARKET ECONOMY

AN OVERVIEW

In our discussion of the circular flow model of the economy we assumed that the system represented a "market economy in which there is private ownership of all resources." Actually, the system that we are primarily concerned with can more appropriately be called a "mixed-market economy." It is not a centrally planned economic system directed by a supreme economic czar of sorts, nor is it void of governmental influence and control. Most economic decisions are made by individuals acting in their own self-interest, but the role of government is strong and becoming more dominant over time.

FREE ENTERPRISE AND PERSONAL FREEDOM

The economies of most Western nations are based on the principle that individuals have the right to engage in the occupation of their choice and to use the rewards of their enterprise to obtain whatever benefits they find personally most satisfying. There are restrictions imposed on our range of choices both in employment and in consumption. These restric-

15

tions are not always consistent within any one country, much less between the countries that can be characterized as having a mixed-market economy.

Until 1978 people could not legally employ their productive resources to set up a gambling casino in Atlantic City but could do so in Las Vegas. In view of the commercial "success" of the relaxation of this restriction on economic freedom in Atlantic City, one might predict that more opportunities for this type of employment will become available.

On the consumption side we are, at present, not permitted to consume certain substances such as marijuana, heroin, or "angel dust" (at least not legally). There was a relatively brief period of time when we were restricted from the legal consumption of alcoholic beverages. Less complete restrictions exist on a fairly broad scale that limit how we can allocate our earnings for personal consumption benefits. For example, an individual may not be permitted to hunt a moose in Montana in a given big game season because the number of moose permits is limited and the hunter failed to have the good fortune of getting a permit in the draw.

Although these kinds of restrictions on employment and consumption exist, they really do not limit our personal economic freedoms by very much. The array of things that we can spend our income for is seemingly infinite (but countable, I suppose). And so too with employment opportunities. At any point in time we have some unemployment problem, but yet for the vast majority of people there exists a plethora of alternative occupations available to us. I could quit my job as a university professor to become an auto mechanic or a dentist. In my case, both would imply further training to develop the appropriate skills. Nevertheless, the opportunity is there. We are free not only to select the type of job we want but to choose the location as well, subject to job availabilities.

What constitutes acceptable employment and/or consumption is a fluid concept, ever changing as societal norms take different forms and become institutionalized within the legal framework of society. Acceptable economic behavior is defined within the context of the needs and mores of society at any time.

All of the participants in the sphere of economic affairs are driven by their own self-interest when the system is characterized by economic freedom. As individuals, we seek to maximize our personal satisfaction. This does not mean that we are necessarily selfish. Maximization of personal satisfaction does not rule out charitable behavior. It simply means that we must derive pleasure or satisfaction from such behavior or we would not voluntarily do those things.

PRIVATE AND PUBLIC GOODS

In this text the terms *goods*, *products*, and *commodities* are used interchangeably to mean anything that is wanted by someone. This is a very broad definition and includes both physical items and the class of things we frequently refer to as services.

For something to be a good, it need not have universal appeal. Some goods are wanted by some people but are avoided carefully by others. Some people will pay to obtain a particular good, whereas others might not take the good at a zero price (except perhaps for resale or to trade for some other more desirable good). Cigars may represent a good example.

How goods are classified depends on the purpose of the analysis. The meaning of the term *good, product,* or *commodity* is usually clear from the context of discussion. In some cases it makes sense to talk about food as a good. For other purposes finer classifications may be necessary: such as cereal grains, oats, or packages of Quaker Oats. The determination of what constitutes a product or commodity is of major importance in many court cases involving antitrust.

One important distinction between broad classes of goods involves the distinction between private goods and public goods. Private goods are those for which the right of use and the right of exchange are assignable to particular individuals (or a group of individuals). For a good to be a private good the *exclusion principle* must hold. This principle states that for private goods persons can exert their property rights to exclude others from receiving benefits from the consumption of the product.

A public good, on the other hand, conveys benefits to all who choose to take advantage of the availability of the good. One person's consumption does not diminish the benefit others can receive and no one person can invoke the exclusion principle to obtain compensation from another for benefits from consuming the good or to prevent others from consumption entirely. National defense, public concerts, and the interstate highway system represent examples of public goods. Some of these, like a highway system, are "truly" public goods only up to the point of congestion of some type. Beyond such a point, one person's use can reduce the ability of others to consume the good.

The analysis of public goods differs in many respects from that of private goods. Our emphasis throughout this text will be on private goods, although the methodology developed can be readily adapted to the analysis of problems involving public goods.

THE MARKET SYSTEM

The economy is composed of a complex network or system of markets. The term *market* is a fairly nebulous abstraction that economists use to represent the contacts between buyers and sellers—or simply a collection of buyers and sellers. There need not be any geographic area implied by the term *market*. It is sufficient to consider a market as a mechanism or structure that facilitates exchange among various economic units (persons, households, businesses, governments, and nonprofit organizations).

Exchange could take place on the basis of barter, but in a complex economy the use of money allows the system to operate much more smoothly than would be possible otherwise. But the existence of money also complicates the economic system. In addition to commodity markets, we also have money markets. Just as there is some demand and supply for each type of commodity, there is a demand and supply for money and various monetary instruments, such as in the bond market.

In order to understand how markets function we must first become more than casually familiar with the concepts of supply and demand. These concepts are introduced and applied in some rudimentary ways in the remaining sections of this chapter. But to appreciate fully how the market system works (or when it fails to work) we must develop an extensive background understanding of demand, production, cost, and market structures. This will be the task of the rest of Part 1 of this text.

DEMAND

The demand for a product is defined as the quantities that consumers are willing and able to purchase at various prices. We will investigate the concept of demand thoroughly in Chapters 3 through 6, but for now we shall assume that there is generally an inverse relationship between price and quantity: the higher the price, the fewer the number of units sold in a given time period, and vice versa. This is called the "law of demand."

Demand may be represented with an equation, a schedule (table of prices and quantities), or a graph called a *demand curve*. A *demand schedule* is given in Table 2.1 and the corresponding demand curve is drawn in Figure 2.1. Each of these represents how the quantity purchased varies as price changes with other influences on demand held constant. These other determinants include income, tastes and prefer-

Table 2.1 A DEMAND SCHEDULE

PRICE (P)	QUANTITY (Q_D)
12	10
11	20
10	30
9	40
8	50
7	60
6	70
5	80
4	90
3	100
2	110
1	120

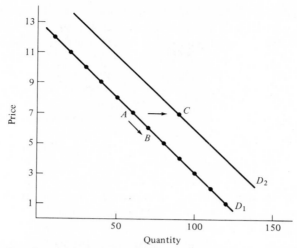

Figure 2.1 Graphic Representation of Demand Demand curve (D_1) for the price/quantity data given by the demand schedule in Table 2.1. Each dot along the demand curve D_1 corresponds to one of the 12 observations in the demand schedule. A second demand curve, D_2, represents an increase in demand.

ences, other prices, consumer expectations, and the size of the population.

Movement from one point to another in a given demand schedule, or along a given demand curve, is called a *change in quantity demanded*. A change in quantity demanded is caused by just one thing: a change in the price of the product. Movement from A to B in Figure 2.1 represents such a change in quantity demanded. As price declines from $7 to $6, consumers increase the quantity they demand from 60 to 70 units. This can also be seen from the corresponding points in Table 2.1.

The increase in quantity demanded may be due to two effects: a substitution effect and an income effect. The former results because this product is now relatively less expensive than others and may be substituted for other goods. For example, a decline in the price of beef may encourage consumers to substitute beef for chicken. The income effect results because as the price of anything we purchase declines our real income or purchasing power increases. For most goods more will be purchased at higher levels of real income than at lower levels.

If the other determinants of consumer demand change, the entire demand relationship may shift. For example, if incomes increase, more of most products would be purchased at each price. This is represented by an increase in demand to D_2 in Figure 2.1. Movement from D_1 to D_2 is a *change in demand* and may be caused by a change in any of the determinants of demand (other than the product's own price). At a constant product price of $7 the change in demand from D_1 to D_2 results in consumer purchases increasing from 60 to 90 units (from point A to point C).

The demand given in Table 2.1 and Figure 2.1 is the *market demand* for the product. That is, it represents the total amount purchased by all consumers at each possible price. As we shall see in Chapter 4, the market demand is simply the horizontal summation of the demand for all individual consumers.[1]

SUPPLY

Supply represents the quantities of a product that producers are willing and able to make available for sale at various prices. In general they will be willing and able to sell more at higher prices than at lower prices. Thus there is a positive relationship between price and quantity which is frequently called the "law of supply."

As with demand, we can represent supply with an equation, a schedule (or table), or a graph called a supply curve. A supply schedule is given in Table 2.2 and the corresponding supply curve is graphed in Figure 2.2. Note that the "law of supply" is evident in both: A decrease in price is associated with fewer units being offered for sale.

A given supply schedule or supply curve represents the way in which the quantity supplied changes as price changes. Such a change is

Table 2.2 A SUPPLY SCHEDULE

PRICE (P)	QUANTITY SUPPLIED (Q_S)
12	120
11	110
10	100
9	90
8	80
7	70
6	60
5	50
4	40
3	30
2	20
1	10

[1] Strictly speaking, market demand is the horizontal sum of individual demands only for private goods. For public goods the market demand is the vertical sum of individual demands. Since our emphasis throughout is on private goods, we shall always assume that the market demand is as defined here (as the horizontal sum) unless otherwise specified.

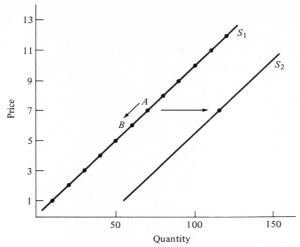

Figure 2.2 Graphic Representation of Supply Supply curve (S_1) for the price/quantity data given by the supply schedule in Table 2.2. Each dot along the supply curve S_1 corresponds to one of the 12 observations in the supply schedule. A second supply curve, S_2, represents an increase in supply.

illustrated by movement from point A to point B in Figure 2.2 (or the corresponding points in Table 2.2). At A, the price is $7 and 70 units are offered for sale. When price falls to $6 (point B), the quantity offered for sale drops to 60 units. The only thing that will cause a *change in quantity supplied* is a change in the price of the product.

In Figure 2.2 a second supply curve S_2 is drawn to illustrate an increase in supply. This is a change in supply that might be caused by a more sophisticated technology, more efficient production by labor, or a decrease in the cost of inputs. We see that, along S_2, 115 units would be offered for sale at a price of $7 rather than 70 units for the original supply, S_1.

The supply curves in Figure 2.2 are market supply curves representing the combined output of all firms at each price. A market supply curve is the horizontal sum of the supply curves for individual producers. As with the "law of demand," we are taking the "law of supply" as given here, since both are consistent with our common sense. The concepts underlying this principle are developed in Chapters 8 and 9.

MARKET EQUILIBRIUM

Since the quantity demanded is inversely related to price and the quantity supplied is directly related to price, it is likely (though not necessary) that there is some price at which the quantity demanded exactly equals the quantity supplied. This is called an *equilibrium price* because once it is established (for a given supply and demand) there is no tendency for natural economic forces to cause price to change from that level. The quantity associated with the equilibrium price is the *equilibrium quantity*.

The demand curve from Figure 2.1 and the supply from Figure 2.2 are reproduced in Figure 2.3 to illustrate the determination of the equilibrium price and quantity. We see that at a price of $6.5 the quantity that consumers are willing and able to purchase is 65 units, which exactly equals the quantity that producers are willing and able to offer for sale. This price-quantity configuration occurs at point *E*, the intersection of the supply and demand curves.

Suppose the price were above the equilibrium price for some reason, such as a price of $10. At that price consumers would purchase 30 units, but producers would see that relatively high price as incentive to produce 100 units. Thus there would be a surplus of the amount *AB* (i.e., 70 units), or the difference between the quantity supplied and the quantity demanded. When a surplus exists in a free market, natural economic

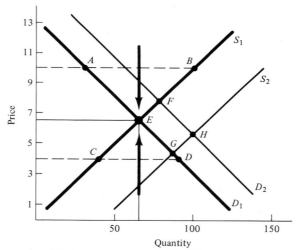

Figure 2.3 Determination of the Equilibrium Price and Quantity The determination of the equilibrium price ($6.50) and the equilibrium quantity (65) is at the intersection of the supply (*S₁*) and demand (*D₁*) curves. At any price above $6.50 (such as $10) a surplus exists (*AB* = 70 units) and natural economic forces will put downward pressure on price. At any price below $6.50 (such as $4) there is a shortage (*CD* = 50 units) and natural economic forces will put upward pressure on price. The equilibrium price is established at *E*, where the quantity demanded exactly equals the quantity supplied.

forces will exert downward pressure on price. Suppliers with growing inventories will cut back on production and offer the product at reduced prices. Although the market conditions are not entirely analogous, this type of phenomenon has been observed when automobile manufacturers have overproduced and accumulated inventories of excess cars. To help clear the market the companies offered rebates, which essentially represented a method of price reduction.

If price is below the equilibrium price a shortage exists because at that price the quantity consumers are willing and able to purchase exceeds the quantity suppliers will make available for sale. For example, consider a price of $4 in Figure 2.3. The quantity demanded is 90 units, whereas the quantity supplied is just 40 units. There is a shortage of CD (50 units) at that price. When such a shortage exists, price will tend to rise. Some consumers are more willing (and able) than others to pay a high price. Producers recognize this fact and adjust the price upward until the market clears (the quantity demanded equals the quantity supplied).

Now suppose that there is a shift in supply (to S_2) and/or in demand (to D_2). If the only change is to S_2, the new lower equilibrium price would be $4.25 (see point G) and there would be an increase in the quantity demanded. If supply remained constant (at S_1) but demand shifted to D_2, the equilibrium price would rise to about $7.80 (see point F) and thus stimulate an increase in the quantity supplied. If both demand and supply shift to D_2 and S_2, respectively, the new equilibrium price would be roughly $5.70 (see point H). Price would have fallen from the initial equilibrium ($6.50) because the increase in supply is relatively greater than the increase in demand. With an increase in both supply and demand, the equilibrium quantity will always increase, but equilibrium price may increase or decrease depending on the magnitude of the increases.

An ability to work with shifts in supply and/or demand in either direction can be a valuable aid in developing an understanding of many economic phenomena. The serious student will do well to practice drawing diagrams such as in Figure 2.3, with various types of changes in supply and/or demand, and analyzing the effect on the equilibrium price and quantity. Three applications of supply-and-demand analysis are discussed briefly in the following sections of this chapter. Other examples are developed in greater detail in subsequent chapters, especially in Part 2 of the text.

APPLICATION 1: PRICE SUPPORTS

From time to time various special-interest groups ask the government to intervene in the functioning of the market to establish a price above the normal equilibrium price. Such a price is called a "support price" or alternatively a "price floor" since it is the lowest level price to which price would be permitted to fall. Figure 2.4 can be used to analyze the effect of such a policy.

The particular context of the diagram is not material to the analysis but it is probably helpful to think in terms of a typical application. Two such cases are agricultural price supports and minimum wage legislation. In the former case quantity refers to output of an agricultural product such as wheat, while in the latter case quantity represents a level of employment.

In Figure 2.4 the free-market equilibrium is at point E, with price P_E and quantity Q_E. If the price floor is established at P_F ($P_F > P_E$), producers receive a higher price (or labor a higher wage) but fewer units of the product are purchased (less labor is employed). The quantity supplied (Q_S) at P_F exceeds the quantity demanded (Q_D) by the amount AB. This surplus creates an additional policy problem. If the situation involves wheat production, for example, the government must purchase this excess production at some (perhaps substantial) cost and must either store it or otherwise dispose of it (it has at times been dumped in the ocean). If the situation involves a minimum wage at P_F there is AB amount of unemployment created since Q_S persons would be willing and able to work while only Q_D would be hired. Some previously employed persons would even lose their jobs: ($Q_E - Q_D$) represents these people.

Whether the price floor is of any net advantage depends on a number of things. Farmers of workers as a group may receive more, less, or a

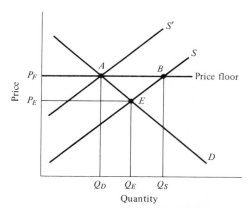

Figure 2.4 Effect of a Price Support Program   Diagram illustrating the effect of a price support program (establishing a price floor at P_F). The free-market equilibrium price and quantity are P_E and Q_E. At the support price P_F, the quantity supplied (Q_S) exceeds the quantity demanded (Q_D) by the amount AB. This surplus creates additional problems. Restriction of supply to S' is another alternative policy that results in establishing the same price (P_F).

constant amount of money depending on the elasticity of the demand function (elasticity is discussed in Chapter 5). In the agricultural setting it is clear that consumers pay more per unit and purchase fewer units. It is also clear that in the case of a minimum wage some workers are put out of work while others do obtain a higher wage.

One alternative to using a mandated price floor to get price up to P_F is to restrict supply to S'. The new equilibrium at point A yields the same general result but avoids the problem of the surplus AB. This may be done by acreage allotments or by stringent entrance requirements to be employed in a certain trade, depending on the context of the problem.

APPLICATION 2: EFFECT OF A SPECIFIC EXCISE TAX

A specific excise tax is a tax of a fixed dollar amount on each unit of a good that is sold (examples include taxes on cigarettes, liquor, gasoline, and tires). For purposes of discussion we will assume that an excise tax of $3 per unit is levied on the product represented by the supply and demand curves of Figure 2.5. The market equilibrium (without the tax) is at E, with the equilibrium price and quantity P_E and Q_E, respectively.

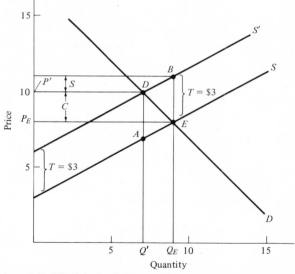

Figure 2.5 Effect of an Excise Tax   Illustration of the effect of imposing a $3 per unit specific excise tax (T) on a commodity. The effective supply curve shifts from S to S' since sellers now must obtain $3 more at each level of sales than prior to the tax. The equilibrium shifts from E to D, with the equilibrium price increasing from P_E to P' and the equilibrium quantity decreasing from Q_E to Q'. Given these demand and supply curves, the consumer pays $2 of the tax ($C$) while the seller absorbs the remaining $1 of the tax ($S$).

The supply curve S shows the quantities that sellers will make available for sale at various prices, or alternatively the price they must receive in order to be induced to make any given quantity available. For example, for suppliers to be induced to offer 7 units for sale the price must be $7 (see point A in Figure 2.5). Now with a $3 excise tax they must get $10 to offer 7 units for sale: $7 for the firm and $3 to pass on to the government for the tax (see point D).

Thus, the effect of the tax is to shift the supply curve to S', where S' lies above S by $3 at every point. At the original equilibrium, $P_E = \$8$ and $Q_E = 9$ units. Now with the tax, consumers will not purchase 9 units at the original price plus the tax ($11). A new equilibrium is formed at D, where consumers purchase 7 units at a consumer price of $10. As we have seen, $7 of that $10 goes to the seller and the remaining $3 to the government.

So who really pays the tax? The answer is that both the consumer and the producer share the tax burden, as long as neither the supply curve nor the demand curve is either perfectly horizontal or perfectly vertical. Exactly how the tax burden is split between the two parties depends on the exact nature of supply and demand. In the case illustrated in Figure 2.5, the consumer pays $2 ($C$) while the seller pays $1 ($S$).

We will be in a better position to more fully analyze the effect of such taxes after we have developed a more solid understanding of supply and demand concepts.

APPLICATION 3: REDUCING CONSUMPTION OF A PRODUCT

Suppose that the government would like to encourage consumers to use less of some product, such as electric energy. There are many types of policies that could be used to achieve such an end. Two of these, and their joint effect, are analyzed in Figure 2.6.

One policy that has been used is to discourage consumers from wasteful use of electric power (such as leaving lights on when it is not necessary for some function or for safety, or running dishwashers at less than full capacity, or using air conditioners to excess, and so on). By changing people's attitudes their demand curve may be shifted to the left (reduced) as depicted in Figure 2.6(a) by the shift from D to D'. With a constant supply function, consumption and price would both be reduced to Q' and P', respectively. Forming policies to successfully influence attitudes is not easy, however. Consider the difficulty in getting people to accept a 55-mph speed limit, for example.

One other alternative is to impose a specific excise tax on electric consumption. The effects of such a tax have been discussed in the preceding section, so we can simply summarize here by noting that consump-

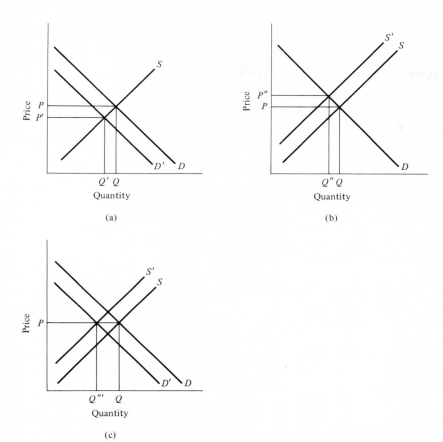

Figure 2.6 Policies to Reduce Consumption of a Good Three of the many possible ways to encourage reduced consumption of a good. (a) Consumer's attitudes are changed resulting in a lower demand, a lower price $(P' < P)$, and a reduced level of consumption $(Q' < Q)$. (b) A specific excise tax is imposed, shifting supply to S', raising price to P'' and reducing consumption to Q''. (c) Here both policies are adopted resulting in the largest reduction in consumption and, for the functions illustrated, no change in price. The effect on price in part (c) depends on the nature of the supply and demand functions: Price may either rise, fall, or remain constant.

tion would be reduced to Q'' while price would rise to P'', as illustrated in Figure 2.6(b).

It is entirely reasonable to expect more than a single policy measure to be brought to bear on any particular problem. In Figure 2.6(c) the combined effect of encouraging less use of electricity (shifting demand from D to D') and of imposing an excise tax (shifting supply from S to S')

is illustrated. As one would expect, the reduction in consumption (from Q to Q''') is greater than when either policy is used alone. In the case depicted here the net effect on price is zero (P remains constant). However, this result is not general. Price could either rise or fall depending on the nature of the demand and supply curves, the amount by which demand shifts, and the dollar value of the excise tax.

SUMMARY

The functioning of a free-market economy, or a mixed-market economy, is dependent on the existence of economic freedom (i.e., the freedom to use our resources for whatever productive end we desire and to use the returns from that employment to purchase goods and services so as to maximize our own satisfaction). The fact that self-interest is a driving force in the economy does not, however, imply selfishness. There is room for any type of charitable activity in the context of enhancing one's self-satisfaction.

The government does limit our economic freedoms to some extent, but only when the collective judgment of society deems it desirable to do so. This is a very fluid concept and what is prohibited today may be permissible tomorrow, and vice versa.

The existence of property rights and the ability to enforce the exclusion principle distinguishes private from public goods. A private good, such as a car, may be bought and sold through the market system and the owner can prohibit others from reaping benefit from its use. A public good, such as national defense, cannot be exchanged in the marketplace because there is no corresponding property right or ability to exclude others from the benefit derived from the product. (Public goods are discussed further in Chapter 16.)

The concept of a market in which goods and services are bought and sold is not geographically defined, but rather is an abstraction representing a set of conditions that facilitate exchange. In a free competitive market the forces of supply and demand determine the amount of goods exchanged and the price at which exchange takes place.

An understanding of supply and demand can be very useful in evaluating a wide variety of economic problems. Three of these (price supports, effect of an excise tax, and efforts to curtail consumption of a product) have been introduced in this chapter. A more complete analysis awaits our development of a deeper understanding of the economic forces at work in the marketplace.

Selected Readings

Bell, Frederick W. "The Pope and the Price of Fish." *American Economic Review* (December 1968), 1346–1350.

Brozen, Yale. "The Effect of Statutory Minimum Wage Increases on Teenage Unemployment." *Journal of Law and Economics* 12 (April 1969), 109–122.

Dahl, Dale C., and Jerome Hammond. *Market and Price Analysis.* New York: McGraw-Hill, 1976.

Friedman, Milton. *Capitalism and Freedom,* Chicago: University of Chicago Press, 1962.

Suits, Daniel B. "Agriculture." In Walter Adams, ed., *The Structure of American Industry,* 5th ed. New York: Macmillan, 1977, pp. 1–39.

QUESTIONS

1. Write a short explanation of the following terms or concepts that were used in this chapter:
   (a) demand
   (b) economic freedom
   (c) exclusion principle
   (d) free enterprise
   (e) market equilibrium
   (f) market system
   (g) private goods
   (h) public goods
   (i) supply

2. Give some examples of conflict between the desirability of a completely free-enterprise system with absolute economic freedom and social needs or goals. Explain some potential means of resolving these conflicts.

3. Distinguish between public and private goods and give some examples of each. Why is it important to consider such differences in types of goods?

4. Develop hypothetical, but reasonable, demand and supply schedules that combine to form an equilibrium price and quantity. Graph these schedules as demand and supply curves identifying the equilibrium. Use these curves to show a change in quantity demanded and a change in quantity supplied. Illustrate changes in demand and supply on the same graph.

5. Use the concepts of supply and demand to explain why the cost of a college education increased throughout the 1970s and yet the number of college students increased. Does this violate the idea that demand curves are generally expected to have a negative slope?

6. Think of two situations in which you might suggest establishing a price floor for a particular good or service and explain why such action might be desirable. Also, explain what market ramifications are likely to result.

7. Suppose that you would like to reduce the consumption of cigarettes among teenagers. Suggest several economic policies that might be used and explain their consequences.

8. Price fluctuations due to changes in demand and supply forces are fairly common in agricultural markets. Explain factors that might contribute to such price changes for beef, chicken, wheat, and soybeans. Use supply and demand graphs to illustrate your answer.

9. A "price ceiling" functions in the opposite direction of a "price floor." To be .effective such a ceiling price must be below the market equilibrium price. Illustrate this concept using a supply and demand graph. Identify a situation

in which you might advocate a price ceiling and carefully explain the market ramifications of such a policy.

10. Most college students have some employment objective in mind for when they graduate at the end of an undergraduate or graduate degree program. Identify the type of employment you plan to find and then list factors that will affect the demand for such people and factors that will affect their supply over the next five years.

CHAPTER 3
AN ECONOMIC THEORY
OF CONSUMER BEHAVIOR

It should be noted that the title to this chapter is "An Economic Theory of Consumer Behavior." There are sociological, psychological, and various hybrid theories of consumer behavior; however, our purpose is not to provide a comprehensive study on the subject. Rather it is the objective of this chapter to develop an understanding of the way in which economists analyze the behavior of consumers. In particular, we want to establish a method for determining the conditions that must be met for consumers to obtain the greatest possible benefit from their limited resources. In the process we will be able to formulate an equilibrium condition that will help us to predict the manner in which consumers will allocate their money income among alternative bundles of commodities.

THE REASON FOR CONSUMPTION

Although we are all consumers of a vast array of goods and services, we seldom give thought to the question of why we consume as we do. As a starting point, it is reasonable to assume that we consume in order to achieve some benefit or satisfaction. When we buy a hamburger and fries for lunch, we do so because of the benefit we expect from the purchase. When we make the decision to purchase a $200 ten-speed bike, we must

31

expect to obtain satisfaction from owning the bike or we would not buy it. And so it is with everything we consume.

As long as individuals are free to purchase (or not) according to their personal preferences, then it is logical to expect that they do so because of the satisfaction they expect to receive. No one is likely to have ever placed a gun at your head and forced you to make a purchase you would not have made otherwise.[1] We are, however, influenced in our consumption decisions in numerous ways, some of which may be construed as a reduction in personal freedom. For example, some would argue that we are so greatly influenced by massive promotional programs that we are not capable of making rational consumer decisions. It may be true that we are heavily influenced by advertising and other forms of promotion. However, we are also influenced by the opinions of members of our family, our peers, and other reference groups. All of these influences interact to determine the mind set that establishes the expected benefit from consumption. The origin of the influence is not the important issue.

The fundamental issue is that when we walk up to the counter and order a hamburger, fries, and a shake, we do so voluntarily, with the anticipation that the benefit we receive will in some sense be worth the cost. For example, suppose that I bought a CB radio and antenna for my car at a cost of $245. Implicitly, I must have reasoned that it was worth that amount of money to me or I would not have made the purchase. Obviously, it is hard to say what it means for something to be worth $245. However, if we look at this in the context of opportunity cost,[2] it is more meaningful. The purchase of the CB unit for $245 meant that I had to give up the consumption of $245 of other goods and services. Thus I must have believed that I would get more (or at least as much) satisfaction from the CB radio than from alternative potential purchases.

The difficulty involved in expressing the "worth" of things we consume brings us to an important aspect of the economic theory of consumer behavior. For the model we shall develop it is not necessary that we be able to actually measure the satisfaction one receives from consumption in a numerical way. In economics we usually use the term *utility* to indicate the want-satisfying characteristic of consumption and often refer to "utils" as a hypothetical measure of utility. But we have no

---

[1] In one sense, we are "forced" to purchase certain goods and services when we pay taxes. Taxes are generally nonvoluntary payments to a government that "purchases" such things as police protection, public libraries, national defense, highways, and so on. Conceptually, at least, we collectively determine how the tax money is used through the political marketplace rather than through economic markets. More will be said in this regard in later chapters.

[2] Economists define the opportunity cost of a decision as the value of the next most attractive alternative use of the economic resources allocated to the action resulting from that decision.

scale by which to measure the intensity of utility, or satisfaction, obtained from consumption. That is, we really cannot measure utility in a cardinal manner.

You can illustrate this for yourself by asking someone to tell you how much they enjoy their favorite beverage. They will not be able to give you a definite numeric answer, but will probably explain it in relative terms. That is, they may say that they like Coke better than Pepsi (or vice versa). It is this ability to rank or order alternatives that is important to the development of the economic model of consumer behavior. Our model will ultimately be dependent only on the concept of ordinal utility, or the ability of consumers to rank alternative bundles of commodities according to their respective want-satisfying power (utility).

Throughout our discussion of consumption, we will assume that consumers prefer more to less, *ceteris paribus* (i.e., all other things being the same). During the late 1960s and early 1970s it seemed fashionable for students to object to this assumption claiming that our society had turned the corner relative to the quest for the accumulation of the material things of life. They would often claim that all they wanted were the basic essentials of a simple life. Perhaps for a small segment of society this was, or still is, true. But for the vast majority of the people of the world, more is indeed preferred to less. Try offering people a choice between a five-dollar bill and a one-dollar bill as a gift with no strings attached. It is doubtful that you'll find anyone who takes the one rather than the five. In a similar vein, how many people do you know who would refuse a pay raise because there was nothing more they wanted to spend the money for anyway?

THE PRINCIPLE OF DIMINISHING MARGINAL UTILITY

Although our consumptive desires may be virtually unlimited in relation to the total of the goods and services available in the world, if we consider any one good there is likely to be some limit to the amount we would voluntarily consume during a given period of time. The reason for this relates to the principle of diminishing marginal utility. We have already defined utility as being roughly synonymous with satisfaction. The term *marginal* is used in economics to refer to the effect of a small change in one variable on some other. Marginal utility is then the additional utility that results from a small amount of additional consumption of some product. Thus, the *principle of diminishing marginal utility* means that as we consume additional units of some commodity (in a given time period), the added satisfaction that we receive from successive units becomes less and less.

The verbal description of this model can be translated into a graphic depiction rather simply. If you label the vertical axis of a graph *MU* (marginal utility) and the horizontal axis Q (quantity consumed), a line can be drawn in that space to represent the principle stated in the preceding paragraph. From that verbal statement we know that the second unit consumed provides less satisfaction than the first, the third unit less than the second, and so on. This tells us that the graphic relationship, or the graphic depiction of the marginal-utility function, will have a negative slope. Such a geometric model of the principle of diminishing marginal utility is represented in Figure 3.1.

At times I have used a simple experiment in class to illustrate this principle as well as some of the ideas discussed in the previous section. You could replicate this experiment with any group. First ask members of the group who among them likes chocolate candy. You'll almost certainly have several to many who respond positively. Then ask them to determine who likes chocolate the most. This illustrates the impossibility of making interpersonal comparisons of utility because they lack a common ground of measurement. Often they will resort to comparisons, as in our Coke versus Pepsi example. After it becomes clear that they cannot determine unequivocally who likes chocolate the most, select one of the more avid chocolate lovers to be the subject of the experiment.

Give that chocolate lover a Hershey Kiss (or other small chocolate candy), and after they have eaten it ask them how much they enjoyed it, or how much satisfaction they received from having consumed it. Once again, they will have difficulty giving a specific answer, but suggest that they pick an arbitrary index of measurement. For example, let 20 be the measure of satisfaction from the first chocolate consumed. That is, assign

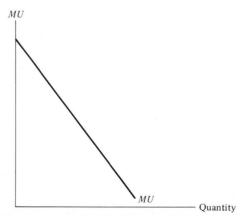

Figure 3.1 Diminishing Marginal Utility Marginal utility as a function of the quantity consumed. This illustrates the graphic model of the principle of diminishing marginal utility (it is possible that for some goods *MU* may at first increase but will decline after some rather small *Q*).

a hypothetical measure of the "utils" derived from that consumption. Now give them another piece of the candy and ask how much satisfaction they get from it relative to the first. Answers will vary but usually will be close to the original index: 19 is a common response. Then give them another candy and ask them to rate it on the same scale. Then give them a fourth, fifth, sixth, and so on, asking them to rate each in turn. The satisfaction rating tends to diminish at varying rates for different people, but has never failed to decline in my experiences.

You should try to think of other examples where the concept of diminishing marginal utility is very evident. The consumption of beer after some physical activity on a hot summer afternoon provides a good example for some people. The first beer may be very satisfying, but successive

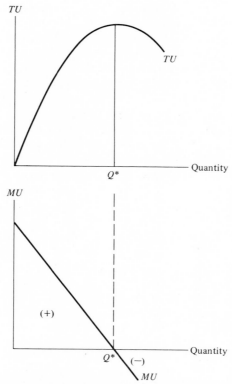

Figure 3.2 Relationship Between Total and Marginal Utility   Total-utility and marginal-utility functions showing that total utility increases where marginal utility is positive, reaches a maximum where marginal utility is zero, and decreases where marginal utility is negative. For some goods marginal utility may not become negative but approach zero, in which case total utility continues to increase but at a very slow rate.

beers typically yield less and less satisfaction. Shoes may be another good example. If you had no shoes, the satisfaction obtained from the first pair would provide considerable benefit (especially in a cold Montana winter). Additional pairs of shoes do provide us with satisfaction, but the increment to our total satisfaction diminishes.

This brings us to an important relationship. The fact that additional consumption of some commodity gives us diminishing marginal satisfaction means that our total satisfaction from consuming that good must be increasing at a decreasing rate. Thus, if we were to graph total utility (*TU*) as a function of the quantity of a good consumed (*Q*), the line would have a positive slope but the slope would become flatter as *Q* increases. Recall that slope represents the rate of change of a function, so the idea of *TU* having a decreasing slope is consistent with the idea of diminishing marginal utility since marginal utility is the change in total utility for a small change in quantity consumed. Figure 3.2 illustrates a typical total-utility function and the corresponding marginal-utility function.

We see that total utility increases even though the additional utility from increased units consumed (marginal utility) decreases in the range of consumption up to *Q**. That is, as long as marginal utility is positive, even if diminishing, total utility increases, but at a decreasing rate. At *Q**, where *MU* is zero, total utility reaches a maximum. Beyond *Q** the marginal utility is negative which means that the individual's total satisfaction would decrease as illustrated by the two graphs in Figure 3.2.[3]

Students frequently question the idea of negative marginal utility from consumption and the idea that increasing the consumption of a commodity may decrease total satisfaction. However, consider our earlier example of eating chocolate candies. At some point people's appetites for chocolate become saturated and they will not voluntarily eat more because they may become ill. With shoes, beyond some point additional pairs would surely become a nuisance. Most students have ob-

---

[3] Using the basic calculus, we can express this relationship in general form as follows: let $TU = f(Q)$, then $MU = dTU/dQ$. Since *TU* will be maximized where the first derivative equals zero, *TU* is a maximum where $MU = 0$. Consider a more specific case: let $TU = 100Q - Q^2$. Then $MU = dTU/dQ = 100 - 2Q$. Setting this equal to zero and solving, we have:

$$MU = 100 - 2Q = 0$$
$$2Q = 100$$
$$Q = 50$$

Thus, *TU* is a maximum at $Q = 50$ and at that point $TU = 2500$ (and, of course, $MU = 0$). You should try graphing these functions (*TU* and *MU*) in a manner similar to Figure 3.2 to illustrate the relationships further. You should also note that the derivative of *MU* is negative (-2), which illustrates the principle of diminishing marginal utility and verifies the conclusion that *TU* is a maximum at $Q = 50$.

served (or experienced) the consumption of alcoholic beverages beyond the point of positive increments to satisfaction. In general, it can be said that people will not choose to consume beyond a point such as Q^* in Figure 3.2 ceteris paribus. However, other things are not always equal and we occasionally witness such consumption. Peer group pressure may be one influence that will "force" a person to consume beyond Q^*, such as in the consumption of alcoholic beverages.

A UTILITY SURFACE

As we have noted earlier, the amount of satisfaction we obtain from one good is related in part to how much of other commodities we have. Confronted with a plate of homemade brownies, we might consume along one utility function, but if we also have a quart of milk, our satisfaction from each additional brownie may be considerably greater; that is, we would be on some other utility function. Similar relationships can be seen for most of the things that we consume. Thus, it is desirable for us to be able to develop a model of consumer behavior that incorporates more than one commodity.

In an algebraic treatment, we could state total utility as a function of any number of goods (X_1 to X_n):

$$TU = f(X_1, X_2, \ldots, X_n)$$

and proceed to analyze consumer behavior. However, such an approach necessitates the use of calculus and is usually so abstract that students find it difficult to grasp the most important conclusions because they become too enmeshed in following the mathematics. Therefore, our approach will be to develop the necessary concepts graphically in a manner that permits us to reach the same conclusions without much sacrifice in generality.

The use of graphic analysis limits us to three dimensions, which means that we will only be able to view utility as a function of two goods (one dimension for utility and the other two for commodities). However, the conclusions we will reach for the two-good case are the same as would be derived using mathematics for the n-good world in which we live.[4] To illustrate the way in which utility may vary for two commodities X and Y, we can construct a utility surface such as in Figure 3.3. In this diagram the amount of good X consumed is measured along the dimension $O\bar{X}$, increasing from zero units of X (at O) to all the X available to the

[4] For a good mathematical treatment of this and other aspects of microeconomics, see James M. Henderson and Richard E. Quandt, *Microeconomic Theory: A Mathematical Approach*, 2d ed. (New York: McGraw-Hill, 1971).

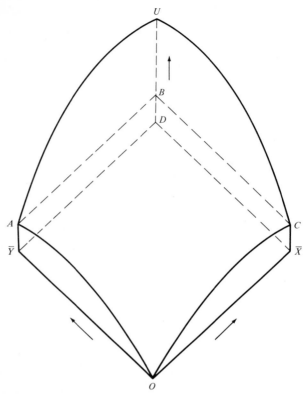

Figure 3.3 A Utility Surface This three-dimensional drawing illustrates how utility (*U*) varies as the consumption of two goods (*X* and *Y*) varies. As the consumer increases consumption of *X* and/or *Y* by moving away from the origin (*O*), a higher level of utility is realized.

consumer at $\bar{X}$. The amount of Y consumed is measured in a similar manner along the dimension $O\bar{Y}$. Utility is measured in the third dimension along the line DBU.[5]

The surface $OAUC$ represents a utility surface on which the amount of utility obtained from the consumption of goods X and Y is measured by the height of the surface at various points above the X-Y plane. For example, if zero units of both X and Y are consumed, the individual obtains no satisfaction from X or Y, and therefore the height of the utility surface is

[5] You can visualize a three-dimensional model of these relationships for yourself by considering your desk or table top to be the X-Y plane and utility as distance above that plane.

at zero. This is represented by point O in Figure 3.3. The curves OA and OC represent the manner in which utility increases as the consumption of Y or X increases respectively, holding the other constant at zero.

Consumption of zero X and $\bar{Y}$ of Y would yield satisfaction measured by the distance from $\bar{Y}$ up to A, or the distance DB on the utility axis. Likewise, if $\bar{X}$ of X were consumed but no Y, the level of utility would be the distance from $\bar{X}$ up to C. For simplicity we have constructed the diagram such that this is also DB, but it is not necessary that this be true. If, however, the consumer does obtain the same amount of satisfaction from zero of Y and $\bar{X}$ of X as from zero of X and $\bar{Y}$ of Y, then it stands to reason that the consumer would not care which of these two bundles of goods he or she actually consumes.

Would there be other combinations of X and Y that would also yield the level of satisfaction DB? Most likely the answer is yes. If the consumer starting with zero X and $\bar{Y}$ of Y would trade all the Y for $\bar{X}$ of X and maintain the same level of satisfaction, that person might well trade a lesser amount of Y for less compensation in terms of X. Such a case is illustrated in Figure 3.4, in which the consumption of the bundle of commodities X_1 and Y_1 also gives the level of satisfaction DB (i.e., $FE = DB$).

To see why this is true, suppose we cut through the utility surface at the level DB. Making certain that the slice represents a constant level of satisfaction, it would have to be parallel to the X-Y plane and pass through points A and C, as well as B. This would provide a ridge along the utility surface representing a constant level of satisfaction.[6] The line AEC in Figure 3.4 illustrates this ridge representing a constant height (DB) above the X-Y plane. Each point along that ridge (AEC) corresponds to some combination of the two goods X and Y that would provide the level of satisfaction DB. Point E is one such point. The corresponding point in the X-Y plane is F, at which X_1 and Y_1 are the respective amounts of goods X and Y that are consumed.

In the case illustrated, the consumer at point A on the utility surface would be willing to trade $(\bar{Y}-Y_1)$ amount of Y for (X_1-0) amount of X without changing the level of satisfaction derived from the consumption of X and Y. Doing so would move them from A to E on the utility surface. For the individual to be willing to give up the remaining Y_1 units of Y, you would have to provide compensation of more units of X (equal to the amount $\bar{X}-X_1$) to keep the consumer at the same level of satisfaction (DB).

---

[6] If you were to cut through a tennis ball, the cut surface would provide an analogous type of ridge.

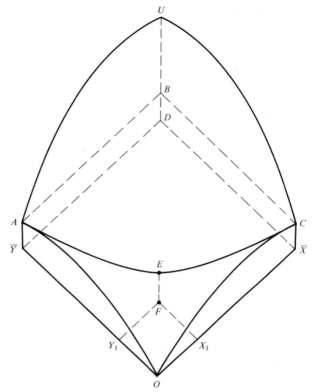

Figure 3.4 Points of Equal Utility on a Utility Surface By slicing through the utility surface at a constant height above the *X-Y* plane, we obtain a ridge, depicted by the line *AEC,* which represents alternative points at which the consumer has a constant level of satisfaction. The level of satisfaction given by the ridge *AEC* is the height *DB,* which equals *FE* since the slice is parallel to the *X-Y* plane.

We have now established that there are alternative bundles of X and Y that would provide the same level of satisfaction to the consumer. In fact, every point along the ridge AEC corresponds to a combination of X and Y that yields the level of satisfaction indicated by the distance DB. Because the consumer obtains the same level of satisfaction from each of these points (such as A, E, or C), we say that the consumer is indifferent between the corresponding bundles of commodities. In this simple two-good case, each such bundle can be represented as a point in the X-Y plane. The point labeled F, corresponding to X_1 and Y_1, represents one such bundle of the commodities X and Y.

INDIFFERENCE CURVES

Having developed the idea of consumer indifference among some set of alternative combinations of commodities, it is but a short step moving from analysis in three dimensions to just two dimensions. The diagram in Figure 3.5 is helpful in this transition. This figure is identical to Figure 3.4 except that we have now taken a slice through the utility surface (parallel to the X-Y plane) at a higher level of satisfaction (represented by the height DG, where $DG > DB$). Each point along the ridge created by

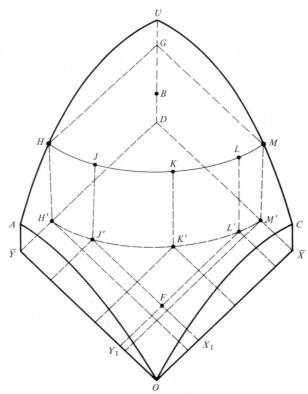

Figure 3.5 Derivation of an Indifference Curve From any slice through a utility surface which is parallel to the X-Y plane, we can determine the combinations of X and Y which yield the level of satisfaction determined by the height of the slice. This is done by projecting the ridge on the utility surface down to the plane below, such as from $HJKLM$ to $H'J'K'L'M'$. These points in the X-Y plane are called an indifference curve because they represent alternative combinations of the two goods that yield the same level of satisfaction (DG in this diagram).

this new slice represents an equal level of satisfaction. Five such points are labeled, H, J, K, L, and M in Figure 3.5.

Because DG is greater than DB, we know that the consumer is better off (has a higher level of satisfaction) at any point on the new ridge in Figure 3.5 than along the ridge in Figure 3.4. For example, let us compare point A on the first ridge (Figure 3.4 or 3.5) with point H on the second ridge (Figure 3.5). We can see in the latter diagram that these two points on the utility surface correspond to the same amount of Y (i.e., $\bar{Y}$), but at point H the consumer also has some of good X (rather than zero of X as at point A). Since more is preferred to less, H must be preferred to A. You should be able to show in a like manner that point M on the utility surface is preferred to point C.[7]

For each point along the ridge $HJKLM$ there is a corresponding bundle of the commodities in the X-Y plane below. These are identified as H', J', K', L', and M' in Figure 3.5. Each of these bundles of commodities must yield the same level of satisfaction because they are all derived from points that are equidistant above the X-Y plane. Since they yield the same satisfaction, the consumer would be indifferent between the bundles H', J', K', L', and M'. If we connect all such points (these five are only representative), we have what is called an indifference curve. An *indifference curve* is defined as the locus of points representing alternative bundles of the two commodities that yield the same level of satisfaction. There would be one indifference curve for every possible slice through the utility surface (parallel to the X-Y plane).

For any two goods we can draw indifference curves in two-dimensional space, thus simplifying the analysis of consumer behavior considerably.[8] Three representative indifference curves are drawn in Figure 3.6 and are labeled I_0, I_1, and I_2. The indifference curve I_1 corresponds to the one derived in Figure 3.5 (i.e., the curve $H'J'K'L'M'$), and I_0 passes through the point F from Figures 3.4 and 3.5. The space bounded by these axes (to the right of OY and above OX) is frequently referred to as the *commodity space* because it represents all possible combinations of commodities X and Y that are potentially available for consumption.

The indifference curves drawn in Figure 3.6 represent only three of an infinite number of potential indifference curves that could have been drawn through this commodity space. That is, there could be an indifference curve through any point in Figure 3.6. The curve I_0 that passes

---

[7] As a further test of your understanding, explain why point J or point L on the ridge in Figure 3.5 would be preferred to point E on the ridge in Figure 3.4. It will help to know that the points labeled F are identical in the two diagrams.

[8] We shall use just two goods and two-dimensional diagrams throughout the text. This simplifies the analysis (and permits us to avoid the use of calculus); moreover, the results are applicable to as many different goods as one might want to incorporate into the analysis.

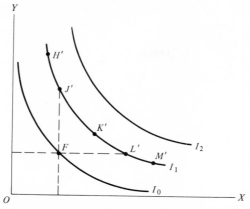

Figure 3.6 Representative Indifference Curves   Each slice through a utility surface would yield a separate indifference curve. Three such curves are depicted here. The curve I_2 represents the greatest level of satisfaction (i.e., is from a higher slice through the utility surface than I_1 or I_0). As illustrated here, indifference curves are negatively sloped and are convex to the origin.

through point F represents combinations of X and Y that yield a constant level of satisfaction, as determined by the slice through the utility surface in Figure 3.4 at the height DB. Indifference curve I_1 depicts combinations of X and Y that yield a higher level of satisfaction as determined by the slice through the utility surface at the height DG in Figure 3.5. In that figure we see clearly that DG is greater than DB, and thus points along I_1 must represent greater satisfaction than points along I_0.

This leads us to another important property of indifference curves. That is, an indifference curve that lies farther from the origin represents a greater level of satisfaction than one closer to the origin. This also follows from our previous observation that more is preferred to less. For example, J' and L' are preferred to F because the former represents the same amount of X but more Y, whereas the latter represents the same amount of Y but more X. Thus, in Figure 3.6, points along I_2 are preferred to points along I_1, and points along I_1 are preferred to points along I_0. It follows that points along I_2 are also preferred to points along I_0.

Still another property of indifference curves implied by the discussion above is that indifference curves cannot intersect one another. The reason can be illustrated by referring to Figure 3.7. By definition, a consumer would be indifferent among alternative amounts of X and Y along I_1 and also indifferent between bundles along I_2. Thus, if we look only at I_1, we would say the consumer is indifferent about having the bundle represented by A or the bundle represented by C. Looking at I_2, we would reason that A is also equal to B since they are on the same indiffer-

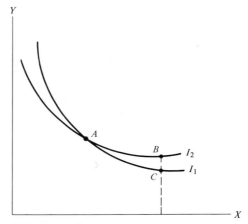

Figure 3.7 Inconsistent Indifference Curves Because each
indifference curve represents a given level of satisfaction, they
cannot intersect. In this diagram point B would definitely be
preferred to point C. If both B and A are on indifference curve I_2,
they must provide equal satisfaction, and if C and A are both on
indifference curve I_1, they must provide equal satisfaction.
However, if $B > C$, then both B and C cannot equal A. Thus, by the
definition of indifference, I_1 and I_2 cannot intersect.

ence curve. But clearly B is preferred to C since more is preferred to less.
Herein lies the contradiction. If B is preferred to C, A cannot have the
same utility value as both B and C. Thus it would be inconsistent for
indifference curves to intersect one another.

Indifference curves are negatively sloped because, as indicated
above, for a consumer to maintain a constant level of satisfaction (indifference) if we decrease the amount of Y that the consumer has, we must
compensate for that loss by increasing the amount of X. The rate at which
a consumer is willing to substitute X for Y, while maintaining a constant
level of satisfaction, is called the *marginal rate of substitution* of X for Y.
If consumers had very little X and a great deal of Y (such as at point H' in
Figure 3.6), we would expect them to be more willing to give up Y for
one unit of X than if they had lots of X and little Y (such as at point M' in
Figure 3.6). Thus, we should expect that the marginal rate of substitution
of one good for another will be dependent upon the amount of each good
that the consumer has.

We can measure the marginal rate of substitution (MRS) as the negative of the value of the slope of an indifference curve (i.e., as the absolute
value of the slope of an indifference curve). In Figure 3.8, we see that at
H' the slope of I_1 is steeper than at M'. Thus at H' the amount of Y that a
consumer would give up to obtain one more unit of X is greater than at
point M' (the absolute value of the slope of I_1 is greater at H' than at M').

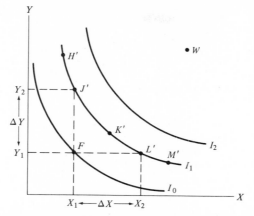

Figure 3.8 The Slope of an Indifference Curve   The absolute value of the slope of I_1 between J' and L' is $\Delta Y/\Delta X$. This can be shown to equal the ratio of the marginal utility of X to the marginal utility of Y.

This is consistent with, but an alternative way of stating, what we said in the previous paragraph in comparing the willingness of a consumer to substitute X for Y. In general, the more consumers have of any one good, relative to the amounts of other goods they have, the less important that good becomes to them. For example, suppose Y is scotch and X represents soda. At H', you might be quite willing to substitute more soda for some of the relatively large supply of scotch. But, as you move along I_1 towards M', you have less and less scotch but more soda and would thus be less willing to continue to substitute soda for the decreasing amount of scotch you have.

It is because of this type of relationship with respect to consumers' willingness to substitute one good for another that we generally assume that the *MRS* of X for Y diminishes. This is reflected in the way we have drawn the indifference curves in all our graphs. All indifference curves will be assumed to be of this general shape: bowing toward the origin, or convex to the origin.

We know that the slope of any curve is measured by the ratio of the change in the vertical direction to the change in the horizontal direction or, in general terms, as $\Delta Y/\Delta X$. We can then approximate the slope of I_1 between J' and L' as the ratio $(Y_2 - Y_1)/(X_1 - X_2)$. Since $Y_2 > Y_1$ and $X_1 < X_2$, this ratio has a negative value. Referring to Figure 3.8, we can then say that between J' and L' the *MRS* of X for Y is:

$$MRS = -\frac{Y_2 - Y_1}{X_1 - X_2} = -\frac{\Delta Y}{\Delta X}$$

It will be very useful to us to be able to relate MRS to the marginal utilities of the goods.

To do this, recall that the marginal utility of any good is defined as the change in total utility per unit change in the amount of the good consumed holding constant the consumption of other goods. Suppose we hold consumption of Y constant at Y_1 and increase X from X_1 to X_2. The marginal utility of X would be:

$$MU_X = \frac{I_1 - I_0}{\Delta X}$$

because $I_1 - I_0$ is the change in the level of satisfaction or utility. In a like manner, holding X constant at X_1 and increasing Y from Y_1 to Y_2, we could define the marginal utility of Y as:

$$MU_Y = \frac{I_1 - I_0}{\Delta Y}$$

If we divide MU_X by MU_Y, we have:

$$\frac{MU_X}{MU_Y} = \frac{(I_1 - I_0)/\Delta X}{(I_1 - I_0)/\Delta Y} = \frac{\Delta Y}{\Delta X}$$

Thus, the slope of the indifference curve between J' and L' is equal to the ratio of the marginal utility of X to the marginal utility of Y. Further, we know that the slope of the indifference curve is negative. We shall find that these relationships will be of great significance to us in the section following the next one. But first we must consider one other important aspect of consumer behavior.

THE BUDGET CONSTRAINT

We can all think of some things we do not have that we might like to have. I might, for example, like to have a chalet in Vail, an ocean cottage on the shore of South Carolina, a private jet, and many other goods or services. The reason I don't have all of these is most likely clear: Their cost far exceeds my ability to pay. In general, we would like to consume some bundle of goods far from the origin in our commodity space, such as point W in Figures 3.8 and 3.9. We are, however, constrained from reaching such a point by the limit imposed by our income.

Economists refer to this as our *budget constraint.* Suppose that we have an income of M dollars. Our expenditures on goods and services are then limited to those M dollars.[9] If $M = \$100$, while X represents hockey

---

[9] We will assume that consumers have no stock of wealth to draw on for use in purchasing goods and services, and that they can only consume out of current income (i.e., they cannot borrow). Neither of these assumptions is critical to our analysis, but they allow us to reach meaningful conclusions without incorporating a time dimension and other complexities that are beyond the scope of this text.

tickets that sell for \$5 each ($P_X = 5$) and Y represents tickets to a dinner theater at \$10 each ($P_Y = 10$), then the maximum amount of each type of entertainment we could purchase would be 20 hockey tickets or 10 dinner theater tickets. These are clearly determined by dividing the available income by the price of each good, respectively, as follows:

$$\text{Max } X = \frac{M}{P_X} = \frac{100}{5} = 20$$

$$\text{Max } Y = \frac{M}{P_Y} = \frac{100}{10} = 10$$

We see then that if a consumer purchases no Y, the maximum amount of X that can be obtained is equal to M/P_X and if no X is purchased, the maximum amount of Y that can be bought is M/P_Y.

The total amount spent on X will equal the price of X times the number of units of X purchased, or $P_X X$, whereas the total amount spent on Y will equal the price of Y times the number of units of Y purchased, or $P_Y Y$. If we assume that money is not of value except in exchange for goods and services, it is reasonable to assume that a person will use money to obtain want-satisfying goods or services such as X and Y (CB radios, bikes, scotch, soda, Pepsi, Coke, hockey tickets, and dinner theater tickets are examples we have cited above). Thus the amount spent on all goods and services will equal M. Assuming that there are just these two goods, X and Y, to purchase, it follows that

$$M = P_X X + P_Y Y$$

Solving this expression for Y yields

$$Y = \frac{M}{P_Y} - \frac{P_X}{P_Y} X$$

This is a linear equation in X and Y and is sketched in Figure 3.9 as the consumer's budget constraint.

If $X = 0$ in the above equation, Y would equal M/P_Y, and if $Y = 0$, we could solve for X finding that it would be equal to M/P_X. These are the Y and X intercepts of the budget constraint respectively and represent the maximum amount of each good that could be consumed if no units of the other were purchased. It is unlikely that a consumer would choose to spend all income on just one good. Rather, consumers typically allocate their income to a variety of goods and services. The rate at which a consumer can afford to substitute X for Y is given by the slope of the budget constraint as graphed in Figure 3.9 or as given by the equation above. In either form we see that the slope of the budget constraint is the negative of the ratio of the price of X (i.e., P_X) to the price of Y (i.e., P_Y).

For example, in our case of hockey and dinner theater tickets, assume that a consumer allocated all income (\$100) to theater tickets

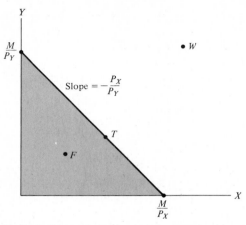

Figure 3.9 The Budget Constraint Graphic representation of the budget space, or the alternative bundles of commodities a consumer can afford to purchase with income M and the commodity prices P_X and P_Y.

$(Y = 10)$. If that consumer gave up one dinner theater ticket (Y), two hockey tickets (X) could be purchased. The rate at which that consumer can afford to substitute hockey tickets for dinner theater tickets is two of the former for one of the latter. The change in the horizontal direction $(X =$ hockey tickets) is $+2$, while the change in the vertical direction $(Y =$ dinner theater tickets) is -1. The slope of the budget constraint is thus $-$ ($\frac{1}{2}$). This is, of course, equal to the negative of the ratio of the price of X ($5) to the price of Y ($10):

$$\text{Slope of budget constraint} = -\frac{P_X}{P_Y}$$

$$= -\frac{5}{10}$$

$$= -\frac{1}{2}$$

The space bounded by the two axes and the budget constraint is often called the *budget space* because it represents all the possible combinations of the commodities that a consumer can purchase with a given level of income (a given budget) and a given set of product prices. In Figure 3.9, consumption of any bundle of goods along the line from M/P_Y to M/P_X, such as at the point T, would exhaust all of the consumer's income (M). The consumer could also purchase the bundle represented by point F, but would have money left over that could have been used to purchase want-satisfying goods or services. Since we assume that more is preferred to less, we can expect that the consumer will prefer some bundle such as T along the budget constraint to any bundle below the budget constraint. Which of these possible combinations is most preferred will be the subject of our discussion in the next section. Before going on, however, we should note that points, such as W, that lie outside the budget constraint may be desirable in the eyes of a consumer but are unobtainable given his or her income and the product prices.

UTILITY MAXIMIZATION AND CONSUMER EQUILIBRIUM

In this section the focal point of our attention will be on determining how consumers can allocate their relatively scarce money income in a manner that will maximize their utility or satisfaction. To accomplish this we shall want to combine all of the relationships developed earlier in this chapter into a single framework for analysis. Prior to doing this, let us first take a more intuitive approach and see whether both lines of reasoning lead to the same conclusion.

Suppose that you are faced with the alternative of buying either a Pepsi or a Coke from a machine for 50 cents. If you prefer Pepsi to Coke, you will purchase the Pepsi. Why? Because if you prefer Pepsi to Coke, you must believe that you get more satisfaction or utility from the Pepsi. But what if Cokes (of the same size) were just 25 cents? In that case, you might well select the Coke. With the price of Coke one-half the price of Pepsi, you would have to believe that an additional Pepsi would provide you with at least twice as much satisfaction in order for you to stick with your original decision to buy the Pepsi. We can generalize this to say that a consumer will always purchase the commodity that yields the *greatest amount of additional satisfaction per dollar* (in algebraic terms, the good with the greatest value of the ratio of *MU/P*), subject to limited money income.[10]

An alternative way of visualizing this type of allocation process in a situation familiar to all students is frequently used. Suppose you have two exams tomorrow, one in chemistry and one in English literature, and that you have just six hours available to study. In this case, the measure of benefit is the score on the exams rather than utility, and the scarce resource is time rather than money. The objective is to allocate the resource so that you maximize the test scores.

Let's assume that you have kept up pretty well in chemistry but have let yourself get behind in reading the English assignments so if you don't study any chemistry you could get 50 percent; but, without studying the

---

[10] With the price of Pepsi at 50 cents and the price of Coke at 25 cents, even if you have a *very* strong preference for Pepsi, if you have just 30 cents, you must purchase the Coke or neither.

English the best you could do, based on just listening to class discussions, is 5 percent. This is shown by the first row of Table 3.1, which relates test scores to the number of hours you study each subject for this round of tests. We will assume that final grades will be based on total points earned on tests in each class so that the important objective is to maximize the overall total of the test scores. We see that without studying, your overall total score would be 55. If you had just one hour to study, you could improve this score the most by reading English literature as indicated in the column headed "Marginal Score" under English. Thus, at least one hour should be allocated to studying English.

If we look at the marginal contribution of each hour's study for each subject, it would always be best to allocate the time to the subject with the greatest marginal score per hour. Doing this, we would be led to allocate two hours to Chemistry and four hours to English. The overall total score would then be:

$$82 + 73 = 155$$

Any other allocation of the six hours would yield a lower overall total. It is important to note that at this allocation the marginal score per hour is equal for both subjects. Thus, we are led to the same general conclusion we reached above: The allocation should be such that the greatest amount of additional benefit per unit of the scarce resource is obtained at each point. With diminishing marginal benefits (utility, additional score on a test, or whatever), we will be led by this principle to an allocation such that in using all our available resources (money or time in our examples) *the marginal benefit per unit of resource is equal for all items.* In the example of allocating the six hours of available study time, we found that the overall total score would be maximized when the marginal score per hour spent on each subject was equal to 14.

Table 3.1 EFFECT OF HOURS STUDIED ON TWO EXAM SCORES*

	CHEMISTRY		ENGLISH	
HOURS	TOTAL SCORE	MARGINAL SCORE	TOTAL SCORE	MARGINAL SCORE
0	50	—	5	—
1	68	18	25	20
2	82	14	43	18
3	92	10	59	16
4	96	4	73	14
5	99	3	85	12
6	100	1	95	10

* Note that each exam is subject to diminishing marginal scores. This is generally realistic and is comparable to the concept of diminishing marginal utility in consumption.

Let us return to our model of consumer behavior based on indifference curves, and the budget constraint imposed by limited money income and product prices. We have already defined a *commodity space* as the amounts of goods available for consumption (the amounts of X and Y in our two-good case), and a *budget space* as the combinations of those goods we can afford to purchase given their prices and our income. These are depicted in Figures 3.8 and 3.9, respectively. Our objective is to find that combination of goods that will maximize satisfaction (be on the highest possible indifference curve) while at the same time satisfying the budget constraint. For this purpose both the commodity space and budget space are drawn together in Figure 3.10.

Recall from the preceding section that the consumer can purchase any combination of X and Y in the space bounded by the two axes and the line from M/P_Y to M/P_X (including points along those boundaries). Six such points are labeled in Figure 3.10: M/P_Y, R, T, S, M/P_X, and F. Which of these will provide maximum satisfaction (i.e., put the consumer on the highest possible indifference curve)? To answer this question, let us evaluate several of these alternatives.

First, we can say that the combination represented by point F would not yield the greatest possible satisfaction because the consumer can reach higher indifference curves by moving from F along arrows 1 or 2 or

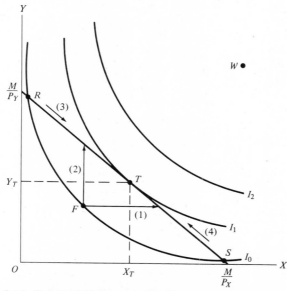

Figure 3.10 General Consumer Equilibrium   Graphic depiction of consumer equilibrium at T given income (M) and prices P_X and P_Y for two goods X and Y, respectively. At point R the consumer can increase satisfaction by substituting X for Y along the budget constraint, while at S the reverse is true.

between them toward the budget constraint. All such points would represent more of X or Y, or both, and would lie along indifference curves representing a greater level of satisfaction than I_0 (on which point F is found). Recall that there is an indifference curve through every point in the commodity space even though we have drawn just three for illustrative purposes.

Let us now consider the point labeled R. We see that the indifference curve through this point (I_0) is more steeply sloped than the budget constraint. From our earlier discussion we know that at R the following must be true:

$$\frac{MU_X}{MU_Y} > \frac{P_X}{P_Y}$$

If we divide both sides of this inequality by the same number (P_X) and multiply both sides by a given value (MU_Y), the direction of the inequality will remain the same, and we have

$$\frac{MU_X}{P_X} > \frac{MU_Y}{P_Y}$$

Thus, the consumer is getting greater marginal utility per dollar spent on X than per dollar spent on Y.

If this consumer were to allocate one less dollar to Y and use it for X, total utility would increase since the loss from reducing the consumption of Y would be less than the gain from increasing consumption of X. That is, the consumer could increase total utility by substituting X for Y and moving along the budget constraint in the direction of arrow 3. This leads us to an important conclusion:

If the marginal rate of substitution of X for Y (the slope of the indifference curve) is greater than the ratio of the price of X to the price of Y (the slope of the budget constraint), the consumer can increase utility by substituting more X for less Y. Stated alternatively, if

$$\frac{MU_X}{MU_Y} > \frac{P_X}{P_Y}$$

or, equivalently, if

$$\frac{MU_X}{P_X} > \frac{MU_Y}{P_Y}$$

the consumer would obtain greater satisfaction by consuming more X and less Y.

Let us consider what happens as the consumer moves along the budget constraint from R in the direction of arrow 3. Given that P_X and P_Y are constant, and if X and Y are subject to diminishing marginal utility,[11] then as the amount of X consumed increases (MU_X decreases) and the consumption of Y decreases (MU_Y increases), the MRS of X for Y becomes closer to being equal to the ratio of P_X to P_Y. Further, movement from R in the direction of arrow 3 will move the consumer to indifference curves higher than I_0.

If we consider the bundle of goods represented by point S in an analogous manner, we find that at that point the indifference curve is less steeply sloped than the budget constraint. Thus, at S,

$$\frac{MU_X}{MU_Y} < \frac{P_X}{P_Y} \qquad \text{or} \qquad \frac{MU_X}{P_X} < \frac{MU_Y}{P_Y}$$

and the consumer is getting greater marginal utility per dollar from Y than from X. In this case, the consumer can increase utility by purchasing more Y and less X. We find that:

If the marginal rate of substitution of X for Y (the slope of the indifference curve) is less than the ratio of the price of X to the price of Y (the slope of the budget constraint), the consumer can increase utility by substituting more Y for less X. Stated alternatively, if

$$\frac{MU_X}{MU_Y} < \frac{P_X}{P_Y}$$

or, equivalently, if

$$\frac{MU_X}{P_X} < \frac{MU_Y}{P_Y}$$

the consumer would obtain greater satisfaction by consuming more of Y and less of X.

This would lead the consumer to move along the budget constraint from S in the direction of arrow 4, and to indifference curves representing higher levels of satisfaction.

If at point R we can move down the budget constraint to improve total satisfaction and from point S we can do the reverse, there must then

---

[11] Both X and Y need not exhibit diminishing marginal utility (although one must), but since most goods are likely to have this characteristic, we shall assume that both X and Y do as well.

be some point along the budget constraint between R and S for which further change would result in less total utility. That point is labeled T corresponding to the purchase of X_T of good X and Y_T of good Y. At point T the indifference curve I_1 is just tangent to the budget constraint, so their slopes must be equal at that point. This means that the *MRS* of X for Y must equal the ratio of the price of X to the price of Y.

Any movement along the budget constraint (or interior to it) would put the consumer on a lower indifference curve and therefore X_T, Y_T must be the optimum bundle of the two commodities for the consumer to maximize utility. Thus we find that:

If the marginal rate of substitution of X for Y (the slope of the indifference curve) is equal to the ratio of the price of X to the price of Y (the slope of the budget constraint), there is no reallocation of expenditure that will increase the consumer's utility. Stated alternatively, if

$$\frac{MU_X}{MU_Y} = \frac{P_X}{P_Y}$$

or, equivalently, if

$$\frac{MU_X}{P_X} = \frac{MU_Y}{P_Y}$$

the consumer is obtaining the maximum possible satisfaction from the income (M) available.

The combination of X and Y represented by point W would be preferred to X_T, Y_T, but it is outside the budget space, as are all points along indifference curve I_2.

We have found that the optimum allocation principle derived from our model of consumer behavior is consistent with the results we found intuitively in the examples of buying Coke or Pepsi or in the allocation of study time. However, the results based on the deductive logic of this model are more powerful and more general. These results can be extended to any number of goods (n) such that utility is maximized when:

$$\frac{MU_1}{P_1} = \frac{MU_2}{P_2} = \cdots = \frac{MU_i}{P_i} = \cdots = \frac{MU_n}{P_n}$$

where i represents any one of the plethora of goods and services available for our consumption.

SUMMARY

In this chapter we have developed an economic theory of consumer behavior based on relatively few, but important, assumptions. We have assumed that people consume in order to obtain satisfaction or utility and that, in general, for the bulk of the world's population, more is preferred to less. The amount of satisfaction or utility obtained from consumption cannot be measured in a cardinal manner given the current state of the art. However, it is only necessary for the development of the economic model that consumers are able to rank various bundles of commodities in an ordinal way. That is, they can say whether bundle A is preferred to bundle B, or B to A, or that they are indifferent between the two.

There may be a seemingly endless array of commodities and services that we would like to consume and that we would obtain satisfaction from. However, for any single item there is likely to be diminishing marginal utility from consuming additional units. The first drink after a tennis match on a hot summer's day yields greater satisfaction than the fourth, sixth, or tenth. And so we find that the total utility from consuming any single good (ceteris paribus) increases at a decreasing rate, and may eventually decline if so much of the good is consumed that marginal utility becomes negative.

Given a given set of product prices and a fixed level of money resources to use for consumption, most (if not all) people are unable to afford to purchase all the things they might desire. Consumers must therefore make decisions about how to allocate their resources so as to obtain the maximum level of satisfaction. Using just two goods, we can show how utility changes as the quantity of each good consumed changes by using a three-dimensional graph of a utility surface. From this model in three dimensions we can develop a two-dimensional mapping of indifference curves that becomes the basis for the economic model of consumer behavior. This mapping defines the commodity space of all goods and services.

There is some indifference curve through each point in this two-dimensional commodity space with the following properties: points along an indifference curve represent bundles of commodities that yield the same level of satisfaction to the consumer; they are negatively sloped; they cannot intersect one another; the further an indifference curve is from the origin (along a straight line through the origin) the higher the level of satisfaction obtained from the bundles of commodities represented by that indifference curve; each indifference curve is convex to the origin. The slope of an indifference curve is the marginal rate of substitution of X for Y, which may be measured as the ratio of the marginal utility of X to the marginal utility of Y.

Although there may be many things consumers would like to purchase, they are limited by their money income. Given the prices of commodities and the consumer's income, we can define a budget space as the combinations of goods and services the consumer can afford to purchase. This space is bounded by the budget constraint and the two axes. Combining the commodity and budget spaces, we see that a consumer will maximize utility by consuming the bundle of commodities where the budget constraint is just tangent to an indifference curve.

The slopes of the two curves are equal at the point of tangency, and the slope of the indifference curves can be measured by the ratio, MU_X/MU_Y, whereas the slope of the budget constraint is P_X/P_Y. Thus we find the equilibrium condition for maximizing utility is

$$\frac{MU_X}{MU_Y} = \frac{P_X}{P_Y}$$

which may be written as

$$\frac{MU_X}{P_X} = \frac{MU_Y}{P_Y}$$

That is, the consumer will maximize utility by allocating money income such that the marginal utility per dollar spent is equal for all goods.

Selected Readings

Alchian, Armen A. "The Meaning of Utility Measurement." *American Economic Review* 43 (March 1953), 26–50.

Friedman, Milton, and L. J. Savage. "The Utility Analysis of Choices Involving Risk." *Journal of Political Economy* 56 (August 1948), 279–304.

Hughs, George D. *Demand Analysis for Marketing Decisions.* Homewood, Ill.: Irwin, 1973.

MacCrimmon, K. R., and M. Toda. "The Experimental Determination of Indifference Curves." *Review of Economic Studies* (October 1969), 433–451.

QUESTIONS

1. Write a short explanation of the following terms or concepts that were used in this chapter:
   (a) budget constraint
   (b) ceteris paribus
   (c) commodity space
   (d) consumption
   (e) diminishing marginal utility
   (f) indifference curve
   (g) opportunity cost
   (h) utility surface

2. Explain the "principle of diminishing marginal utility." Pick three goods or services that you consume and evaluate how this principle influences your consumption of them. Is it conceivable that the marginal utility of any of them could be negative? If so, explain how this would be recognized and what the consequences would be.

3. Give a detailed explanation of what is meant by an indifference curve. Include the various properties of indifference curves and explain the significance of these properties.

4. Give a detailed explanation of the concept of budget constraints including their properties. Explain what factors might cause a budget constraint to: shift in a parallel manner; become more steeply sloped; become less steeply sloped.

5. Use a graphic representation of three indifference curves and a budget constraint to explain the determination of the bundle of commodities that would maximize a consumer's satisfaction given some limited income and constant product prices. Explain the relevance of the condition that the marginal utility per dollar should be equal for all goods.

6. Identify several groups of people that influence your personal consumption behavior and explain how each effects your decisions. Are there any social institutions that you can identify as influencing your consumption? In what ways?

7. The model of consumer equilibrium can be thought of as a general "choice model." Explain how this choice model involving benefits and costs (opportunity costs perhaps) could be applied to decisions regarding: the choice of a school to attend; the choice of what you will do next weekend; and the choice of what you will do after college.

8. Four indifference mappings representing a person's preference structure for several goods are illustrated. From these graphs write a paragraph interpreting this person's likely consumption pattern, and carefully explain how each of the four separate indifference mappings should be interpreted.

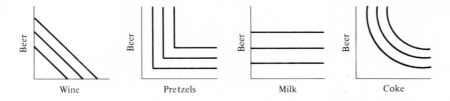

9. For the indifference mappings shown in the figures given in Question 8 explain how the following budget constraints would influence the utility maximizing combination of commodities. Draw a graph to illustrate your answer to each.

   (a) The price of beer is greater than the price of wine.
   (b) The price of beer is less than the price of wine.
   (c) The prices of beer and wine are equal.
   (d) The price of beer is greater than the price of pretzels.
   (e) The price of beer is less than the price of pretzels.
   (f) The prices of beer and pretzels are equal.

(g) The price of beer is greater than the price of milk.
(h) The price of beer is less than the price of milk.
(i) The prices of beer and milk are equal.
(j) The price of beer is greater than the price of Coke.
(k) The price of beer is less than the price of Coke.
(l) The prices of beer and Coke are equal.

CHAPTER 4
CONSUMER DEMAND

CHANGES IN THE BUDGET CONSTRAINT
THE PRICE–CONSUMPTION CURVE
THE INCOME–CONSUMPTION CURVE
THE CONSUMER'S DEMAND
MARKET DEMAND
ENGEL CURVES
EFFECTS OF PRODUCT PROMOTION
SUMMARY
SELECTED READINGS
QUESTIONS

The primary objective of this chapter is to use the constructs developed in Chapter 3 to derive a consumer's demand curve. The term *demand* has a very specific meaning in economics. *Demand is defined as the quantities of a good or service that consumers are willing and able to purchase at various prices during a given time period, ceteris paribus.* Note that consumers must be both willing and able to purchase in order for their demand to be meaningful in the marketplace. A public school teacher may be willing to purchase a $250,000 home, but due to limited money resources be unable to do so. The same teacher, however, may be able to purchase a pack of cigarettes but be unwilling to spend money in that way.

In addition to deriving a consumer's demand we shall consider what determines the level of that demand and the manner by which individuals' demands are aggregated to arrive at the market demand for the good or service. The relationship between consumption and income will also be investigated, and an Engel curve will be derived. *An Engel curve represents the quantities of a good or service that consumers will purchase at various levels of income during a given time period, ceteris paribus.*

CHANGES IN THE BUDGET CONSTRAINT

The quantity of a good that a consumer purchases depends on such things as that good's price, the consumer's income, the prices of other goods, and the consumer's tastes and preferences. In Chapter 3 we saw that the consumer's attitude toward a good (tastes and preferences) can be represented by an indifference map in what is frequently called the commodity space. However, we also saw that prices and income combine to limit the number of alternative bundles of goods available to the consumer into what is referred to as the budget space. The bundle of goods that maximizes consumer satisfaction is determined, for a given level of income, by the following condition (for just two goods):

$$\frac{MU_X}{P_X} = \frac{MU_Y}{P_Y}$$

This condition can be generalized to any number of goods, and simply stated means that the consumer's income should be allocated among alternative purchases such that marginal utility per dollar is equal for all goods.

Recall that this condition for maximizing a consumer's satisfaction was derived from the analysis that led us to the conclusion that the highest level of satisfaction (highest indifference curve) would be reached at the point at which a given budget constraint was just tangent to an indifference curve. At a point of tangency two curves have the same slope, so at the utility maximizing point the slopes of the indifference curve and budget constraint are equal. The slope of an indifference curve (MRS_{XY}) is equal to the ratio $-MU_X/MU_Y$ and the slope of the budget constraint is the negative of the ratio of the price of X to the price of Y (i.e., $-P_X/P_Y$). Therefore, the condition for consumer satisfaction must be $MU_X/MU_Y = P_X/P_Y$, which can be written in the alternative form given above: $MU_X/P_X = MU_Y/P_Y$.

The slope of the budget constraint is determined by the prices of X and Y, but what determines the distance between the budget constraint and the origin? In Figure 3.9 we saw that the budget constraint would intercept the X and Y axes at M/P_X and M/P_Y, respectively, where M represents the consumer's money income. If prices remain constant an increase in income will cause these intercepts to shift outward because the consumer would find it possible to purchase more of X or Y. The opposite is true for a decrease in income. As income falls, the consumer would be able to purchase less of X or Y, with constant prices, and the intercepts would shift toward the origin. Note, however, that as long as prices are constant, the slope of the indifference curve (measured as

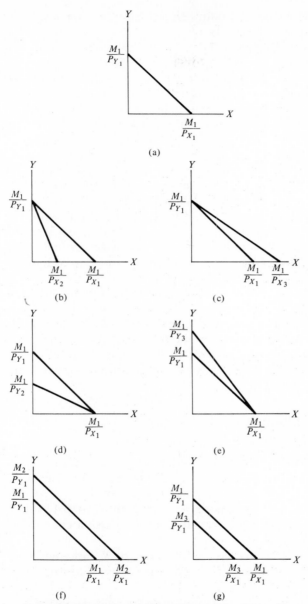

Figure 4.1 Changes in the Budget Constraint   The effect of
changing income (M), the price of Y (P$_Y$), or the price of X (P$_X$) on
the budget constraint. (a) Original budget constraint. (b) Effect of
a higher P$_X$. (c) Effect of a lower P$_X$. (d) Effect of a higher P$_Y$. (e)
Effect of a lower P$_Y$. (f) Effect of a higher M. (g) Effect of a lower M.

$-P_X/P_Y$) will remain constant.[1] Thus, changes in income result in parallel shifts in the budget constraint.

Figure 4.1 illustrates the effect of various price and income changes on the position of a budget constraint. Figure 4.1(a) depicts an original budget constraint for a given level of income (M_1) and given prices for X and Y (P_{X_1} and P_{Y_1}). In (b) the price of X is assumed to have increased to P_{X_2} while the price of Y and income remained constant. The result is that the Y intercept does not change but the slope ($-P_X/P_Y$) becomes steeper and the X intercept is at a lower quantity of X. Part (c) shows the effect of a decrease in the price of X from P_{X_1} to P_{X_3} with the resultant flatter budget constraint having the original Y intercept but a higher X intercept.

Figure 4.1(d) and (e) represent the effect of similar changes in the price of Y (ceteris paribus). We see that an increase in the price of Y results in a less steeply sloped budget constraint while decreasing the price of Y has the effect of increasing the budget constraint's slope (with the X intercept constant in both cases). P_{Y_1} represents the original price of Y in both (d) and (e), while P_{Y_2} is the higher price of Y and P_{Y_3} the lower price.

The last two portions of Figure 4.1 illustrate the effect of a change in income on the budget constraint while prices are kept constant at P_{X_1} and P_{Y_1}. Part (f) shows an income increase from M_1 to M_2 and part (g) shows the effect of a decrease in income from M_1 to M_3. Note that in both cases the result of a change in income is a parallel shift of the budget constraint: further from the origin for a higher income and closer to the origin for a lower income.

THE PRICE–CONSUMPTION CURVE

The diagram in Figure 4.2 depicts the indifference mapping for a consumer (just two of the indifference curves illustrated), along with that consumer's budget constraint. The consumer's income is assumed to be $120, the price of Y is $7.50 and the price of X is $8.00. We see that the equilibrium bundle of goods is: $X = 9$ and $Y = 6.4$ (this is marked as point A in the diagram). The slope of the budget constraint is $-P_X/P_Y = -8/7.5 = -1.07$.

How would a change in the price of X influence this consumer's choice of how much of each good to purchase with the $120 income? To

---

[1] It is only relative prices that must remain constant for the slope of the budget constraint to be constant. If both prices increase or decrease in the same *proportion* (not dollar amount) then the slope of the budget constraint will remain the same. If both prices increase by 25 percent, the budget constraint would shift toward the origin in the same manner as if income had fallen by that percent.

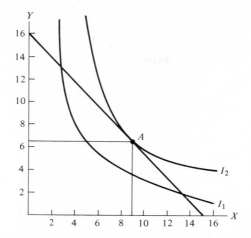

Figure 4.2 Specific Consumer Equilibrium Indifference map with budget constraint showing the combination of X and Y that yields maximum satisfaction ($X = 9, Y = 6.4$) given: income = 120, $P_Y = 7.50$, and $P_X = 8$.

answer this question, let us assume that the price of X increases from $P_{X_1} = \$8.00$ to $P_{X_2} = \$15.00$. From the discussion above concerning the effect price changes have on the budget constraint we know that the slope of the budget constraint will increase when the price of X increases, while income and the price of Y remain constant. With the price of X at $\$15$ and the price of Y at $\$7.5$ the slope of the budget constraint is: $-P_X/P_Y = -15/7.5 = -2.0$. This new budget constraint is shown in Figure 4.3, along with the original budget constraint and indifference map that were given in Figure 4.2.

We see that with the now higher price of X the consumer would maximize satisfaction by purchasing 4 units of X and 8 units of Y. Note that the increased price of X, with constant income and price of Y, results in the consumer equilibrium at a lower level of satisfaction than originally (the tangency now occurs on I_1 rather than on I_2). Although only two possible prices of X are illustrated in Figure 4.3, we could show the effect of any number of alternative prices for X in the same manner. The higher the price of X the steeper the budget constraint, and the lower the price of X the flatter the budget constraint.

If we were to show all the possible equilibrium points (tangencies of budget constraints with indifference curves) for changes in the price of X, they would form a line called a *price–consumption curve.* For the two prices of X depicted in Figure 4.3 we can determine two points, A and B, along the price–consumption curve. Although we cannot tell the exact

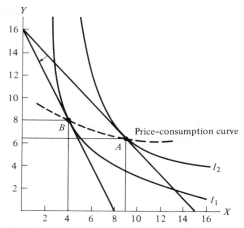

Figure 4.3 The Price–Consumption Curve Determination of a price–consumption curve from an indifference map and budget constraints given: income = 120, $P_Y = 7.50$, $P_{X_1} = 8.00$, and $P_{X_2} = 15.00$.

shape of the curve from just two observations, we do know that points A and B will lie on the curve. The entire curve may look something like the dashed line drawn through these points in Figure 4.3. We see that the points along the price–consumption curve represent the quantities of each good that would be purchased at various different prices of one of the goods, holding income and the other price(s) constant. A price–consumption curve could be derived for changes in the price of Y in a strictly analogous manner.

THE INCOME–CONSUMPTION CURVE

We have seen that a change in a consumer's income has the effect of shifting the budget constraint in a parallel manner: away from the origin for an increase in income and toward the origin for a decrease in income. This movement of the budget constraint causes changes in the bundle of commodities the consumer would select in order to maximize satisfaction. Two examples are illustrated in Figure 4.4.

In Figure 4.4(a) the case of two *normal goods* is illustrated. A normal good is one for which consumption increases (decreases) as income increases (decreases). In this case both X and Y are normal goods because the level of consumption of both changes in the same direction that income changes. Equilibrium points, such as A and B, trace out an *income–consumption curve*, which shows how the bundle of commodities consumed varies as the level of income changes.

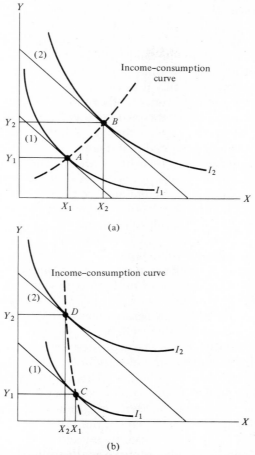

Figure 4.4 The Income–Consumption Curve Determination of income–consumption curves illustrating both normal and inferior goods. (a) X and Y both normal goods. (b) X an inferior good, Y a normal good.

Most of the things we spend our income for would be classified as normal goods. However, there may be some things that people would purchase less of at a higher level of income than at a lower level. Potatoes may represent an example for some households at some income levels. If less is purchased as income increases the good is called an *inferior good*. In Figure 4.4(b) the good represented by X is an inferior good. If either X or Y is an inferior good, the income–consumption curve will have a negative slope, such as the one shown by the dashed line through equilibrium points C and D.

THE CONSUMER'S DEMAND

An *individual consumer's demand* represents the quantities of a particular good or service that the consumer is willing and able to purchase at various prices during a given time period, ceteris paribus. How should we expect the quantity purchased to vary as price changes if everything else (income, tastes and preferences, other prices) remains constant? It is intuitively appealing to say that consumers will generally purchase more of a commodity at a lower price than at a higher price. In fact, this relationship is so widely accepted that it is frequently cited as the "law of demand." The term *law* may be a bit of an overstatement if it suggests that the relationship must hold in every possible case, but the relationship described is certainly prevalent enough to allow us to consider price and quantity to be inversely related as a general rule. Goods for which this would not be true are surely the exception.

Is this "law of demand" consistent with the model of consumer behavior that we developed in Chapter 3? It is easy to verify that the answer to this question is affirmative from the example shown in Figure 4.3. We saw that for a given set of preferences (as reflected by the indifference mapping), a given level of income ($120) and a constant price of Y ($7.50) the *quantity* of X purchased *decreased* from 9 to 4 units when the *price* of X *increased* from $8 to $15.

This inverse relationship between price and quantity is frequently shown graphically by a *demand curve,* which is simply a geometric way of depicting the negative (inverse) relationship that normally exists between price and the quantity of a good a consumer is willing and able to purchase. Such a curve may be derived directly from the indifference curve analysis of consumer behavior. In the upper part of Figure 4.5 the information from Figure 4.3 is reproduced and in the lower part of the figure the corresponding demand curve is illustrated.

In Figure 4.5 the bundles of commodities that maximize the consumer's satisfaction are determined by the tangencies of the budget constraints with the indifference curves in the upper portion of the graph. The quantities (Q) of X so determined are then projected down to the lower part of the graph where their respective prices are plotted on the vertical axis. Only two points are used for ease of exposition; however, there would be one point in this price-quantity space for each possible price of X. Connecting all such points gives us the demand curve for X. From just two observations one cannot tell whether the demand curve is linear or curved, but we can see that it has the negative slope that we expected. We have drawn the demand curve as a linear function through the two observations derived above because it will simplify our subsequent discussion while not restricting the generality of the principles discussed in relation to the concept of demand.

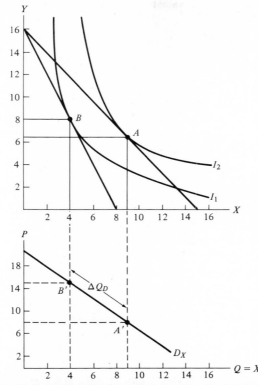

Figure 4.5 An Individual's Demand Curve Derivation of the demand curve for X from an indifference map and budget constraints given: income = 120, $P_Y = 7.5$, $P_{X_1} = 8.00$, and $P_{X_2} = 15.00$.

A demand curve is just one way of representing the relationship between price and quantity. The same information can be put in tabular form, which is then referred to as a *demand schedule*.[2] The demand schedule is a listing of the quantities that would be purchased at each of the possible prices. For every demand curve there is a related demand schedule, and vice versa. The demand curve for X that is graphed in the lower part of Figure 4.5 can also be represented by the demand schedule given in Table 4.1. We see in this table that a price of $8 is associated with a quantity purchased of 9 units, while 4 units are purchased at a price of $15. These data points correspond to points A' and B', respectively, in Figure 4.5.

[2] The demand relation can also be presented in the form of an algebraic equation. For the demand that is graphed in Figure 4.5 and given as a demand schedule in Table 4.1 the corresponding demand equation is: $P = 20.6 - 1.4Q$.

Table 4.1 DEMAND SCHEDULE FOR X

PRICE (P)	QUANTITY (Q)
$20.60	0
19.20	1
17.80	2
16.40	3
15.00	4
13.60	5
12.20	6
10.80	7
9.40	8
8.00	9
6.60	10

Movement from one level of consumption to another within a de-mand schedule, or along a demand curve, is defined as a *change in quantity demanded*. For example, using the demand schedule or the demand curve given above, if price changes from $15.00 to $8.00 the quantity demanded changes from 4 to 9 units. This change is identified by ΔQ_D along the demand curve for X in Figure 4.5 (movement from B' to A'). Note that a change in quantity demand is caused by a change in the price of the good.

This is not to say that other things will not influence the amount of a good that a consumer may purchase. Certainly as income, tastes and preferences, or the prices of other goods vary we should anticipate that there may be some effect on the consumption of X (any particular good). However, changes in these factors cause a change in the overall level of demand, which is reflected in a shift of the demand schedule: to the right for an increase in demand, or to the left for a decrease in demand.

Figure 4.6 illustrates an increase in demand for X in comparison to the original level of demand as shown in Figure 4.5. The higher level of demand is labeled D_X' while the original level is D_X. The change in demand (ΔD) is the horizontal distance between the two curves. With an increase in demand we see that more will be purchased at each possible price. For example, at a price of $8 the original demand was 9 units, and after the change 13 units would be purchased at that price. The reverse would be true of a decrease in demand.

For virtually all goods, an increase in income will stimulate an in-crease in demand. This has been evident in recent years in the increased demand for recreational equipment from skis and tennis racquets to travel trailers and motor homes. The opposite is true as well (i.e., for most goods demand will decrease if income falls).

Changes in consumers' tastes and preferences may also cause a change in demand. Many fads and style changes represent examples.

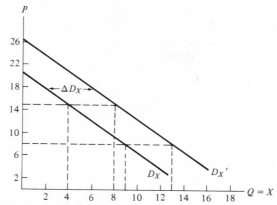

Figure 4.6 An Increase in Demand A change in demand for *X* (Δ*D*) from the original level D_X to a higher level D_X' results in a greater quantity being purchased at every price.

Consider the surge of demand for skateboards during the early 1960s, followed by an almost complete decline, and then an even greater increase in demand during the decade of the 1970s.

In some cases the demand for a particular product will be affected by changes in the price of related products. If the price of a substitute product increases (decreases) demand for the product in question will rise (fall). This has been evidenced in recent years with home insulation and home heating fuel prices. Increases in the price of natural gas and electricity have stimulated greater demand for home insulation (and other substitute products such as wood stoves). If the price of a complementary product increases (decreases), demand for the product in question will fall (rise). Substantial increases in the price of gasoline, for example, might be expected to cause a decline in the demand for passenger car tires as people drive less.

MARKET DEMAND

The market demand for a good or service is the quantities that the sum of all consumers are willing and able to purchase at various prices. Market demand may be presented as a schedule, such as in Table 4.2. In this table, the total market is assumed to be composed of just three consumers: *A*, *B*, and *C*. In practice, any number of consumers may be considered. As we see, the market demand is simply the sum of what each individual consumer is willing and able to purchase at each price.

Market demand may also be shown in terms of a graph in which individual consumer demand curves are added horizontally to arrive at the market demand curve. This is illustrated in Figure 4.7 for the data

Table 4.2 DETERMINATION OF MARKET DEMAND

PRICE	CONSUMER A	+ B	+ C	= MARKET DEMAND
10	1	0	0	1
9	2	0	0	2
8	3	0	1	4
7	4	1	2	7
6	5	2	3	10
5	6	3	4	13
4	7	4	5	16
3	8	5	6	19
2	9	6	7	22
1	10	7	8	25

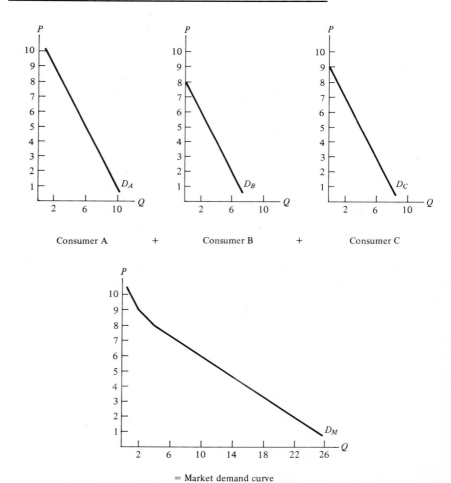

= Market demand curve

Figure 4.7 The Market Demand Determination of the market demand (D_M) by the horizontal summation of all individual consumer demand curves (D_A, D_B, and D_C).

given in Table 4.2. Note that the market demand curve has a negative slope just as do individual consumer demand curves.

ENGEL CURVES

In addition to being interested in the relationship between price and quantity, we are usually concerned with how the consumption of various goods is affected by the consumer's income level. The model of consumer behavior developed in Chapter 3 can be used to analyze this problem in a manner very similar to the analysis of how price influences consumption as in our derivation of demand curve.

By now the equilibrium condition, that a consumer will maximize satisfaction by allocating income such that the bundle of commodities purchased is at the point of tangency of an indifference curve and the individual's budget constraint, should be well established. Combining this principle with the way by which budget constraints shift as income changes, as illustrated in Figure 4.1(f) and (g), we can evaluate the relationship between the level of income and the quantity of a good or service consumed.

In the upper panel of Figure 4.8 two budget constraints, representing constant product prices but different levels of income, are drawn along with the two indifference curves which are tangent to those budget constraints. Budget constraint BC_1 represents a lower level of income than does BC_2. We see that at the higher level of income more X (X_2 units) are consumed than at the lower income (at which X_1 units are consumed).

If we project these quantities of X consumed at the two levels of income down to the lower panel of Figure 4.8 and plot them opposite the income corresponding to BC_1 and BC_2 (M_1 and M_2, respectively), we have what is defined as the *Engel curve* for the commodity X. Thus, *the Engel curve depicts the relationship between a consumer's level of income and the amount of some good consumed.* The Engel curve for X is labeled E_X and is positively sloped in this diagram. For most goods this will be the case. As income increases consumers will purchase more of what we define as *normal goods*. Clothing, recreational equipment, jewelry, vacations, and cameras represent a few examples from a vast array of normal goods. In our diagram in Figure 4.8 we could define X as a normal good because of the positive relationship between income and the amount of X consumed.

Although most goods are in fact normal goods, the consumption of some will increase more rapidly with increasing income than others. Things that are necessities are likely to be much less sensitive to income changes than are things that may be more of a luxury. In the left diagram of Figure 4.9 two Engel curves are drawn to illustrate how the relationship between consumption and income will vary between a necessity

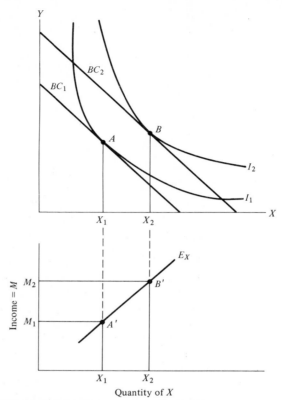

Figure 4.8 An Engel Curve Derivation of the Engel curve for X from an indifference map and budget constraints. If X is a normal good an increase in income from M_1 to M_2 (shifting the budget constraint from BC_1 to BC_2) will increase the consumption of X.

(e.g., clothing) and a luxury (e.g., vacations). These are represented by E_N and E_L, respectively. The consumption of both increases as income increases so both are normal goods, but we see that the Engel curve for necessities may come very close to being vertical at some point, indicating that further increases in income would stimulate virtually no additional consumption. On the other hand, the curve for a luxury good will tend to be more flat, indicating that at a higher level of income consumption may increase appreciably.

Not all goods are normal goods, however. There may be some things that people will consume less of at a higher income than at a lower income. Such goods are called inferior goods and will have an Engel curve with a negative slope (i.e., an inverse relationship between income and consumption).

Potatoes and ground meat are frequently cited as examples of inferior goods, at least for some households. As a low-income household

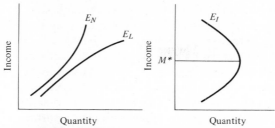

Figure 4.9 Engle Curves for Different Types of Goods Engel curves comparing the relationship between income and consumption for a necessity (E_N), a luxury (E_L), and a good that is inferior (E_I) above some level of income, M^*.

moves to higher levels of income, its members may consume more fresh green vegetables and more steak rather than staple items like potatoes and ground meat. Such relationships depend critically on the preference structure of the particular consumer, as represented by the indifference curves.

The right portion of Figure 4.9 shows an Engel curve (E_I) that has a positive slope up to the income level M^* and then becomes negatively sloped. A good with an Engel curve such as this would be a normal good at lower income levels and an inferior good at a higher income. This type of relation may be more common than the case of an Engel curve that is negatively sloped throughout. This is particularly likely if we define goods in a narrow sense (such as a brand of pen) rather than as a broad class (such as pens in general). For example, a low-income individual may be more likely to buy Bic pens for less than a dollar than gold Cross pens for more than $20. However, with increased income the reverse might well be true, in which case the Bic pen becomes an inferior good. Note that this does not imply that the Bic pen is an inferior product in a quality sense. Rather in the view of our hypothetical consumer it is viewed as inferior according to our particular definition of an inferior good as one for which the rate of consumption varies inversely with income, ceteris paribus. You should be able to think of other examples of this type such as Fords versus Cadillacs, or Cutty Sark scotch versus Chivas Regal.

EFFECTS OF PRODUCT PROMOTION

We have seen that changes in product prices and income influence a consumer's pattern of consumption through shifts of one form or another in the budget constraint, with the preference structure (i.e., the indifference curves) remaining constant or fixed. But many things may cause an individual's preference structure to change such that consumption patterns are altered.

We are all influenced in various ways each day of our lives with respect to our attitudes toward various goods and services. Reference groups such as families, members of clubs to which we belong, and church groups are examples of this set of influences on our consumptive behavior. Perhaps a more obvious and direct influence comes by way of product promotions—point-of-purchase displays; magazine, television and radio advertising; coupons and contests; free samples; and so forth. The source of the influence is not particularly important to the analysis of its effect on consumption. Whether it stems from the church, a Madison Avenue advertising agency, family members, or a government, we can use the same basic model of consumer demand to analyze how consumption may be changed.

Suppose that some factor arises to cause consumers to alter their preference structure between tea and coffee such that tea is more preferred than prior to the influence. In particular, we will assume that an association of tea producers has put on a promotional blitz with extensive advertising, free samples of various teas being distributed door to door, and so on. If the promotion is successful, it would be expected to increase the sale of tea at the expense of the substitute product, coffee in this case.

The change would not be brought about by changes in income or in the relative product prices since we have assumed these to be constant. Rather, the change results from consumers developing a different "mind set" or preference structure due to the promotion. They may become more aware of, and sensitized to, the advantages of tea and the disadvantages of coffee as a beverage. In Figure 4.10 such an effect is illustrated, where point A represents the prepromotion equilibrium and point B the equilibrium established after the promotion for tea.

We see that the budget constraint is fixed and that the different equilibrium points are established by movement of the individual's preference structure (indifference curves). This new view of tea and coffee by the consumer results in an increase of tea consumption from T_1 to T_2 and a decrease in coffee consumption from C_1 to C_2.

It is important to note that the diagram in Figure 4.10 does not violate our earlier statement that indifference curves cannot intersect, despite the fact that it may appear that way if we are not careful to consider exactly what is being depicted. What we really have in this figure is two different preference functions superimposed on a single diagram with one budget constraint.[3] Thus we can't say that I_1 is preferred to I_2, or vice versa. It is entirely possible that the two levels of satisfaction represented are equal. Each represents a preference struc-

---

[3] In our earlier diagrams we have superimposed more than one budget constraint on a single preference structure (indifference map) to analyze the influence of price or income changes on the pattern of consumption.

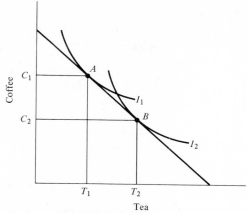

Figure 4.10 Advertising and Consumer Equilibrium The effect of a promotion for tea on the equilibrium consumption of tea and coffee with constant product prices and income and no change in the promotion of coffee.

ture at different points in time during which the consumer's perception of the two products has been altered by the promotional activity on behalf of the tea industry.

SUMMARY

Building on the model of consumer behavior developed in Chapter 3, we have shown that a consumer's budget constraint becomes flatter as the price of X decreases *relative* to the price of Y (alternatively, the budget constraint becomes steeper as the price of Y decreases *relative* to the price of X). Further, we have demonstrated that changes in income shift the budget constraint in a parallel manner, further from the origin for increases in income and closer to the origin as income declines.

Combining these relationships with a constant preference structure (fixed indifference curves), we are able to analyze the effect of price or income changes on the pattern of consumption. As the price of one good changes we can trace out a price–consumption curve that illustrates the changing pattern of consumption for those price changes. The equilibrium points so determined can be used to derive a demand curve, as was done in Figure 4.5.

We find that individual demand curves can normally be expected to follow the "law of demand," which postulates an inverse relationship between price and the quantity consumed. This is certainly consistent with observations we might make in various marketplaces (i.e., consumers are likely to purchase more at lower prices than at higher prices, ceteris paribus). Market demand curves are simply the horizontal sum of individual demand curves and thus, also typically, have a negative slope.

An income–consumption curve traces out the manner in which consumption changes as income changes. From the equilibrium points that determine the income–consumption curve we can derive an Engel curve. The Engel curve depicts the relationship between the level of a consumer's income and the amount of a particular good consumed, ceteris paribus. Engel curves for normal goods are positively sloped, with necessities having a steeper curve than luxuries. If the Engel curve for some good has a negative slope (in some range), the good is defined as being an inferior good (in that range).

Product promotion is seen to affect the consumer's preference structure as represented by the indifference map. The shifting of the preference structure, with constant prices and income, is likely to lead to a new equilibrium position in which the product being promoted is consumed at a higher level than prior to the promotion (such as illustrated in Figure 4.10). Preference structures may be shifted by our association with various reference groups (families, churches, clubs, etc.), as well as by promotional campaigns developed by some advertising agency. The analysis of the effects would be the same, however.

Selected Readings

Boulding, Kenneth E. *Economic Analysis,* 4th ed., vol. 1. New York: Harper & Row, 1966, chap. 24.

Hicks, John A. *A Revision of Demand Theory.* New York: Oxford University Press, 1956.

Leibenstein, Harvey. "Bandwagon, Snob, and Veblen Effects in the Theory of Consumer Demand." *Quarterly Journal of Economics* (May 1950), 183–207.

Stigler, George. "The Development of Utility Theory, I," *Journal of Political Economy* 58 (August 1950), 307–324.

Stigler, George. *The Theory of Price.* New York: Macmillan, 1966.

QUESTIONS

1. Write a short explanation of the following terms or concepts that were used in this chapter:
   (a) change in demand
   (b) change in quantity demanded
   (c) consumer demand
   (d) Engel curve
   (e) income–consumption curve
   (f) "law of demand"
   (g) Market demand
   (h) price–consumption curve

2. Use an indifference mapping and budget constraints to derive a price–consumption curve for the commodity measured along the vertical axis. Explain carefully what the graph shows.

3. Derive a price–consumption curve for the good measured along the horizontal axis of a graph showing a consumer's indifference mapping and budget constraints. On a separate graph immediately below derive the demand curve for that good and explain how points in the two graphs are related.

4. What is the "law of demand"? Does this law hold true for all goods? Some people might say that the law of demand does not hold true for pizza because despite rising prices more pizzas are sold each year in the United States. What is wrong with such reasoning?

5. Construct five hypothetical individual demand schedules for some product. Graph each of these demand schedules on the same graph paper. Then derive the market demand for that product assuming these are the only five consumers in the market and graph the market demand curve. Explain the relationship between individual demand curves and the market demand curve.

6. Pick any advertisement from a popular magazine and explain how you believe that ad would change an individual consumer's demand curve. Show both pre-ad and post-ad demand curves on a graph. Do the same for the market demand for the product. Explain why this ad would be expected to have the effects you've shown.

7. Gasoline consumption and gas prices have been the subject of considerable attention in recent years. Do you think there has been a change in the demand for gas? Has there been a change in the quantity of gasoline demanded? Explain your answer using a graph to illustrate.

8. During the 1970s the growth of sales for fast-food restaurants averaged about 7% per year. At the turn of the decade this growth rate dropped dramatically. The major chains introduced new features (e.g., more started to serve breakfast, salad bars were introduced, a wider variety of sandwiches were offered, etc.). What relevance does the theory of consumer behavior and demand have in this regard?

9. Draw Engel curves for the following three goods on the same graph and explain why they are drawn as they are with relation to one another: food, jewelry, and electricity. Explain any assumptions you make with regard to these goods.

CHAPTER 5
REVENUE AND ELASTICITY CONCEPTS

According to the "law of demand," we can expect that more units of a product will be sold at a lower price than at a higher price, ceteris paribus. But thus far we have not concerned ourselves with the important factor of how many dollars are received by the seller(s) of the product or, equivalently, how many dollars are spent by the consumer(s) of the product. Price changes will usually affect the amount of revenue that changes hands in the exchange process. But this is not always true. In some cases revenue changes in a way that is not expected by those who haven't carefully analyzed the economic forces at work.

In this chapter we shall focus our attention on how various revenue concepts are related to product prices and the resulting number of units sold. For the most part our discussion here will relate to market demand rather than the demand for the output of any individual producer or the demand of a particular consumer. In addition to investigating these revenue concepts we shall discuss several measures of responsiveness of sales to such factors as the product's price, the income level of consumers, and the prices of other products.

TOTAL REVENUE

The *total revenue (TR)* received from the sale of a product is simply *the price (P) at which the product is sold times the number of units sold (Q).* Thus

$$TR = P \cdot Q$$

It should be clear that the amount received by producers *(TR)* must be equal to the total expenditure *(TE)* by consumers of the product (unless *TR* is reduced by taxes, as discussed in Chapters 2 and 16).

In Table 5.1 we have constructed a simple linear demand schedule in columns (1) and (2). We see that for each $5 decrease in price the quantity sold increases by 10 units.[1] In general, every $1 change in price stimulates a 2-unit change in quantity sold (in the opposite direction). In column (3) total revenue (or total expenditure) is calculated by multiplying each price by the number of units sold at that price.[2]

We see that even though there is a constant 2-to-1 ratio between quantity increase and price decrease, total revenue at first increases but then declines. This phenomenon will be explored in detail as we progress through this chapter, but for now it is important to realize that revenue will not necessarily be increased when an increase in the quantity sold is stimulated by a price cut. Also note that in some cases a price increase will result in fewer sales but greater revenue (e.g., if price increases from $10 to $15).

The relationship between total revenue and quantity is graphed in Figure 5.1. In this form it is easy to see that total revenue reaches its peak

Table 5.1 LINEAR DEMAND SCHEDULE

DEMAND SCHEDULE		TOTAL REVENUE(OR EXPENDITURE) ($)
(1)	(2)	(3)
P ($)	Q	TR = TE = P · Q
30	0	0
25	10	250
20	20	400
15	30	450
10	40	400
5	50	250
0	60	0

[1] The algebraic expression for this demand function is $Q_D = 60 - 2P$, where Q_D is the quantity demanded at each price P.
[2] The equation for total revenue is: $TR = P \cdot Q$. From footnote 1 we can solve the demand equation for P as $P = 30 - 0.5Q$. Thus, $TR = (30 - 0.5Q)Q = 30Q - 0.5Q^2$.

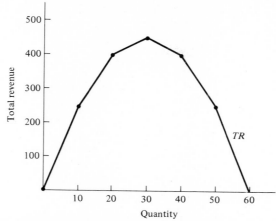

Figure 5.1 Total Revenue The total-revenue function based on the data from Table 5.1. Note that total revenue increases at a decreasing rate, reaches a maximum, and then declines.

at sales of 30 units. From Table 5.1 we find that this many units would be sold when the price is $15.

AVERAGE REVENUE AND MARGINAL REVENUE

Average revenue (AR) is defined as total revenue divided by the number of units sold to generate that revenue. It can be shown that average revenue is always equal to price by the way in which the terms are defined, as follows:

$$AR = \frac{TR}{Q} \frac{(P \cdot Q)}{Q} = P$$

Thus column (1) of Table 5.1 could be headed either average revenue or price. It follows that there will be an inverse relationship between average revenue and quantity.

Marginal revenue is perhaps the most important of the revenue concepts we shall discuss because of the extensive use of "marginal analysis" in the study of economics.[3] *Marginal revenue (MR) is defined as the*

---

[3] The concept of marginal analysis will become apparent as we progress through our study of microeconomics. The term *marginal* is roughly synonymous with incremental (only for very small increments) and thus it is convenient to think of marginal analysis as evaluating various costs and benefits of decisions for the changes implied by the decision.

Table 5.2 TOTAL, AVERAGE, AND MARGINAL REVENUE

P ($)	Q	$TR = P \cdot Q$ ($)	$AR = TR/Q$ ($)	$MR = \Delta TR/\Delta Q$ ($)
30	0	0	30	
25	10	250	25	25
20	20	400	20	15
15	30	450	15	5
10	40	400	10	−5
5	50	250	5	−15
0	60	0	0	−25

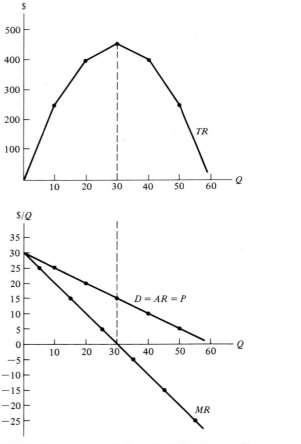

Figure 5.2 Total, Average, and Marginal Revenue The relationship between the total-revenue function (*TR*), the demand curve (*D = AR = P*), and the marginal-revenue function (*MR*). Total revenue increases as long as marginal revenue is positive, reaches its maximum when marginal revenue is zero, and decreases when marginal revenue is negative.

change (Δ) in total revenue per unit change in output sold. In algebraic terms,[4]

$$MR = \frac{\Delta TR}{\Delta Q} \qquad \text{for small changes in } Q$$

In this form we see that marginal revenue is a measure of the rate of change (or slope) of the total-revenue function.

These revenue concepts are all given in tabular form in Table 5.2, the first three columns of which are identical with Table 5.1. The two right-hand columns give the data for average revenue and marginal revenue. Note that the values for marginal revenue are written between the other lines to indicate that those numbers represent the (average) marginal revenue over each interval.

As quantity increases we see that total revenue at first increases and marginal revenue is positive. But eventually total revenue begins to decline as quantity increases and in this range marginal revenue is negative. Looking at Figure 5.2, we see this relationship even more clearly. Remember that marginal revenue measures the rate of change, or slope, of total revenue. We should then expect that when the slope of total revenue is high, marginal revenue will be fairly large. As the slope of the total revenue function declines, marginal revenue becomes less. Ultimately, when the total-revenue curve turns downward, we see that marginal revenue is negative. The marginal-revenue points in Figure 5.2 are plotted at the midpoints of each interval to emphasize that these values represent the average change in total revenue over the interval.

ELASTICITY: A MEASURE OF RELATIVE RESPONSIVENESS

We know that the quantity of a good or service that is sold (or produced) will depend on a number of factors. For example, the quantity sold has been seen to be influenced by the price, consumers' income, and the prices of other products. It is frequently desirable to know the relative degree of responsiveness of sales to changes in one or more of these factors. Further, it may be useful to be able to compare several goods or services in terms of how sensitive their sale is to these changes. To make such comparisons we need a measure of responsiveness that is unaffected by the type or size of the units of measurement involved.

A fairly large family of measures of relative responsiveness have been developed that are referred to as *elasticities.* In the most general form, *an elasticity (E) is the percentage change in some dependent vari-*

---

[4] For those readers familiar with calculus it may be more meaningful to think of marginal revenue as: $MR = dTR/dQ$. For the total-revenue function given in footnote 2 we have: $TR = 30Q - 0.5Q^2$ and $MR = dTR/dQ = 30 - Q$.

able divided by the percentage change in the causal variable that is assumed to have stimulated that change, ceteris paribus. For our purposes the dependent variable will always be quantity (Q) and various causal variables will be considered. For now, we will use X to represent any one of these causal variables. We can then write a general definition of any elasticity as:

$$E = \frac{\%\Delta Q}{\%\Delta X}$$

The larger the value of E the more elastic, or responsive, Q is to changes in X. Since percentage changes are used in the calculation, the elasticity measure is a pure number, void of units, and comparable among various different products.

For each type of elasticity there are two alternative forms: the arc elasticity and the point elasticity. The former is used to calculate an elasticity over some interval, whereas the latter refers to the elasticity at a particular point (i.e., a particular set of values for the variables). Throughout this text we shall use only arc elasticities since the determination of point elasticity is cumbersome without the use of calculus.[5] Further, often only a few observations of the values for each variable are available, an insufficient number for determining the functional relationships necessary to calculate a point elasticity, but this is enough information to calculate the arc form of the elasticity.

There are alternative methods of calculating the percentage changes to use in determining an elasticity. In order to have results that are consistent regardless of the direction of change in the variables it is best to use the midpoint of the intervals as the basis for calculating the percentages. Thus the general form we shall use to calculate arc elasticities is as follows:

$$E = \frac{\dfrac{Q_1 - Q_2}{(Q_1 + Q_2)/2}}{\dfrac{X_1 - X_2}{(X_1 + X_2)/2}} = \frac{\dfrac{\Delta Q}{\text{average } Q}}{\dfrac{\Delta X}{\text{average } X}}$$

where the subscripts refer to the two observations of Q and X being used for the calculation. The 2's in this expression cancel each other algebraically, so we can simplify the expression somewhat as follows:

$$E = \frac{\dfrac{Q_1 - Q_2}{Q_1 + Q_2}}{\dfrac{X_1 - X_2}{X_1 + X_2}}$$

[5] The expression for a point elasticity is $E = (dQ/dX)(X/Q)$. This implies that the function $Q = f(X)$ is known. Unless quite a few data points are available, we would have little confidence in the significance of such a function.

This general form will be used throughout the remainder of the text with price (P), income (M), or some other causal variable replacing X as necessitated by the situation being discussed.

PRICE ELASTICITY OF DEMAND

The most commonly used measure of elasticity is the price elasticity of demand, which measures the percentage change in quantity divided by the percentage change in price, ceteris paribus. We shall use E_P to represent the arc price elasticity of demand; thus

$$E_P = \frac{\%\Delta Q}{\%\Delta P}$$

For purposes of calculation, the form to be used is

$$E_P = \frac{\dfrac{Q_1 - Q_2}{Q_1 + Q_2}}{\dfrac{P_1 - P_2}{P_1 + P_2}}$$

Since price (P) and quantity (Q) are inversely related, E_P will be a negative value (as long as the demand curve has a negative slope). It has become a fairly standard convention to refer to the absolute value of E_P (written $|E_P|$) rather than always saying "minus 0.5" or "minus 2.3" and so forth.

To illustrate the calculation of the arc price elasticity we will use the demand function given initially in Table 5.1 above. That demand schedule and the absolute value of the arc price elasticity for each interval are presented in Table 5.3. Two of these elasticities are calculated below to show exactly how the values were determined.

Table 5.3 CALCULATION OF ARC PRICE ELASTICITY

P	Q	$|E_P|$
30	0	
		11.00
25	10	
		3.00
20	20	
		1.40
15	30	
		0.71
10	40	
		0.33
5	50	
		0.09
0	60	

For the interval from $P = 30$ to $P = 25$,

$$E_P = \frac{\dfrac{0 - 10}{0 + 10}}{\dfrac{30 - 25}{30 + 25}} = \frac{\dfrac{-10}{10}}{\dfrac{5}{55}} = -11.00$$

$$|E_P| = 11$$

For the interval from $P = 10$ to $P = 5$,

$$E_P = \frac{\dfrac{40 - 50}{40 + 50}}{\dfrac{10 - 5}{10 + 5}} = \frac{\dfrac{-10}{90}}{\dfrac{5}{15}} = -0.33$$

$$|E_P| = 0.33$$

Several things should be noted from these elasticities in Table 5.3. First, even though the demand curve is linear (the slope is constant), the relative responsiveness of sales to changes in price, as measured by the arc price elasticity, varies throughout the demand function. This will frequently be the case.[6] Thus, when we hear someone report that the demand for a given product has a particular price elasticity we should interpret that as only being true for the ranges of price and quantity being evaluated (and recognize that in some other range the elasticity may be quite different).

Second, observe that the absolute value of the price elasticity declines as price declines. In Figure 5.3 we see that as we move downward to the right along the demand curve $|E_P|$ is greater than one until the price reaches $15 ($Q = 30$) and below that price (or for Q greater than 30) $|E_P|$ is less than one. By definition,

Demand is price elastic if $|E_P| > 1$.
Demand is price inelastic if $|E_P| < 1$.
Demand is unitarily elastic if $|E_P| = 1$.

Thus we see that demand is more elastic (relatively more responsive to price changes) at higher prices than at lower prices.

In the interval from $P = 30$ to $P = 25$, the percentage change in quantity is 11 times as great as the percentage change in price ($E_P = \%\Delta Q / \%\Delta P = 11.00$). That is to say that in this range quantity is very responsive to price changes. Thus a small percentage decrease in price stimulates a relatively large percentage increase in sales. If this is true, one should expect total revenue to increase. Referring to Figure 5.3, we see that this is true. As long as $|E_P|$ is greater than one, total revenue

[6] There are certain types of demand functions that have constant elasticities throughout, but it is probably accurate to say that most will not. An example of a form of demand function with a constant price elasticity is $Q = aP^{-b}$. In this case, $|E_P| = b$ throughout.

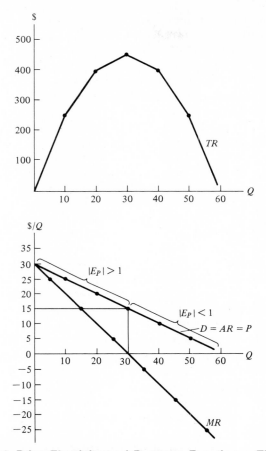

Figure 5.3 Price Elasticity and Revenue Functions The relationship between the coefficient of arc price elasticity (E_P), the demand curve ($D = AR = P$), the marginal-revenue (MR) curve, and the total-revenue (TR) curve. Demand is price elastic when marginal revenue is positive and inelastic when marginal revenue is negative.

will increase with a price decrease (and vice versa). When $|E_P|$ is less than one, a decrease in price will result in a decline in total revenue (the reverse being true again). In cases for which $|E_P| = 1$, price changes will be exactly offset by quantity changes such that total revenue remains unchanged.

There are four factors that tend to influence the price elasticity of demand for various products. The most important of these factors is the number of substitutes available and how close these substitutes are for the product in question. If there are many quite close substitutes available, demand will tend to be fairly elastic. For example, the demand for one brand of milk will generally be quite elastic because alternative brands provide nearly perfect substitutes. The total market demand for milk is likely to be more inelastic, on the other hand, because other beverages are not as good a substitute for milk as one brand of milk is for another. This relationship between the price elasticity for a brand and for the product class is true for most goods (e.g., gas, soap, soft drinks, television, beer, etc.). An extension of this line of reasoning leads us to conclude that the relative necessity of a good also may influence price elasticity. A necessity (such as insulin to a diabetic who must rely on this drug) is likely to be quite inelastic with respect to price.

The percentage of consumer income that is spent for a good is likely to influence elasticity as well. For example, table salt is generally considered to be price inelastic. One reason for this is that expenditures for salt represent a small fraction of personal income. If salt were currently selling at 25 cents for a one-pound box and the price increased by 20 percent to 30 cents, it is probable that very few households would reduce their consumption of salt. The product is purchased so infrequently and has such a low price that it accounts for a very small percent of any one household's total budget.

A third factor that affects the price elasticity for a product is the variety of uses the consumer may have for the product. The more potential uses there are for a product, the more elastic its demand will be. If, for example, tennis shoes could be used only for actual tennis play, not much change in sales could be expected to result from a price change. However, since tennis shoes can in fact be worn for a very wide variety of situations, the elasticity of demand is greater than it would be if there were just the one use.

The fourth factor influencing elasticity is the time horizon being considered. In general, we can say that the shorter the period of time the more inelastic the price elasticity of demand. If, for example, the price of natural gas increases sharply, ceteris paribus, in the short run people will continue to use it for heating and cooking if they have gas appliances. However, over a longer period people would switch to other energy sources and perhaps add insulation to reduce their dependence on gas.

It is usually difficult to separate out each of these influences since more than one may operate at any given time for any particular good or service. They may act in the same direction (e.g., salt being inelastic because there are few substitutes, it is a small part of total expenditures, and it has few potential uses) or in opposite directions (e.g., a car represents a substantial expenditure, but in the opposite direction there are few close substitutes in the eyes of most Americans).

Because elasticity measures are calculated on the basis of percentage changes and are pure numbers, they can be compared among different products regardless of the price-quantity values for the products being compared.

Let us consider a few examples of price elasticities that have been reported in the economic literature. Roger W. Schmenner has studied the fare elasticities of demand for urban bus transit in Hartford, New Haven, and Stamford, Connecticut, and has found them to range from 1.82 to 3.45.[7] Given the relationship between price (fare) elasticity and total revenue discussed above, we might suggest that, unless the buses are currently used to capacity, the transit authority should reduce the fare. With elasticities in this range, ridership is apparently quite sensitive to price changes and would increase proportionately more than the cut in fare (in the current range of fares). Thus lower fares would result in greater total revenue to the transit authority from the increased value of use.

Danielson and DeLorme have estimated the coefficient of price elasticity for crude oil in the United States for two time periods separated by World War II: 1929 to 1941 and 1948 to 1973. Their estimate was 0.02 for both periods. This indicates a very inelastic demand for crude oil, an observation that is certainly consistent with our observations of the sale of crude following the price hikes that resulted after the formation of the OPEC cartel.[8]

In a study of the effect of price increases on participation in a school lunch program in Pittsburgh, Braley and Nelson found that the price elasticity varied from 0.47 at a low price to 1.27 at a high price and on up to 2.95 at a still higher price.[9] This empirical evidence is certainly consistent with the analysis given in Figure 5.3 and the related discussion.

INCOME ELASTICITY OF DEMAND

Income elasticity of demand is defined as the percentage change in sales divided by the corresponding percentage change in income, ceteris paribus. If we let M represent a consumer's money income, we can represent the arc income elasticity of demand as E_M. Thus

$$E_M = \frac{\%\Delta Q}{\%\Delta M}$$

[7] Roger W. Schmenner, "The Demands for Urban Bus Transit: A Route by Route Analysis," *Journal of Transport Economics and Policy* 10 (January 1976), 68–86.

[8] Albert L. Danielson and Charles D. DeLorme, Jr., "Elasticity of Demand for Crude Oil in the United States, 1929–1941 and 1948–1973," *Review of Business and Economic Research* 11 (Winter 1975–1976), 19–29.

[9] George A. Braley and Paul E. Nelson, Jr., "Effect of a Controlled Price Increase on School Lunch Participation: Pittsburgh, 1973," *American Journal of Agricultural Economics* 57 (February 1975), 92–94.

For purposes of calculation, we use the following form:

$$E_M = \frac{\dfrac{Q_1 - Q_2}{Q_1 + Q_2}}{\dfrac{M_1 - M_2}{M_1 + M_2}}$$

For normal goods the value of E_M will be positive since consumption is directly related to income. As we saw in Chapter 4, these are goods for which the Engel curve has a positive slope. As illustrated in our discussion of Engel curves, consumption of necessities tends to be less sensitive to income changes than the consumption of luxuries. It follows that the income elasticity of demand for luxuries will generally be greater than for necessities.

If the income elasticity of demand for a product is greater than one, the product is said to be income elastic; if it is equal to one, the product has unitary income elasticity; and if E_M is less than one, the product is income inelastic. If the coefficient of income elasticity is negative, the commodity is an inferior good.

Suppose that we have two observations of sales of some product Q at two different levels of income M, for which it is safe to assume other influences on sales have been relatively constant. These values are:

$$Q_1 = 100{,}000 \text{ units/year} \qquad M_1 = \$12{,}500\text{/year}$$
$$Q_2 = 150{,}000 \text{ units/year} \qquad M_2 = \$15{,}800\text{/year}$$

The income elasticity of demand would be:

$$E_M = \frac{\dfrac{100{,}000 - 150{,}000}{100{,}000 + 150{,}000}}{\dfrac{12{,}500 - 15{,}800}{12{,}500 + 15{,}800}} = \frac{\dfrac{-50{,}000}{250{,}000}}{\dfrac{3{,}300}{28{,}300}} = 1.72$$

In times of economic growth and expansion the sale of goods that are income elastic will tend to exceed the rate of growth in consumers' incomes, while those that are income inelastic will lag behind. Thus an understanding of income elasticity can be a very useful aid in forecasting future demand.

CROSS-PRICE ELASTICITY OF DEMAND

Cross-price elasticity of demand provides a measure of the responsiveness of the sales of one product to changes in the price of some other product. If we let A represent the good whose quantity changes and B represent the good which has a price change, we can define *cross-price elasticity of demand E_C as the percentage change in the quantity of good A which is sold divided by the percentage change in the price of some* *other good B, ceteris paribus.* That is:

$$E_C = \frac{\%\Delta Q_A}{\%\Delta P_B}$$

The fact that two different goods are involved necessitates using some additional subscripts in the algebraic formulation of the arc cross-price elasticity of demand (E_C). These additional subscripts A and B simply allow us to keep straight the product whose price is changing and the one for which we are evaluating quantity changes. The calculation is:

$$E_C = \frac{\dfrac{Q_{A_1} - Q_{A_2}}{Q_{A_1} + Q_{A_2}}}{\dfrac{P_{B_1} - P_{B_2}}{P_{B_1} + P_{B_2}}}$$

The cross-price elasticity is useful in evaluating whether pairs of goods can be considered substitutes for one another, complementary to one another, or independent of one another. *Goods are substitutes if the cross-price elasticity is positive.* Let us reason through an example using the sale of margarine as it might be affected by changes in the price of butter. If the price of butter were to increase, we would expect the quantity of butter sold to decrease. If less butter is sold, we would further expect consumers to use more margarine. Thus the direction of change in the quantity of margarine and the price of butter would be the same and the ratio of the two percentage changes would be positive.

We classify goods as complements if the cross-price elasticity is negative. For example, consider what would happen to the sale of eight-track tape players if the cost of tapes was to increase substantially (perhaps due to shortages in the supplies of petrochemical inputs). Tape players are not of much use without tapes, so we would expect that an increase in the denominator of E_C $(\%\Delta P_B)$ would, in this case, be accompanied by a decrease in the numerator $(\%\Delta Q_A)$ with the result that E_C would be negative.

If a price change for B has no effect on the sales of A, the numerator of E_C $(\%\Delta Q_A)$ will be zero, so E_C will be zero as well. *We say that the two goods are independent of one another if the cross-price elasticity is zero.* For example, an increase in the price of lead pencils would probably have no influence on the sale of dictionaries in the college book store. If so, we would calculate a zero cross-price elasticity for this pair of (independent) goods.

Because cross-price elasticity provides some insight into the degree and type of relationship between goods this measure is useful in defining what constitutes an industry, or product group. In antitrust cases it becomes important to be able to define industry boundaries. Section 7 of the Clayton Act requires that the "line of commerce" be defined in such cases and cross-price elasticities are helpful in making this determination. The higher the value of E_C the stronger the argument that the two goods are in the same industry (i.e., are substitutes for one another). It can also be suggested that the lower E_C is (a large negative number) the more likely the two goods are to be strongly complementary. In either situation, a merger could "lessen competition" and thus be in violation of the Clayton Act. Thus, firms contemplating merger may hope to be able to show a near-zero cross-price elasticity between product lines.

Before leaving our discussion of cross-price elasticity we might mention some additional results from Braley and Nelson's study of participation in school lunch programs. As the price of school lunches increased, their study shows that more students found ways to qualify for the special "free" lunch program. Clearly, we would expect the "free" lunch program to be a substitute for "paid" lunches. This was confirmed by their estimates of the cross-price elasticity of demand which ranged from 0.18 to 0.34.[10] It was consistently positive, and the relatively low values indicate that the two are not very close substitutes. Conceptually, one might think they should be perfect substitutes, but we must recognize the constraint imposed by various eligibility requirements for the "free" lunch program (which rules out substitution for a large segment of the relevant population).

PRICE ELASTICITY OF SUPPLY

The quantity producers (or sellers) are willing and able to sell may also be influenced by changes in price. The measure of this degree of responsiveness is the *price elasticity of supply* (E_S), *which is defined as the percentage change in the quantity supplied* (Q_S) *divided by the corresponding percentage change in price;* that is,

$$E_S = \frac{\%\Delta Q_S}{\%\Delta P}$$

For purposes of calculation we use a form analogous to that used for price elasticity of demand, as follows:

$$E_S = \frac{\dfrac{Q_{S_1} - Q_{S_2}}{Q_{S_1} + Q_{S_2}}}{\dfrac{P_1 - P_2}{P_1 + P_2}}$$

We will only consider the arc form once more as given above.

Since the quantity supplied is generally positively related to price (i.e., supply curves usually have a positive slope), the price elasticity of

---

[10] Braley and Nelson, "School Lunch," p. 94.

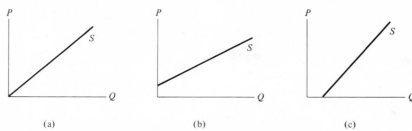

Figure 5.4 Price Elasticity of Supply Supply curves that are (a) unitarily price elastic, (b) price elastic, and (c) price inelastic.

supply will be a positive value. We categorize supply price elasticities as follows:

If $E_S > 1$ supply is elastic.
If $E_S < 1$ supply is inelastic.
If $E_S = 1$ supply is unitarily elastic.

It can be shown that: (1) if a supply curve is linear and intercepts at the origin, $E_S = 1$; (b) if it is linear and intercepts the vertical axis (the price axis) at a positive value, supply is elastic ($E_S > 1$); and (c) if the supply curve is linear and intercepts the horizontal axis (the quantity axis) at a positive value, supply is inelastic ($E_S < 1$).[11] Each of these cases is illustrated in Figure 5.4.

The price elasticity of supply is also influenced by the length of the time period being considered. If the period is so short that no adjustment can be made in the quantity available for sale regardless of price, supply will be perfectly inelastic. In this case the supply curve would be a perfectly vertical line at the existing quantity. As the time period being considered lengthens, the price elasticity of supply will tend to increase because producers (or sellers) have a greater ability to respond to price changes. The elasticity of supply will be influenced by technological forces as well (this will be more apparent once we have discussed production and cost concepts in subsequent chapters).

SUMMARY

The total revenue derived from the sale of any good or service is exactly equal to the total expenditure by consumers (ignoring taxes for now) and is defined as price times quantity ($TR = TE = P \cdot Q$). Because price and quantity generally change in opposite directions, a price increase (de-

---

[11] For nonlinear supply functions the price elasticity of supply can be put into one of these three categories by evaluating the line that is tangent to the supply curve at any point in a similar manner.

crease) and the resulting decrease (increase) in quantity sold may cause total revenue to rise, to fall, or perhaps remain the same depending on the price elasticity of demand.

If demand is price elastic, price reductions, and resulting quantity increases, will cause total revenue to increase. However, if demand is price inelastic the opposite will be true. In Figure 5.3 these relationships are illustrated. We see in that figure that when demand is elastic, marginal revenue ($MR = \Delta TR/\Delta Q$) is positive; when demand is inelastic, marginal revenue is negative. It follows that marginal revenue will be zero when demand is unitarily elastic with respect to price. When this is true, a change in price (and quantity) will not result in any change in total revenue.

Just as price elasticity measures the relative responsiveness of sales to changes in price, other forms of demand elasticities measure the relative responsiveness of sales to other factors. Income and cross-price elasticities are the most common (after price elasticity) of these other measures. The former reveals the relative responsiveness of sales to changes in consumer income, whereas the latter indicates how responsive the sale of one product is to price changes for some other product.

All of the elasticity concepts discussed must be determined and evaluated with careful attention to the ceteris paribus assumption. For example, with price elasticity we want to evaluate the relative influence of just price changes on sales. If at the same time that price declines income increases, we cannot say how much of the increase in sales was due to the price change and how much was due to the changing level of income.

Selected Readings

Baumol, William J. *Economic Theory and Operations Analysis*, 3d ed. Englewood Cliffs, N.J.: Prentice-Hall, 1972, chap. 9 and 10.

Foster, Henry S., and Bruce R. Beattie. "Urban Residential Demand for Water in the United States." *Land Economics* (February 1979), 43–58.

Hogarty, Thomas F., and Kenneth G. Elzinga. "The Demand for Beer." *Review of Economics and Statistics* (May 1972), 195–198.

Jung, J. M., and E. T. Fujii. "The Price Elasticity of Demand for Air Travel." *Journal of Transport Economics and Policy* (September 1976), 257–262.

Suits, Daniel B. "The Elasticity of Demand for Gambling." *Quarterly Journal of Economics* (February 1979), 155–162.

Working, F. J. "What Do Statistical Demand Curves Show?" *Quarterly Journal of Economics* (February 1927), 212–235.

QUESTIONS

1. Write a short explanation of the following terms or concepts that were used in this chapter:

(a) average revenue
(b) complementary goods
(c) cross-price elasticity of demand
(d) elasticity of supply
(e) income elasticity of demand
(f) marginal revenue
(g) price elasticity of demand
(h) substitute goods
(i) total revenue

2. Given the demand schedule in the table below fill in the columns for total revenue (TR), average revenue (AR), and marginal revenue (MR). Draw the total revenue curve in one graph and the average revenue, marginal revenue and demand curves on a separate graph immediately below the total revenue graph. Explain the relationship between your marginal revenue curve and the total revenue curve.

Price	Quantity	TR	AR	MR
8	0			
7	1			
6	2			
5	3			
4	4			
3	5			
2	6			
1	7			

3. Calculate the price elasticity of demand for the following price changes based on the demand schedule in Question 2.

Price Change	Price Elasticity
(a) from $7 to $6	
(b) from $3 to $2	
(c) from $5 to $3	
(d) from $5 to $4	

Which of the above would be an example of an elastic, inelastic, or unitarily elastic demand? Explain how these elasticities relate to the graphs in Question 2.

4. In Question 5 of Chapter 4 you constructed a market demand curve. Using that curve develop a table showing total revenue, average revenue, and marginal revenue (like the table in Question 2 above). Does your market demand have different elasticities in different regions? Calculate at least three elasticities: one near the high-price end, one near the middle, and one near the low-price end.

5. Do you see any relationship between income elasticity and the slope or shape of an Engel curve? How would you expect the income elasticities of food, jewelry, and gasoline to compare? Relate this answer to your answer to Question 9 in Chapter 4.

6. List three pairs of goods that you would expect to have positive, negative, and zero cross-price elasticities (i.e., $E_C > 0, E_C < 0, E_C = 0$)

Pairs of Goods		E_C
1	and	
2	and	
3	and	
4	and	
5	and	
6	and	
7	and	
8	and	
9	and	

Which pairs of goods are complementary, which are substitutes, and which are independent?

7. What types of goods would you expect to have: (a) an elastic demand; and (b) an inelastic demand? Explain why. What are the factors that determine the relative degree of price elasticity? Explain how these factors relate to the elasticity of demand for gasoline? How do they relate to the demand for single-family residential housing? For mass transit?

8. Do you think that the demand for a four-year college education is elastic or inelastic with respect to price (tuition)? With respect to a person's income? Would this vary depending on the four-year school you were considering? Explain.

9. Do you think that local merchants in the retail sector use the concepts of income, price, or cross-price elasticity in making their decisions? Explain. Interview several local merchants to see whether they consider the sensitivity of sales to price in their decisions.

10. Odin K. Knudsen and Paul J. Servelle have estimated the following elasticities for higher education for private schools with nearby public schools:

Price elasticity (for effective tuition and fees) = -0.96
Income elasticity = 2.53
Cross-price elasticity = $+0.13$

Interpret each of these elasticities individually and then write a paragraph commenting on how this information might be useful to the president of a private college. (See "The Demand for Education at Private Institutions of Moderate Selectivity," *The American Economist*, Fall 1978, 30–34.)

11. Better Brand, Inc. has estimated the demand function for their line of ten-speed bikes as follows:

$$Q = 15 - 4P + 0.5DPI + 2.2P_0$$

Q is sales in thousands per year, P is their average price, DPI is disposable personal income per capita in real terms, and P_0 is the average price of their major competitors.

(a) If $P = \$120$, $DPI = \$4000$, and $P_0 = \$140$, how many bikes can Better Brand expect to sell?

(b) If DPI and P_0 remain constant and P is increased to $140, how much would sales change?

(c) What would be the price elasticity of demand for the change from (a) to (b)?

(d) If $P = \$120$, $DPI = \$4000$, and P_0 changes to $130, what will be the effect on Better Brand sales? What is the cross-price elasticity of demand? Does this make sense? Why?

(e) If $P = \$120$ and $P_0 = \$140$, but income falls to $3000, what would be your estimate of the income elasticity of demand?

CHAPTER 6
ADDITIONAL TOPICS
IN DEMAND ANALYSIS

SUBSTITUTION AND INCOME EFFECTS
EFFICIENCY IN EXCHANGE
SUBSIDIES: MONEY OR GOODS IN KIND
THE MARGINAL UTILITY OF MONEY AND INCOME REDISTRIBUTION
CONSUMER'S SURPLUS
SUMMARY
SELECTED READINGS
QUESTIONS

Many of the concepts developed in the previous chapters relating to demand have a wide scope of applications in economic analysis. The patterns of analyses and the logic inherent in them provide the foundation for much of the study of microeconomics throughout the remainder of the text. In this chapter we apply the methodology developed thus far to several interesting and important issues. First, we shall see how changes in the quantity of a good demanded, due to a price change, can be separated into two parts: the substitution and the income effects. Next we shall consider the analysis of exchange within the framework of an "Edgeworth box" and uncover the important principle of "Pareto optimality." We then focus attention on the question of whether it is preferable to provide money subsidies to low-income households or to provide subsidies "in kind," such as food or housing. Fourth, we shall investigate some of the economic relationships involved in income redistribution programs. Finally, the concept of a consumer's surplus will be developed. This concept has important ramifications for a firm's pricing policy as well as for various public sector decisions.

SUBSTITUTION AND INCOME EFFECTS

When the price of something goes up, we know that fewer units will generally be purchased (and vice versa). This change in quantity demanded can be attributed to two effects. First, when the price of one good goes up, other goods appear *relatively* less expensive and, as a result, consumers will substitute them for the now more expensive item. Second, an increase in the price of one product that we purchase has the effect of reducing our "real income" or purchasing power. Thus, the total effect of a price change on the quantity demanded can be partitioned into a substitution effect and an income effect.

The substitution effect is the change in the quantity of X purchased due solely to the change in price, after compensating the consumer for the resulting change in real income. We define real income for this purpose as maintaining the same level of satisfaction (i.e., remaining on the same indifference curve). *The income effect is the change in the quantity of X purchased due to the change in real income, after taking out the substitution effect.*

To see just how these two effects can be separated, let us take a concrete example. In Figure 4.3 we illustrated the total effect of a price increase on the quantity of good X that would be purchased in the context of deriving the demand curve for X. The relevant portion of that diagram is reproduced in Figure 6.1, in which the total effect of that price rise is partitioned into the income and substitution effects.

In this example, income is $120, the price of Y is $7.50 and the price of X increases from $8.00 to $15.00. Given these conditions, we see that the consumer maximizes satisfaction at point A (where the original budget constraint BC_1 is tangent to indifference curve I_2). When the price of X increases to $15.00, the budget constraint becomes BC_2 and the equilibrium combination of X and Y is at point B along indifference curve I_1. The total effect of the price rise on consumption of X is from A to B, or from 9 units to 4 units. The consumer has a lower real income since I_1 lies below I_2.

Suppose we compensate the consumer by providing an income supplement sufficient to permit him or her once more to reach I_2 given the new set of product prices. Such a budget constraint is given by the dashed line (which is labeled BC_H since it is often considered a hypothetical budget constraint). BC_H has the same slope as BC_2 since it represents the new higher price for X. It is tangent to I_2 at point C. Thus, *if* the consumer had the same level of real income (satisfaction) after the price increase as before, consumption of X would be reduced from point A to point C (or from 9 to 7 units) as Y is substituted for the now more expensive X. This then is the substitution effect of the price increase.

The income effect can now be determined by taking away the income supplement (i.e., moving from BC_H to BC_2) but maintaining the higher price of X. This is represented as movement from C to B in Figure 6.1, or from 7 to 4 units of X. We see that X is a normal good in this example since the income effect is positive (income and consumption of

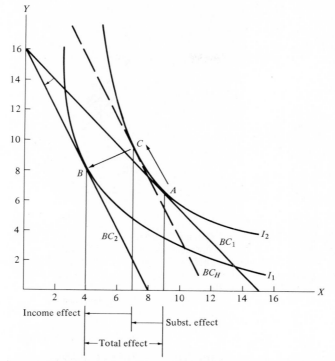

Figure 6.1 Income and Substitution Effects for a Price Increase Determination of the substitution effect ($A \rightarrow C$), the income effect ($C \rightarrow B$), and the total effect ($A \rightarrow B$) for an increase in the price of X.

X move in the same direction; i.e., an income-consumption curve would pass through points B and C and have a positive slope).

The substitution effect of a price change is always negative because a price decrease for S will provide incentive for consumers to substitute X for Y, and an increase in the price of X will provide the opposite incentive. The income effect may be positive (as in the example above), negative (as in the case of an inferior good with negatively sloped income-consumption and Engel curves), or neutral (vertical income-consumption and Engel curves). As we see in Figure 6.1, *a positive income effect reinforces the negative substitution effect,* both causing less X to be consumed as the price of X increases. *If the income effect is negative, it works in the opposite direction of the substitution effect.* This case is illustrated in Figure 6.2.

In an extreme case, a negative income effect may exceed the substitution effect, in which case the demand curve would have a positive slope. If this is true, the good is called a *Giffen good;* see Figure 6.2(b).

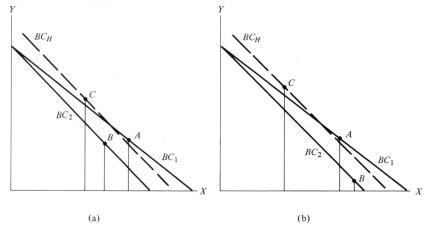

(a)   (b)

Figure 6.2 Inferior and Giffen Goods Partitioning of the total
effect (A → B) of a price increase for X into the substitution effect
(A → C) and the income effect (C → B) for an inferior good (an
income consumption curve through C and B would have a
negative slope). In (b) the negative income effect is greater than
the substitution effect so that illustration is representative of a
Giffen good.

Consider, for example, a poor family that exists on a diet of mostly
potatoes and some ground meat. If the price of potatoes increases, they
may find that the effect on their total purchasing power (real income) is so
great that they no longer can afford any ground meat, and as a result they
purchase even more potatoes.

Since most of the goods we purchase typically account for a small
fraction of our total spending, the income effect is usually relatively
slight. Thus, even if the income effect is negative, it is unlikely to be
sufficient to offset the substitution effect.

To reinforce the concept of separating the income and substitution
effects of a price change, and because prices may move in either direction, we have illustrated these effects in Figure 6.3 for a price decrease.
Note that the procedure is exactly the same regardless of the direction of
the price change. The steps may be summarized as follows:

1. Draw the original budget constraint (BC_1) and locate the original
   equilibrium point (A).
2. Draw the new budget constraint (BC_2) reflecting the price change
   and locate the new equilibrium point (B).
3. Draw the hypothetical budget constraint (BC_H) parallel to the
   new budget constraint (BC_2) but tangent to the original indifference curve (the one A lies on) and locate the point C at the
   tangency.

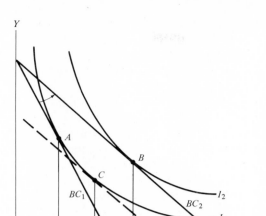

**Figure 6.3 Income and Substitution Effects for a Price
Decrease** Determination of the substitution effect ($A \rightarrow C$), the
income effect ($C \rightarrow B$), and the total effect ($A \rightarrow B$) for a decrease
in the price of X.

4. The substitution effect is the change in the quantity of the good
   whose price changed represented by movement from A to C.
5. The income effect is the change in the quantity of the good whose
   price changed represented by movement from C to B.

EFFICIENCY IN EXCHANGE

Indifference curve analysis can be used to help answer the question:
When will voluntary exchange between consumers take place? The
complex concept of the exchange of a plethora of products among many
consumers can be simplified from these dimensions into a two-
dimensional problem without any loss of generality and with great gains
in terms of ease of exposition and understanding.

Let us take a hypothetical case of two consumers, whom we shall call
Ann and Bob, who have just two products to consume: beer and pretzels.
Each consumer has some utility function for beer and pretzels that can be
represented by an indifference mapping. In Figure 6.4, Ann's indifference curves are convex to O_A (Ann's origin), at the lower left corner. Six of
her indifference curves are drawn, with those further from the origin represent a higher level of satisfaction than those that are closer to the origin
(i.e., $I_6^A > I_5^A > I_4^A > I_3^A > I_2^A > I_1^A$). For Ann, the quantity of beer increases from left to right while the quantity of pretzels increases from
bottom to top (as indicated at the bottom and along the left of the diagram, respectively).

Bob's preference function is represented in a similar manner, except it has been rotated 180° and superimposed on the same commodity space as Ann's. Thus, while Bob's indifference curves have the standard properties, they appear concave from below (*but note that they are convex to Bob's origin, O_B*). Points along I_6^B are preferred to points along I_5^B, and so forth, with I_1^B being the lowest level shown for Bob. Because the axes for Bob have been rotated 180°, the quantity of beer for Bob increases from right to left, and the quantity of pretzels increases from top to bottom (as indicated at the top and along the right of the diagram, respectively).

Each point in this space, called an Edgeworth box (after the English economist F. Y. Edgeworth), represents some allocation of the available beer and pretzels between Ann and Bob. The total amount of the two goods available is represented by the height and width of the box. Suppose the initial allocation is at point F, such that Ann has nearly all the pretzels and relatively little beer, while Bob has most of the beer but very few pretzels. Is a voluntary exchange likely to result? The answer is definitely yes.

At F, Ann's marginal rate of substitution of beer for pretzels is considerably greater than Bob's. This is apparent from the diagram since at F, Ann's indifference curve (I_3^A) is more steeply sloped than Bob's (I_2^B).

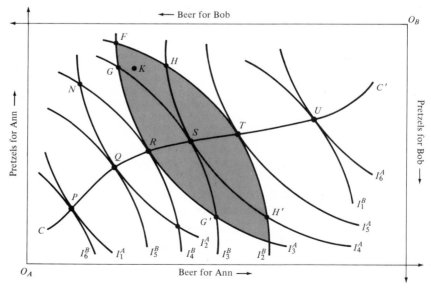

Figure 6.4 Efficiency in Consumer Exchange Edgeworth box diagram of exchange. Given an initial allocation at F, exchange will take place in the shaded region and ultimately end up along the contract curve (CC') in the interval from R to T.

Thus, Ann is willing to give up more units of pretzels for a unit of beer than would be necessary to just compensate Bob for giving up that one unit of beer.

Economic reasoning cannot tell us exactly how exchange will take place, but it does allow us to define some limits to exchange and to specify the set of points which will contain the final point of equilibrium after exchange. Suppose, for example, that Bob offered to make the exchange from F to G. Such a trade would enhance Bob's satisfaction, from I_2^B to I_3^B, while leaving Ann at the same level of satisfaction. If Bob is a persuasive person, this trade might well be consummated since Ann would be no worse off and Bob would be better off. However, Ann is likely to counter with the suggestion that the exchange be made between F and H. This trade would improve Ann's satisfaction while leaving Bob at the same level, a result that would imply that Ann was the better bargainer. Note that exchanges to G' and H' have the same consequences in terms of each consumer's satisfaction as the exchanges to G and H, but very different allocations of the available beer and pretzels.

We might expect a compromise exchange to point K to result since at K both consumers would be on higher indifference curves than at point F. Voluntary exchange to a point such as N would, however, not occur because Ann would be worse off than before the trade.

We can then say that exchange may take place along I_3^A, or along I_2^B, or to any point interior to them, such as K. Given an initial allocation at F, the shaded area represents the region of possible trade. But we see that if exchange occurs such that a new distribution of goods is obtained at G, H, or K, still further exchange is likely since the marginal rate of substitution of beer for pretzels will still be different for Ann than for Bob (i.e., their indifference curves have unequal slopes). And so exchange would continue until a point such as R, S, or T is reached, where the two consumers' indifference curves are tangent (i.e., have equal slopes). Given F as the starting point, we can say that the final distribution, after voluntary exchange, will lie some place along the line segment RT, but beyond that we cannot be more precise.

All of these points of tangency (along with such points as P, Q, and U) form what is called a *contract curve* (CC'), *which represents all possible Pareto optimal distributions of the two goods (i.e., optimal in the sense that no further exchange can take place that will enhance the satisfaction of one person without diminishing the satisfaction of another)*. The fact that these points are all Pareto optimal does not necessarily imply that any one of them is "better" than another. The points along CC' simply represent efficient points of exchange based upon the consumers' utility functions and their voluntary action. Whether the final result is "socially desirable" or "equitable" is beyond the realm of economics to determine.

SUBSIDIES: MONEY OR GOODS IN KIND

In the United States the percentage of the population that qualifies for some type of government subsidy is quite large and increasing. While this is a difficult percentage to measure and avoid double counting, it is probably conservative to say that 20 to 25 percent of the population receives some form of either a food or housing subsidy, or both.

The efficiency of such programs can be analyzed, at least in part, using indifference curve analysis. Let us first consider one form of housing subsidy in which the government pays a portion of the rent for qualifying households. This has the effect of lowering the price (rent) of housing to the individual household, and thus we should expect more units of housing to be purchased with the subsidy than without.

This raises a question of how units of housing should be measured. The number of square feet of space is one obvious measure, but other components of housing (such as number of baths, type of plumbing, type of heating/air-conditioning, amount of insulation, neighborhood, etc.) are also important. For purposes of discussion, we will define a measure of "functional housing units" (FHU) that includes all relevant housing attributes.

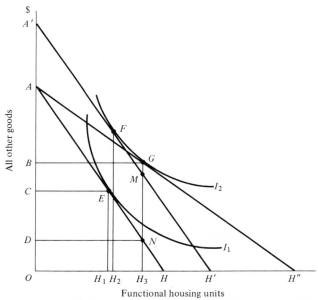

Figure 6.5 The Effect of a Housing Subsidy Analysis of the effect of a housing subsidy on the number of functional housing units (*FHU*) consumed and the cost of such a program to both the consumer and the government.

A representative preference function for housing (FHU) versus money (which can be thought of as "all other goods") is depicted by the indifference curves in Figure 6.5. The original budget constraint (with no subsidy) is given by the line AH. Since the vertical axis measures money (for which the price is $1), the absolute value of the slope of AH is the market rent or price per FHU. For these initial conditions the equilibrium is at E, on indifference curve I_1, with H_1 units of housing consumed.

Now suppose the government offers to pay part of the market rent. The effective budget constraint becomes AH'', which has a flatter slope because the price of housing to the consumer is now less. A new equilibrium is established at G, on indifference curve I_2, with H_3 units of housing consumed. The program has had the effect of increasing consumer satisfaction, from I_1 to I_2, and increasing the quantity of FHUs utilized. Thus, the goal of the program has been reached (at least to some degree).

How much of the housing bill is paid by the government and how much by the consumer can be determined from Figure 6.5 as well. Initially, the consumer used AC dollars to purchase the H_1 FHUs. After the subsidy is established, the consumer has more FHUs (H_3), but pays less (AB dollars). The total market cost of H_3 FHUs is AD dollars. This can be determined from the original budget constraint (AH), whose slope is the market price. Point N represents the purchase of H_3 units at the market price, with D dollars left for other purchases out of the total income of A dollars. Thus, the distance AD represents the total cost for the H_3 units. But with the subsidy the consumer pays just AB dollars, so the cost of the program to the government (taxpayers) is BD dollars.

The consumer could be made just as well off at a lower cost, however. Ask this question: How many dollars would it cost to raise the consumer to satisfaction level I_2? Given the initial market prices, we see that if the consumer had an income of A', this indifference curve could be reached. Thus, a pure money transfer payment of $A'A$ dollars would accomplish the same thing in terms of consumer satisfaction as BD dollars of housing subsidy. Since, by the way in which the diagram is constructed, $A'A = MN$, $BD = GN$, and $MN < GN$, the cost to the government is greater using the housing subsidy than a pure money transfer (ignoring any differentials in the administrative costs of the two programs).

But there is more to be considered. Note that if the pure money grant is used to raise the consumer to I_2, the equilibrium is at point F. This represents H_2 FHUs, which, though greater than H_1, is less than H_3. Thus, if the objective is to increase people's sense of well-being, the pure money transfer is preferred because it achieves the same result as the housing subsidy but at a lower cost. In addition, it preserves the consumer's sovereignty to allocate expenditures to maximize satisfaction according to individual preferences. However, if the objective is to provide some particular level of housing (such as H_3), the subsidy is more efficient since a pure money grant greater than $BD = GN$ dollars would be necessary to induce the consumer to increase housing consumption to that level voluntarily.

To illustrate that this result is not unique to a housing subsidy, let us analyze the food stamp program as well. The conditions assumed are as follows: (1) All food is purchased at market prices regardless of whether payment is with cash money or with food stamps; (2) some direct money expenditure is required by recipients (for example, food stamps worth $150 at the grocery may be purchased for $80 in cash); and (3) a consumer's preference function for money (all other goods) and food is given by indifference curves I_1, I_2, and I_3 in Figure 6.6.

The budget constraint AF represents the situation faced by the consumer without a food stamp program. The absolute value of the slope of AF is the price of food. The consumer would be in equilibrium at point H with F_1 units of food costing AC dollars.

Now let us initiate a food stamp program in which the consumer must pay AB dollars to obtain food stamps, which can be used to purchase $BE = F_3$ units of food (e.g., $AB = \$80$, which buys $150 in food

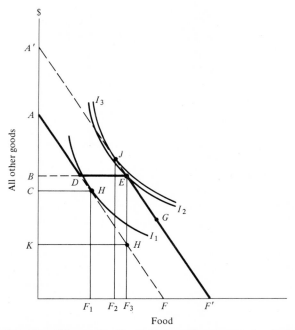

Figure 6.6 The Effect of a Food Stamp Program Analysis of the effect of a food stamp program on the purchase of food and the cost of such a program to both the consumer and the government.

stamps that can be used to purchase F_3 units of food). The budget constraint then becomes $ADEF'$. Beyond F_3 units the consumer continues to pay the market price for food, so EF' is parallel to AF. The consumer is in equilibrium at point E and purchases F_3 units of food. That many units of food has a total cost of AK dollars, of which the consumer has paid AB dollars and the government the remaining BK dollars. The consumer spends less $(AB < AC)$ on food, but gets more $(F_3 > F_1)$ and is at a higher level of satisfaction $(I_2 > I_1)$.

If we took the government cost of BK dollars and gave it to the consumer as a cash grant of $A'A$ dollars $(A'A = EH = BK)$, the consumer would be better off (along I_3), but would purchase fewer units of food $(F_2 < F_3)$ than with the food stamp program. Alternatively, the consumer could get to I_2 with less of an income supplement than $A'A$ dollars. Once again, the effectiveness of the food stamp program versus a cash grant program depends on whether the objective is to maximize consumer satisfaction or to achieve some externally determined level of food consumption by the individual.[1]

THE MARGINAL UTILITY OF MONEY AND INCOME REDISTRIBUTION

It is frequently argued that we should avoid or reduce taxes that are regressive (such as general sales taxes) in favor of more progressive taxes (such as the federal income tax).[2] Further, it is presumed that money collected from such a tax structure could, in part, be redistributed from higher-income taxpayers to lower-income groups, via government programs of various types, to the net benefit of the entire society. To a large extent this supposition is based on certain assumptions concerning the marginal utility of money.

First, one must assume that the marginal utility of money diminishes as the level of income rises. This is not too difficult an assumption to accept on an individual basis. If you were very poor, the additional satisfaction you would receive from having one more dollar to spend would surely be greater than it would if you were a multimillionaire. While the marginal utility for some things may eventually become negative, it does not appear that this is the case with money. Money may be subject to diminishing marginal utility, but it is probably always positive (i.e., more money is always preferred to less).

---

[1] Note that if the consumer's equilibrium along $A'F'$ was below E, such as at G, the cost and results of the two alternative programs would be identical.

[2] A tax is progressive if the *percentage* of income that goes to pay that tax increases as income increases. A tax is regressive if that *percentage* decreases as income increases and a tax is proportional if that *percentage* is constant regardless of the income level. See Chapter 16 for a further discussion of various aspects of tax policy.

Second, we must make an assumption about the rate of decline in the marginal utility of money. If progressive taxes are more equitable, we must be asserting that the larger tax bite, at a higher level of income, has less impact on consumer *satisfaction* than a smaller dollar tax at a lower income. Thus, the marginal utility of income must diminish at a rate faster than the rate of progressivity in the tax structure.

Next we must assume that we can compare utility or satisfaction among various groups. That is, we must be able to say that the loss in *satisfaction* to the high-income taxpayer is less than the gain in *satisfaction* to the lower-income recipient of some government transfer payment. This is a difficult assumption since we have no way to make the comparison. It is much like debating whether my headache is worse than yours. There is no common ground of measurement available to us, at this state of the art, to provide a basis for such an evaluation. However, while strict interpersonal comparisons are not possible, we (as a nation) appear willing to accept the idea that the loss of *satisfaction* to high-income taxpayers is less than the gain in *satisfaction* to lower-income recipients.

Suppose that we have a *social utility* function such that we can obtain the marginal-utility curve for money as given in Figure 6.7. If we also assume that at any given level of income each person has the same marginal utility for money, this diagram can be used to illustrate the effect of a progressive tax and subsequent redistribution of income on society's well-being. Suppose that a tax of *EH* dollars is imposed on a higher-income person and that a transfer payment of *AD* dollars is made to a lower-income individual. Since *AD* < *EH*, we are allowing for some

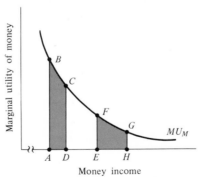

Figure 6.7 The Welfare Effect of Income Redistribution
Illustration of the effect of an income redistribution on the overall welfare of society. A tax of *EH* on a high income with *AD* of the tax redistributed to a lower-income person results in a gain in society's welfare because the loss of satisfaction (*EFGH*) is less than the gain in satisfaction (*ABCD*), assuming that MU_M is derived from a social utility function for money representing the entire society.

administrative cost or other nontransfer use of tax revenue (such as building a hydroelectric dam). The area *ABCD* is the gain in satisfaction to the lower-income individual while the area *EFGH* is the loss of satisfaction to the higher-income person. In this illustration the gain is more than 1.5 times the loss even though only half the tax revenue is assumed to be used as an income transfer.

Thus, given the assumptions stated above, we can conclude that the overall welfare of society is enhanced by progressive taxation combined with a program of income redistribution.

CONSUMER'S SURPLUS

While we are generally inclined to complain that "prices are too high" for most of the things we purchase, in point of fact we would be willing to pay more for many things than we have to rather than do without them entirely. We define the *consumer's surplus as that difference between the total amount the consumer would be willing to pay for a given quantity of some good and the total amount actually paid* (the latter is $TR = TE = P \cdot Q$, as defined in Chapter 5).

A consumer's demand curve for some product is illustrated in Figure 6.8. Given this demand function, we see that if the price is $5, this consumer would purchase 120 units. But we know from the definition of demand that the consumer would have been willing to pay $10 for each of the first 20 units. This is consistent with the principle of diminishing

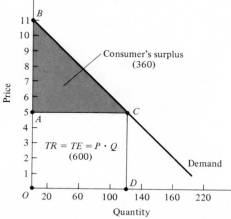

Figure 6.8 Consumer's Surplus Determination of the consumer's surplus for a consumer purchasing 120 units of the product (per unit of time) at a price of $5. The consumer would pay $960 rather than do without the product entirely, but actually pays $600. Thus the consumer's surplus is $360.

marginal utility since the consumer perceives the earlier units as being worth more than later units.

If we were able to charge the consumer the maximum amount for each unit, the total collected would be (approximately) equal to the area under the demand curve up to the total number of units purchased. If 120 units were purchased under such a pricing scheme, the total expenditure would be $960, or the area $OBCD$ in Figure 6.8. However, the consumer actually pays just $600 (i.e., 5×120), or the area $OACD$. Thus, the consumer's surplus is $360, or the area of the triangle ABC.

Although this discussion of consumer's surplus avoids some of the theoretical problems involved,[3] it provides a sufficient intuitive argument to support the more important applications of the concept. In most cases it is not necessary to be as precise as to be able to say that the consumer's surplus is exactly a given value (e.g., $360), but rather to recognize its existence (or perhaps make a broad estimate of the value).

SUMMARY

The basic concepts developed in earlier chapters provide a foundation that can be extended to a broad range of analyses. One of these is the partitioning of the total effect of a price change into income and substitution effects. As the price of a product falls (rises), the consumer's real income, or purchasing power, increases (decreases). This change in real income then influences the level of consumption. This is the income effect and may be positive or negative depending on whether the good is a normal or an inferior good. A change in the price of one good also causes a substitution effect as that product is substituted for other goods (if price declines) or as other goods are substituted for it (if price increases). The substitution effect is always negative (causing consumption to change in a direction opposite to the direction of the price change).

Indifference curve analysis is also useful in evaluating exchange using an Edgeworth box diagram. Given some initial allocation of goods, consumers will find it mutually satisfactory to trade as long as their marginal rates of substitution are unequal. The combinations of commodities for which their MRS are equal define a contract curve. Each point on this curve is Pareto optimal since no further exchange can benefit one person without making another less well off.

Frequently, public sector decisions must be made that involve a choice between giving an individual aid in the form of a pure money transfer or in the form of goods in kind (such as a housing subsidy or food

---

[3] A short but excellent discussion of consumer's surplus, including indifference curve analysis, can be found in George J. Stigler, *The Theory of Price*, 3d ed. (New York: Macmillan, 1966), pp. 78–81.

stamps). If the objective is to enhance the individual's sense of well-being, it is preferable to make the transfer in money. This may not, however, result in an end that is deemed "socially desirable" in terms of an externally determined consumption pattern.

Given certain assumptions about the nature of the marginal utility of income (MU_M), we can give support to the argument that progressive taxation is better than regressive forms of taxation in terms of the general welfare of the society. If MU_M does diminish, which seem plausible, and if we are willing to make interpersonal utility comparisons, then transfers from higher-income taxpayers to lower-income recipients will increase the total utility or welfare of the society.

Since demand curves generally have a negative slope, we find that consumers actually pay less for a given number of units of a good than they would be willing to pay rather than do without the good entirely. The difference between these amounts is defined as the consumer's surplus.

The logic and concepts developed in earlier chapters, and extended in this chapter, will be useful throughout the remainder of the text. The analysis of production that follows is developed in a manner that is strictly analogous to the analysis of consumer demand.

Selected Readings

Bailey, Martin J. "The Marshallian Demand Curve." *Journal of Political Economy* (June 1954), 255–261.

Friedman, Milton. "The Marshallian Demand Curve." *Journal of Political Economy* (December 1949), 463–474.

Leibenstein, Harvey. "Bandwagon, Snob, and Veblen Effects in the Theory of Consumer Demand." *Quarterly Journal of Economics* (May 1950), 183–207.

Winch, D. M. "The Separation of Income and Substitution Effects." *Western Economic Journal* (Summer 1963), 172–190.

QUESTIONS

1. Write a short explanation of the following terms or concepts that were used in this chapter:
   (a) consumer's surplus
   (b) contract curve
   (c) Edgeworth box diagram
   (d) Giffen good
   (e) inferior good
   (f) income effect
   (g) marginal utility of money
   (h) normal good
   (i) substitution effect

2. Use two indifference curves and budget constraints to illustrate the separation of income and substitution effects for a normal good that is measured along the vertical axis.

3. Explain *why* a price change would be expected to have both an income and a substitution effect. Write a brief explanation of how these concepts may relate to the overall effect of the rapidly rising cost of home heating oil.

4. List several goods that you would think might be "inferior goods" in the context discussed in this chapter. Explain why you think so in each case. Can you think of a good that might be a Giffen good?

5. Construct an Edgeworth box to illustrate the exchange of two products between two consumers. Explain carefully what the diagram shows and the equilibrium condition that results along the "contract curve." Why are points along the contract curve preferred to points off that line? Can we say that one point along the contract curve is better than any other point on the same line?

6. The concept of consumer's surplus indicates that we may pay less for many goods than we might be "willing" to pay even though we may complain about high prices. Think about things that you purchase and identify some that you might be willing to pay more for than you actually must pay.

7. Suppose that you have the choice of allocating money for student aid in the form of a cash grant to students or in the form of tuition reductions. Use indifference curve analysis to evaluate the effect of each alternative on the number of credit hours taken and on the student's level of satisfaction.

CHAPTER 7
PRODUCTION

In this chapter we move the focus of attention from the consumer (demand) side of the marketplace to the producer (supply) side. Many of the analytical constructs developed in previous chapters are also useful in explaining the supply side of the market. Thus the reader will find that the analysis that follows contains many familiar concepts.

In the process of production, various inputs are transformed into some type(s) of output. Except for the final section of the chapter, on multiple products, our discussion will involve the production of a single homogeneous product. However, the principles established are applicable to the more general cases as well. The reader should keep in mind that, although the words "product" or "output" are used throughout, the analysis applies to any form of good or service (cars, skateboards, highway construction, police and fire department services, a travel agent's services, retailing, etc.). For our present purpose, a product may be considered anything for which someone is willing to pay. Thus, production may include the washing of a car as well as building the car.

Inputs are broadly classified as land, labor, capital, and entrepreneurship (managerial functions such as organization, risk taking, etc.). Clearly each of these can be further broken down into subsets. For example, we might want to analyze how different types of labor contribute to higher education (a form of production), in which case the following labor classifications might be useful (other or even finer classes might also be identified): administrators, faculty, maintenance personnel, secretarial staff, research staff, work-study students, library staff, and personnel in other support services. In our analysis we will usually couch our discussion in terms of two broad categories of inputs: labor (L) and capital (K). This is done for ease of exposition only, and our results can easily be generalized to any number of inputs.

PRODUCTION FUNCTIONS

Every business engages in production as a means to some end. The particular end result or objective that a firm strives for is not as important to our analysis of production as one might think. The principle objective (and there may be multiple objectives, as well) may be to obtain some specified rate of return on investment or on sales, to achieve a given share of the total market, to maximize profit, to satisfice (i.e., obtain a "satisfactory" but not necessarily maximum profit), to reach a certain growth rate, or perhaps some other objective. Regardless of the form in which the firm's objective is stated, it is reasonable to expect that efficiency in production will help in reaching the objective. By efficiency we mean that the firm will attempt to combine the various inputs in such a manner that as few resources as possible are used for any given level of production (we assume, of course, that the firm must pay for all the resources used).

The amount of output produced depends on the quantities of various inputs that are utilized in the production process, given the state of technology that exists. As the technological superstructure upon which production is based becomes increasingly sophisticated, we find that a given set of inputs can produce greater and greater quantities of output. This is perhaps no more clearly evident than in the agricultural sector of the economy. We have gone from a situation in which 1 in 15 people in the United States were employed in agriculture in 1900 to where just about 1 in 200 were so employed in 1980. This has been due primarily to rapid changes in the technology of agricultural production. Further advances, such as the development of seed strains that can thrive in land irrigated with seawater, promise to continue this trend.

A *production function represents the relationship between the amounts of the various inputs used in the production process and the quantity of output produced therefrom for a given state of technology.* There are three alternative ways in which production functions may be presented: tabular, graphic, and mathematical. In this chapter we shall continue to rely heavily on graphic methods, although some production relationships will be presented in tabular or algebraic form as well.

Table 7.1 TABULAR FORM OF A PRODUCTION
FUNCTION WITH OUTPUT AS A FUNCTION OF
ONE VARIABLE INPUT

LABOR (L)	QUANTITY (Q)	LABOR (L)	QUANTITY (Q)
0	0	8	268.8
1	8.4	9	291.6
2	31.2	10	300.0
3	64.8	11	290.4
4	105.6	12	259.2
5	150.0	13	202.8
6	194.4	14	117.6
7	235.2		

Table 7.1 contains the data for a typical production function in which
the quantity of output is a function of just one variable input (labor) and
some unspecified fixed inputs (such as land, capital, and entrepreneurship). In our discussion, the terms total product (*TP*) and quantity (*Q*) will
be used interchangeably to refer to the output of various production
processes. We see from the data that output at first increases and then
declines as more labor is utilized.

The production function given in Table 7.1 is also represented by the
graph in Figure 7.1. In the graphic form, as well as in the tabular form,
we see that if no labor is used (*L* = 0) there will be no output

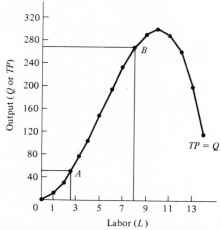

Figure 7.1 A Production Function A production function with
output as a function of one variable input. If 8 units of labor are
used, roughly 270 units of output are produced (point *B*). Using
L = 2.5 yields approximately 50 units of output (point *A*).

($Q = TP = 0$) for this particular production process. For positive integer values of labor (up to 14) the corresponding level of output can be determined from Table 7.1 or Figure 7.1. For example, we see that at $L = 8$, $Q = 268.8$ (from the graph one might have just estimated $Q = 270$ at point B). If we wanted to estimate the level of output for a noninteger value of L (such as 2.5), we could interpolate from the table or make the estimate from the graph. Using Table 7.1 we would find the midpoint between two and three units of labor as follows Q (at $L = 2.5$) = (31.2 + 64.8)/2 = 48. From Figure 7.1 our estimate would be found by going up from 2.5 on the horizontal axis to point A, then reading Q from the vertical axis as 50. While these estimates differ, they would probably be sufficiently accurate for most purposes.[1]

The production function we have been discussing thus far is a *short-run* production function. The *short run may be defined as a period during which the firm can vary the amount of only some of the resources (inputs) used in production while others are fixed*. In the production function of Table 7.1 and Figure 7.1, labor is the input that can be varied while all others (land, capital, entrepreneurship) are held constant. In the *long run the level of use of all inputs can be varied*.

It is important to note that the short-run and long-run concepts are defined without explicit reference to time. These periods are planning horizons for the firm and depend on the ability to adjust the rate of resource use. Thus how much time is associated with the long run or short run may vary from industry to industry, or even from firm to firm within an industry.

For example, let us consider these concepts with reference to a small bakery and an electric utility. A young couple from Connecticut who worked their way through college by baking bread opened a small bakery in Great Falls, Montana, hoping to generate enough income to stay in the Northwest. Their stone ground whole wheat bread and other products sold so well that it wasn't long until they shut down for six weeks to expand operations. New mixing equipment, larger ovens, more floor space, additional labor, and a new sales outlet in a mall were all included in the expansion. Virtually all inputs were increased and all within less than two months. Thus their long run is fairly "short" in terms of a time measure. Contrast this with an electric utility company that seeks to expand in a similar manner. Site availability studies, facility design, environmental impact studies, and regulatory approval are just the beginning of a very time-consuming process. It is not uncommon to consider eight to ten years (or even longer, especially for nuclear facilities) as

---

[1] To be the most accurate in such estimates mathematical functions are the best form of production function to use. In this case, the algebraic function underlying Table 7.1 and Figure 7.1 is: $Q = 9L^2 - 0.6L^3$. At $L = 2.5$ we find that $Q = 9(2.5)^2 - 0.6(2.5)^3 = 46.9$.

the relevant long-run planning horizon. Thus, in such a case, the short run may be quite "long" in terms of time.

Before leaving our general discussion of production functions, we should mention a very common and useful form known as Cobb-Douglas production functions. This type of production function may be written algebraically as:

$$Q = AK^a L^b$$

where A is a positive constant, the exponents a and b are positive functions, Q represents the amount of output, K is the amount of capital input, and L is the amount of labor input. Cobb-Douglas production functions have a number of interesting properties, one of which is that the exponents represent the percentage increase in output for a 1 percent increase in the respective factor, ceteris paribus (holding the other input(s) fixed).

Cobb-Douglas production functions have been used for a wide variety of situations throughout the world. In an excellent survey article, A. A. Walters reports a number of such functions including the following[2]:

| | EXPONENTS | |
INDUSTRY	CAPITAL EXPONENT (a)	LABOR EXPONENT (b)
Gas	0.10	0.83
Foods	0.35	0.72
Coal	0.29	0.79
Metals and machinery	0.26	0.71
Montana livestock	0.94	0.08
Automobiles	0.41	0.96

We see, for example, that for the automobile industry a 1 percent increase in the labor input would increase output 0.96 percent with no increase in capital.

THE LAW OF VARIABLE PROPORTIONS

It is widely recognized that in most production processes the effect (on output) of changing the rate of use of a single variable input varies depending on the amount of that input currently employed. Consider, for example, a wheat farmer with a given set of land, capital, and labor resources, but with the ability to vary the use of fertilizer from none to any positive amount. We might well expect the first units of fertilizer to have the most dramatic effect on wheat yield. Subsequent applications

[2] A. A. Walters, "Production and Cost Functions: An Econometric Survey," *Econometrica* (January–April 1973), 26, 31, 33.

may continue to increase production but not by as much as the first. Ultimately, it is possible to use too much fertilizer and "burn out" the soil (consider what would happen to production in the extreme if fertilizer were spread evenly over the field to a depth of 1 foot).

The *law of variable proportions states that as additional units of a variable factor of production are added to other fixed factors the resulting increments to production will eventually decline, and may become negative.* Note that this definition is stated in terms of what happens with the "increments to product" as "additional units of a variable factor" are used.

In Figure 7.1 (which is reproduced in the upper portion of Figure 7.2), we see that as additional units of labor are used, output (TP) at first increases at an increasing rate, then increases at a decreasing rate, reaches a maximum and eventually declines. That is, the rate of change (or slope) of the total product function varies as the rate of labor use changes. This *rate of change in total product (TP) is called the marginal product (MP) of labor and is defined as*

$$MP_L = \frac{\Delta TP}{\Delta L}$$

where the subscript L indicates that this is the marginal product of labor, and the Δ's mean "change in." As marginal product changes, so does average product, which is defined as

$$AP_L = \frac{TP}{L}$$

Table 7.2 TOTAL PRODUCT, AVERAGE PRODUCT, AND MARGINAL PRODUCT AS FUNCTIONS OF THE AMOUNT OF LABOR EMPLOYED

L	TP	$AP = TP/L$	$MP = \Delta TP/\Delta MP$
0	0	—	
1	8.4	8.4	8.4
2	31.2	15.6	22.8
3	64.8	21.6	33.6
4	105.6	26.4	40.8
5	150.0	30.0	44.4
6	194.4	32.4	44.4
7	235.2	33.6	40.8
8	268.8	33.6	33.6
9	291.6	32.4	22.8
10	300.0	30.0	8.4
11	290.4	26.4	− 9.6
12	259.2	21.6	−31.2
13	202.8	15.6	−56.4
14	117.6	8.4	−85.2

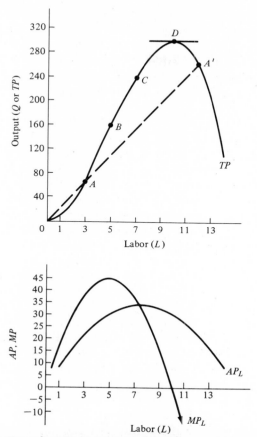

Figure 7.2 Total Product, Average Product, and Marginal Product When the marginal product increases the total product increases at an increasing rate. When the marginal product is decreasing but still positive, the total product increases at a decreasing rate. When the marginal product becomes negative, the total product declines. Average product can be measured as the slope of a line from the origin to the total product curve. For example, the slope of the line 0A is 64.8 ÷ 3, or 21.6, and at $L = 3$ the average product is 21.6. Average product is at a maximum where it is intersected by marginal product.

Both the average product and marginal product for the production function given in Table 7.1 are presented in Table 7.2. Because marginal product almost always eventually declines the "law of variable proportions" is also frequently called the *law of diminishing marginal returns*.

Figure 7.2 illustrates these relationships graphically. In both the tabular and graphic forms we see that total product increases at an increasing rate (marginal product is increasing) up to 5 units of labor, then continues to increase but at a progressively slower rate (marginal product is positive but decreasing) between 5 and 10 units of labor, and finally declines (marginal product is negative) beyond 10 units of labor. Note the direct correspondence between the slope of the total product curve and the value of marginal product. For example, at point D the slope of total product is zero and, at the corresponding level of labor (10), marginal product is also zero.

Just as marginal product can be determined from the total product curve (MP is the slope of TP), the average product can also be determined from the total product curve. The *slope of a line drawn from the origin to any point on the total product curve measures the average product at that point.* For example, the slope of the line through A and A' is 21.6, which is the value of average product at both 3 and 12 units of labor, respectively. By drawing similar lines to points B, C, and D, and measuring their slopes, you should be able to replicate the values of average product in Table 7.2 for $L = 5$, $L = 7$, and $L = 10$.

Average product will be pulled up as long as the marginal product is greater, but if marginal product falls below average product the latter will then decline. Therefore, as shown in Figure 7.2, marginal product will always intersect average product at the peak of average product.

Recall that a given state of technology and a given level of fixed resource use is implied in these production relationships. If there is a technological advancement, or if the variable factor (labor) has more of the fixed factors with which to work (e.g., more capital), each of these curves would be expected to shift upward. That is, in general labor would be more productive with more of other resources to work with, or with a more sophisticated level of technology.

It is conventional to divide production into three phases based on the relationship between AP, MP, and TP. This is done in Figure 7.3. In Stage 1 the average productivity of labor is increasing. If output and input prices are constant the firm will find it profitable to expand production through this stage and into Stage 2. In Stage 3 we see that the marginal productivity of labor is negative. This means that total production would be reduced by employing additional units of labor. Given any positive (or even zero) labor cost, this would clearly be an irrational stage of production. Thus we are led to the conclusion that production should generally take place in Stage 2.[3]

The graphs we have used in this section are meant only to be representative. Some production processes may not have increasing marginal product even at low levels of resource use and for others this phase

---

[3] It can be shown that these stages are symmetric for the fixed and variable factors in the two-input case. That is, Stage 1 for labor is Stage 3 for the fixed factor, and Stage 3 for labor is Stage 1 for the fixed factor. Stage 2 is the same region for both.

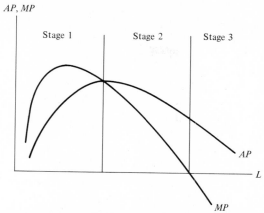

Figure 7.3 Stages of Production The three stages of production. Stage 1, average product increasing; Stage 2, average product decreasing, but marginal product positive; Stage 3, average product decreasing, and marginal product negative.

may be brief. However, most processes will eventually have diminishing marginal productivity. How rapidly it diminishes, and thus the breadth of the three stages of production, depends on the particular process.

ISOQUANT CURVES

In most types of production, inputs can be combined in various combinations. That is, inputs may be substituted for one another in the production process. *An isoquant curve is a line which traces out all of the input combinations that yield the same (iso-) level of output (-quant).* Four such isoquants are illustrated in Figure 7.4. We see that Q_1 units of output can be produced with 2 units of labor and 6 units of capital at point M or with $6L$ and $2K$ at point N. Thus labor may be substituted for capital along Q_1 without changing the level of output.[4]

The two ridge lines marked R and R' delimit the relevant region of production. At points A, B, C, and D the respective isoquants become perfectly vertical, and above those points the isoquants have a positive slope. At points E, F, G, and H the isoquants become perfectly horizontal, and to the right of those points their slopes are positive. A positive slope would imply that if more labor were used (beyond E, F, G, or H), additional capital would also need to be employed to maintain the same level of output, or if more capital were used (beyond A, B, C, or D), additional labor would also need to be hired to maintain the given output. Thus,

---

[4] Such isoquants can be derived from a production surface in the same manner that we derived indifference curves in Chapter 3.

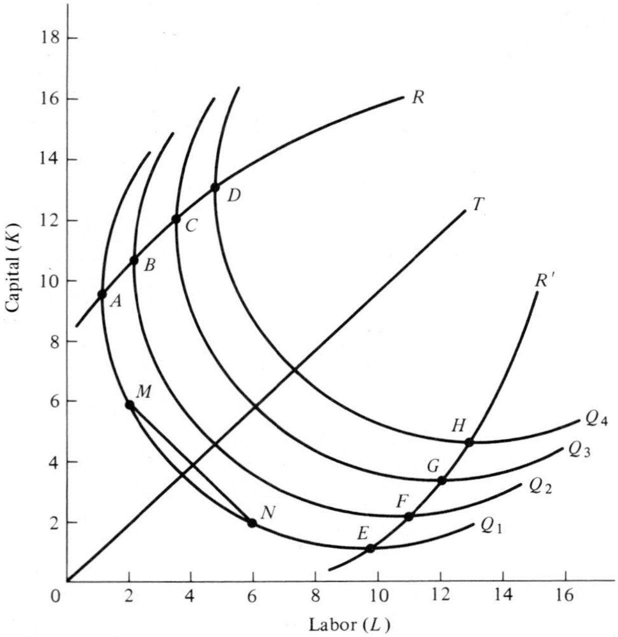

Figure 7.4 Relevant Region of Production Mapping of four isoquants (Q_1 through Q_4) with ridge lines (R and R') marking off the relevant region of production.

above R the marginal productivity of capital becomes negative, while beyond R' the marginal productivity of labor is negative. Thus the space bounded by R and R' is the same as Stage 2 of production as illustrated in Figure 7.3.

The properties of isoquant curves are similar to those of indifference curves. *The farther an isoquant is from the origin* (along a ray such as *OT*), *the greater the level of output* that it represents. (Thus $Q_4 > Q_3 > Q_2 > Q_1$.) *Isoquant curves cannot intersect.* By definition, each isoquant represents a given level of output, and this condition would be violated if two isoquants were to intersect. *Isoquants are also dense;* that is, there is an isoquant for each possible level of output and through each point in the space bounded by the labor and capital axes. We usually only graph a small subset of the isoquant curves, such as the four in Figure 7.4.

The ability to substitute one input for another, in the relevant range of production, means that isoquants will have a negative slope in the region of interest. (If inputs are productive, using more of one implies that less of the other is necessary for a constant Q.) Not only is the slope negative, but in general it will decrease from the upper left to the lower right. Thus *isoquants are generally convex* to the origin, as illustrated in Figures 7.4 and 7.5.

In Figure 7.4 we see that Q_1 units of output could be produced either with the combination of labor and capital given by point M ($L = 2, K = 6$) or with the combination given by N ($L = 6, K = 2$). In moving from M to N the capital input is reduced by four units and, to maintain a constant level of output (Q_1), the labor input must be increased by four units. *The absolute value of this ratio of the change in capital to the change in labor (keeping Q constant) is the marginal rate of technical substitution of labor for capital ($MRTS_{L:K}$).* Over the interval from M to N the $MRTS_{L:K}$ is thus equal to one. As points such as M and N become closer together, the slope of the line between them becomes an approximation for the slope of the isoquant.

The $MRTS_{L:K}$ can then be measured by the absolute value of the slope of an isoquant at any point. For example, the absolute value of the slope of Q_1 at point A in Figure 7.5 is: $MRTS_{L:K} = \frac{10}{5} = 2.0$. At point B we

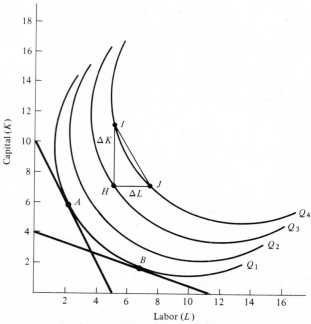

Figure 7.5 The Marginal Rate of Technical Substitution The marginal rate of technical substitution of labor for capital ($MRTS_{L:K}$) diminishes as production becomes more labor intensive for a given level of output. The $MRTS_{L:K}$ at A is the slope of Q_1 at A, or 10/5 = 2.0. The $MRTS_{L:K}$ at B is the slope of Q_1 at B, or 4/11 = 0.36. It can be shown that $MRTS_{L:K}$ is equal to MP_L/MP_K using the triangle *HIJ*.

see that it declines to $MRTS_{L:K} = \frac{4}{11} = 0.36$. This means that for any given level of output (Q_1), the ease with which labor may be substituted for capital diminishes as more labor intensive methods are used (e.g., movement from A to B).

It can be shown that the $MRTS_{L:K}$ is equal to the ratio of the marginal product of capital (MP_K) to the marginal product of labor (MP_L). Referring to Figure 7.5, we know that between I and J the $MRTS_{L:K}$ is equal to the absolute value of the slope of IJ $(= \Delta K/\Delta L)$. We can define the marginal product of capital as follows:

$$MP_K = \frac{\Delta Q}{\Delta K}$$

As we move from H to I (keeping labor constant), output increases from Q_3 to Q_4, so $\Delta Q = Q_4 - Q_3$. Similarly, the marginal product of labor is

$$MP_L = \frac{\Delta Q}{\Delta L}$$

As we go from H to J (keeping capital constant), output also increases from Q_3 to Q_4, so once again $\Delta Q = Q_4 - Q_3$. Dividing MP_L by MP_K, we have

$$\frac{MP_L}{MP_K} = \frac{(\Delta Q/\Delta L)}{(\Delta Q/\Delta K)} = \frac{\Delta K}{\Delta L}$$

This is, of course, the slope of Q_4 between I and J. It then follows that *the marginal rate of technical substitution of labor for capital is equal to the ratio of the marginal product of labor to the marginal product of capital:*

$$MRTS_{L:K} = \frac{MP_L}{MP_K}$$

This is a result that will be of great significance in our analysis of optimization in production later in this chapter.

To illustrate isoquants for a particular productive activity let us look at the transport of crude oil through a pipeline.[5] The output Q is the throughput of oil per day, in barrels, through a 1000-mile pipeline. There are two factors that determine this flow: the diameter D of the pipe and the horsepower H of the pumps. Seventeen isoquants, ranging from 25,000 to 1,500,000 barrels per day (b/d), are shown in Figure 7.6. The relationships illustrated reflect the concepts presented above. If a smaller-diameter pipe is used, more horsepower must be applied to force

[5] D. J. Pearl and J. L. Enos, "Engineering Production Functions and Technological Progress," *Journal of Industrial Economics* (September 1975), 55–72.

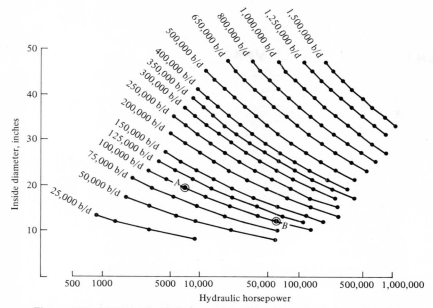

Figure 7.6 Oil Transport Isoquants Seventeen isoquants for the transport of crude oil through a pipeline. Throughput is a function of the diameter of the pipeline and the horsepower supplied by the pumps. (Source: D. J. Pearl and J. L. Enos, "Engineering Production Functions and Technological Progress," The *Journal of Industrial Economics* (September 1975), 56. (Points *A* and *B* added.) Reprinted with permission of Basil Blackwell Publishers.

a given quantity of oil through the pipeline. The marginal rate of technical substitution of horsepower for pipe diameter can be calculated at various points by measuring the slope of the isoquants. For example, along Q = 100,000 b/d, at point A the $MRTS_{H:D}$ is approximately 0.00045; at B it is roughly 0.000033. As the theory suggests, the $MRTS_{H:D}$ diminishes.

In some types of production situations the isoquants may not have the smooth convex shape we have depicted thus far. If inputs must be combined in fixed proportions, the isoquants will be rectangular, as in Figure 7.7(a). For a given amount of one input, such as L^*, a specific quantity of the other, K^*, is necessary to produce Q_2 units of output. If more than K^* units of capital are employed, output would remain at Q_2 unless more labor were used as well. In this case, the inputs cannot be substituted for one another.

In some cases the reverse may be true. The inputs may be perfect substitutes for one another and the $MRTS$ may be constant along any

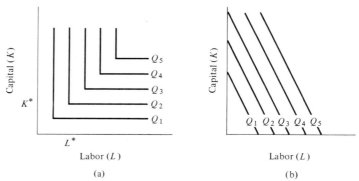

Figure 7.7 Rectangular and Linear Isoquants Isoquants for (a) a production process in which the inputs must be combined in fixed proportions and (b) for a process in which the inputs are perfect substitutes such that the $MRTS_{L:K}$ is constant. Bicycle frames and wheels are an example of the first case while the substitution of fuel oil for natural gas to generate electricity is an example of the second case.

isoquant (i.e., the isoquants have a constant slope throughout). In Figure 7.7(b) this type of relationship is illustrated for a case in which $MRTS_{L:K} = 2$.

ISOCOST CURVES

An isocost curve represents the various combinations of labor and capital that a firm can obtain for a given dollar cost, with a fixed set of input prices. Let C, r, and w represent the firm's total cost, the cost per unit of capital, and the cost per unit of labor, respectively. Then the total cost to the firm of employing (purchasing) inputs is

$$C = wL + rK$$

which, if solved for K, yields

$$K = \frac{C}{r} - \left(\frac{w}{r}\right) L$$

Since C, r, and w are given, this is just a straight line with a negative slope.

The intercepts on the capital and labor axes represent the maximum amount of each resource that could be obtained for a given total cost. Thus, the capital intercept is C/r (or total cost divided by the cost per unit of capital). Similarly, the labor intercept is C/w (or total cost divided by the cost per unit of labor). The slope of an isoquant is simply the negative of the ratio of the per-unit labor cost to the per-unit capital cost (w/r).

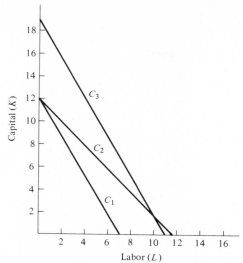

Figure 7.8 Changes in Isocost Curves Three isocost curves (C_1, C_2, C_3), showing the effects of an increase in expenditure on resources (C_1 to C_3) and a decrease in the per-unit cost of labor (C_1 to C_2). The general equation for an isocost curve is $K = (C/r) - (w/r) L$, where C is the total cost of inputs, r is the cost per unit of capital, and w is the cost per unit of labor.

Three isocost curves (C_1, C_2, and C_3) are graphed in Figure 7.8. C_1 represents a total cost of $126, w_1 a per-unit labor cost of $18, and r_1 a per-unit capital cost of $10.50. The labor and capital intercepts are thus $126/18 = 7$, and $126/10.5 = 12$, respectively. The isocost C_2 represents the same total cost as C_1 and the same cost per unit of capital, but a lower cost per unit of labor ($w_2 = \$11$). We see that C_2 has the same vertical intercept but is now less steeply sloped, with a horizontal intercept of 11.45. The slope of C_1 is -1.71 (i.e., $-18/10.5$), whereas the slope of C_2 is -1.05 (i.e., $-11/10.5$).

If the total cost (total amount spent on inputs) changes, with per-unit input costs constant the isocost curve will shift in a parallel manner. This is illustrated by comparing C_1 with C_3. Both curves have the same per-unit input costs ($w_1 = 18$, $r_1 = 10.5$), but the latter represents an expenditure of $198 (whereas $C_1 = \$126$).

Isocost curves are roughly analogous to the budget constraints discussed in Chapters 3 and 4. They are influenced by total cost and per-unit input costs in the same manner that budget constraints are affected by income and product prices, respectively. It may be helpful to refer back to Figure 4.1 to refresh your mind on these concepts. They can be summarized as follows:

Type of Change	Effect on Isocost Curve
C increases	Parallel shift outward
C decreases	Parallel shift downward
w increases	Same vertical intercept but steeper
w decreases	Same vertical intercept but flatter
r increases	Same horizontal intercept but flatter
r decreases	Same horizontal intercept but steeper

For each of these changes other things are assumed to be constant.

OPTIMIZATION IN PRODUCTION

We can now put the concepts developed in the two preceding sections to work in a decision context. There are two particular types of problems we will be able to solve using these concepts: (1) What is the least-cost combination of inputs that will enable the firm to produce a given level of output? (2) What is the combination of inputs that will maximize output for a given total cost?

Let us look at these problems in order. In Figure 7.9 the isoquant curves of Figure 7.4 are reproduced along with the isocost curves C_1 and C_3 from Figure 7.8. If the firm wishes to produce Q_2 units of output, it can do so anywhere along the isoquant Q_2. We know that, given $w = 18$ and $r = 10.5$, Q_2 units could be produced using the input combinations at D, E, or F. (More such points would be possible, of course, if more isocost curves were shown.)

At D and F the total cost would be $198 (along C_3). However, by moving to point E the total cost would be reduced to $126. Note that at E the isoquant Q_3 is just tangent to an isocost curve (C_1). This leads us to an important principle: *A firm will always minimize the cost of producing a given level of output by using the combination of inputs where the relevant isoquant is just tangent to an isocost curve.*

Since two curves have the same slope at a point of tangency, it follows that this least-cost condition may be stated as:

$$\text{Slope of isoquant} = \text{slope of isocost}$$

$$\frac{MP_L}{MP_K} = \frac{w}{r}$$

This equation can be rewritten in a form that has more intuitive appeal, as follows:

$$\frac{MP_L}{w} = \frac{MP_K}{r}$$

That is, *the firm will minimize the cost of producing any given level of*

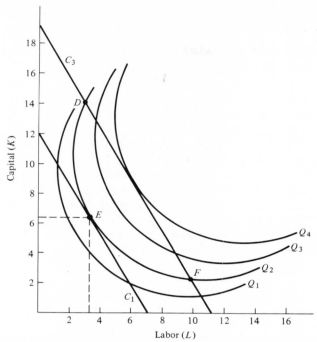

Figure 7.9 Cost Minimization for a Given Output Determination of the least-cost (C_1) combination of labor and capital to produce Q_2 units of output. The optimum combination of labor and capital is determined at the tangency between C_1 and Q_2 at the point E.

output by using resources such that the marginal productivity per dollar is equal for all resources.

Now let us turn our attention to the second question: For a given total cost, what is the combination of inputs that will maximize output? The method of solution is illustrated in Figure 7.10. In this case we use isocost C_2 from Figure 7.8, for which $C = 126$, $w = 11$, and $r = 10.5$. If the $126 were spent such that labor and capital were hired in the amounts represented by either R or V, the firm would produce just Q_1 units. By moving from R to S, or from V to U, output could be increased to Q_2 units. But still further increases in output would be possible until point T is reached. At T the isocost C_2 is just tangent to the isoquant Q_3, the highest isoquant with at least one point in common with C_2. Thus, Q_3 units represents the maximum level of output obtainable for the cost $C_2 = 126$, given the per-unit input costs.

Our conclusion is then: *A firm will always maximize output for a given cost (with constant per-unit input costs) by using the combination of inputs for which the given isocost curve is just tangent to an isoquant curve.* From this tangency condition it once more follows that

$$\frac{MP_L}{w} = \frac{MP_K}{r}$$

That is, *the firm will maximize output for any given cost by using resources such that the marginal productivity per dollar is equal for all resources.*

We see that for either of our decision problems the equilibrium condition for optimization is the same: The marginal productivity per dollar should be equal for all inputs. Suppose this were not true. If $(MP_L/w) > (MP_K/r)$ and we were spending a constant amount (e.g., C_2) on inputs, each dollar taken from capital and used to purchase more labor would increase output. Points R and S in Figure 7.10 represent such cases where the marginal productivity per dollar spent on labor is greater than the marginal productivity per dollar for capital. Note also that, at R and S, $MRTS_{L:K}$ is greater than w/r (the slopes of the isoquants Q_1 and Q_2 are greater than the slope of C_2). When this is true, it will always be better to substitute labor for capital (move toward T).

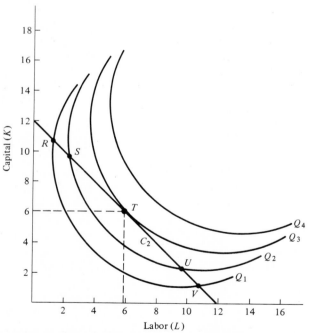

Figure 7.10 Output Maximization for a Given Cost
Determination of the combination of labor and capital that maximizes output (Q_3) for a given cost (C_2). The optimum combination of labor and capital is determined at the tangency between Q_3 and C_2 at the point T.

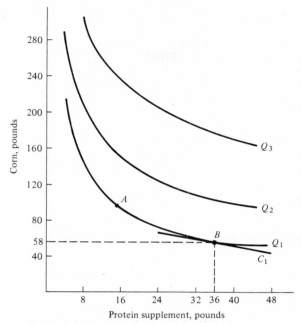

Figure 7.11 Determination of an Optimum Diet Mix
Determination of the least-cost combination of protein
supplement and corn to achieve a weight gain of 40 pounds (Q_1),
given a 0.95 ratio of the price of protein supplement to the
price of corn. The slope of C_1 is 0.95 and that isocost curve is
tangent to Q_1 at B.

At points like U and V the opposite is true. At these points
$MRTS_{L:K} < w/r$ and $(MP_L/w) < (MP_K/r)$. When this is true, each dollar
taken from labor and used for capital will have the net effect of increasing
output at a constant cost.

These concepts can be viewed in a particular applied context by
reference to Sonka, Heady, and Dahm's work with decision models for
swine production.[6] Equations for isoquant curves representing three
levels of weight gain (Q_1, a gain of 40 pounds from 60 to 100; Q_2, a gain of
50 pounds from 100 to 150; and Q_3, a gain of 65 pounds from 150 to 215)
were estimated and are graphed in Figure 7.11. Note that these isoquants
have the same characteristics as predicted by the theoretical constructs
on page 124. Protein supplement P may be substituted for corn C in the
feeding process. Using Q_1, for example, we can calculate the $MRTS_{P:C}$ as

[6] Steven T. Sonka, Earl O. Heady, and P. Fred Dahm, "Estimation of Gain Isoquants and a
Decision Model Application for Swine Production," *American Journal of Agricultural Economics* 58 (August 1976), 466–474.

approximately 3:62 at A, whereas at B it declines to about 0.95 (based on their equations for Q_1).

Sonka, Heady, and Dahm give data on the ratio of the price per pound of protein supplement to the price per pound of corn for every November and April, from November 1970 to April 1975. In April 1971, for example, this price ratio was 0.95. Suppose you had hogs at that time that weighed 60 pounds and you wanted to "fatten them up" to 100 pounds. What combination of protein supplement and corn would do this at the lowest cost? To answer this question all we need to do is draw an isocost curve with a slope of -0.95 and tangent to Q_1. The point of tangency determines the appropriate level of each type of feed. This point is at B, representing about 36 pounds of protein supplement and 58 pounds of corn.

RETURNS TO SCALE

When we refer to the scale of production, we mean the overall level of resource use. It is often useful to think of size and scale as synonymous. For example, Chevrolet Vegas are produced at a larger scale than AMC Sportabouts; that is, the Vegas are produced in a larger factory with more of all inputs being used.

In many types of production processes it becomes technologically more efficient to produce at a larger scale than at a smaller one; hence the phenomenon of mass production. The concept of returns to scale is of a long-run nature because it deals with the overall size of the production process and implies the ability to vary the level of use of all factors of production (inputs). *If the rate of use of all inputs is increased by some proportion and output increases by a greater proportion, there are increasing returns to scale on production.* This is illustrated by movement from A to B in Figure 7.12. Over this interval all inputs (labor and capital) are doubled—and output more than doubles, from 100 to 300 units.

There are two primary factors that contribute to increasing returns to scale. First, as the scale of production increases, it becomes possible to take advantage of greater labor proficiency that results from the *division of labor* and the resulting opportunities for *specialization.* In small-scale operations a worker may have to change from job to job and will not be as adept at some as at others. In addition, time is lost in switching from one job to the other. A worker who specializes in one task is likely to become more highly skilled at it and thus be more efficient. Second, *technological factors* may contribute to increasing returns to scale. Large-sized plants are generally capable of adopting more advanced production technologies. One reason that the limited-edition special-make cars (such as "new" Cords) cost more is that they are produced on a much smaller scale than a Ford, or even a Cadillac Seville.

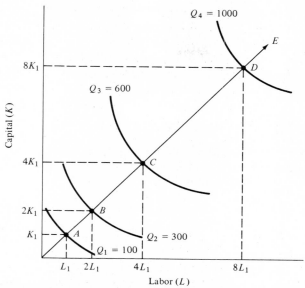

Figure 7.12 Determination of Returns to Scale A mapping of
isoquant curves showing returns to scale. Increasing returns
are evident from *A* to *B*, constant returns from *B* to *C* and
decreasing returns from *C* to *D*.

*If, when all inputs are increased by a given proportion, output in-
creases in the same proportion, there are constant returns to scale.* This
is illustrated by movement from *B* to *C* in Figure 7.12. The level of input
use is doubled for both labor and capital, and the rate of output is also
exactly doubled (from 300 to 600 units).

It is entirely possible that the scale of production could become so
large that it is less efficient. Such *decreasing returns to scale result when
the rate of output increases by a proportion that is less than a given
proportional increase of all inputs.* This is illustrated by movement from
C to *D* in Figure 7.12. Once more both labor and capital are doubled, but
now output less than doubles (from 600 to 1000 units). The principal
reason that is usually given for such decreasing returns to scale is that
organization and control of the production process becomes too complex.
Decision making is delegated to more and more persons, the number of
reports to top management increases rapidly, and general coordination of
the production process is more difficult.

Careful empirical work is usually necessary to determine which
class of returns to scale characterizes a particular activity. We shall return
to this concept in our discussion of long-run costs in Chapter 8, at which
time some empirical results will be reviewed.

For Cobb-Douglas production functions of the form $Q = AK^aL^b$, it is easy to determine the type of returns to scale. It can be shown that if $a + b > 1$ there are increasing returns to scale, if $a + b = 1$ there are constant returns to scale, and if $a + b < 1$ there are decreasing returns to scale. From the data given on page 119 we see, for example, that in the automobile industry there are increasing returns to scale ($a + b = 0.41 + 0.96 = 1.37 > 1$).

PRODUCTION OF MULTIPLE PRODUCTS

Thus far we have dealt with situations involving the production of just one type of output. However, the concepts developed in the process can be generalized to the production of any number of different products, using any number of inputs. In this section we provide the basic framework for such an analysis in the context of producing two products (A and B) with two inputs (labor and capital). To go beyond two inputs or outputs would require formulating the problem in mathematical form rather than graphically. The analysis is based on an Edgeworth box diagram similar to the one used in Chapter 6 in our discussion of exchange between two persons.

In Figure 7.13 we have drawn an Edgeworth box for the production of the two goods, A and B, using labor L and capital K as the only inputs. The origin for isoquants representing levels of production of A is O_A at the lower left corner. Output of A increases from lower left to upper right such that $Q_{A_1} < Q_{A_2} < Q_{A_3} < Q_{A_4} < Q_A^*$, where the dashed isoquant, Q_A^*, represents the maximum production of A that would be possible with the entire amount of labor and capital available. The axes for product B are rotated 180° such that B's origin is at the upper right corner and $Q_{B_1} < Q_{B_2} < Q_{B_3} < Q_{B_4} < Q_B^*$. The maximum possible production of B is Q_B^*.

Suppose the firm was initially using resources to produce A and B at point H. Q_{A_2} units of A and Q_{B_2} units of B would be produced. Now suppose the method for producing A was changed to a more labor intensive method at point E. The same amount of A would be produced but NE more units of labor would be necessary. If these NE (= HM) units of labor are taken from the production of B, MS additional units of capital must be used to maintain the Q_{B_2} level of production at point S. But HN (= ME) units of capital would be freed by the change in the production of A from point H to point E. This is clearly more than sufficient to compensate in the production of B (i.e., $ME > MS$). The SE unused units of capital could be allocated to increase the production of both A and B, without further reallocation of the labor resource. One such point would be W, at which the production of A would be greater than Q_{A_2} and the production of B would be greater than Q_{B_2}.

Once at W the situation is essentially the same as it was at the original

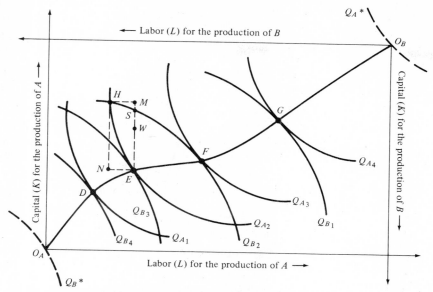

Figure 7.13 Efficiency in the Production of Two Goods
Edgeworth box diagram showing Pareto optimal use of labor and capital in the production of two goods A and B along the contract curve $O_A O_B$.

point H, and similar adjustments could be made to increase the production of A or B, or both. The reason that such changes can increase production in these cases is that the $MRTS_{L:K}$ is different for A than for B at such points. That is, at H and W the isoquants for A and B have different slopes. A reallocation of inputs will always increase production of at least one good, while not decreasing production of any other, unless the $MRTS_{L:K}$ is equal for all goods.

Thus, Pareto optimal points of production are at points of tangencies between isoquants for A and B. These are points such as D, E, F, and G along the contract curve from O_A to O_B. Given a starting point at H, this economic model can tell us that a better use of resources can be obtained by movement to a point between E and F, but which point depends on the relative prices of the products A and B.

We see that labor and capital can be used to produce various different amounts of A and B in an efficient manner (i.e., along the contract curve of Pareto optimal points). These alternative amounts can be graphed, as in Figure 7.14, along what is called a production possibilities curve (or alternatively a product transformation curve). For example, the vertical intercept is Q_A^* and the horizontal intercept is Q_B^*, while F' and D' correspond to points F and D in Figure 7.13.

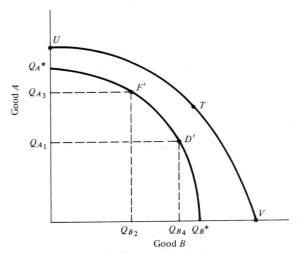

Figure 7.14 The Production Possibilities Curve A production possibilities curve illustrating the trade-off between the production of two goods, A and B. Curve Q_A*Q_B* is derived from the contract curve in Figure 7.13. Curve UV shows the effect of a technological advance on the production possibilities available for a given stock of resources.

Given the technology embodied in Figure 7.13, the combination of A and B represented by point T would be unattainable. However, a technological advance may shift the production possibilities curve outward to one such as UV, making that level of production possible. Technological change is rarely neutral in its effect on various products. The shift shown in Figure 7.14 illustrates a change that favors the production of B slightly more than the production of A.

SUMMARY

Production is the process of transforming various factors of production (land, labor, capital, and entrepreneurship) into goods and services for which consumers are willing to pay a price. A production function specifies the relationship between the inputs and outputs and can be given in tabular, graphic, or mathematical form.

In the short run, at least one factor (or input) is variable while others are fixed. When some factors are fixed, the law of variable proportions states that, after some level of utilization of the variable factor, the increments to production resulting from each additional unit of the variable factor will decline and may become negative.

The rate of change in total product (output) as the level of use of the variable factor changes is the marginal product of that factor

($MP = \Delta TP/\Delta L$, if labor L is the variable factor). Average product is simply total product divided by the rate of use of the variable factor ($AP = TP/L$). Production can be divided into three stages and it can be shown that the relevant region of production is in Stage 2, which extends from the peak of average product to the point at which marginal product equals zero.

Production may be represented as a function of two inputs (say, labor L and capital K) through the use of isoquant curves. An isoquant curve traces out the various quantities of L and K that can be combined to produce a given level of output. They have the following properties: (1) The farther from the origin, along any ray through the origin, the higher the level of output; (2) they cannot intersect; (3) there is an isoquant through each point (i.e., they are dense); (4) they have a negative slope in the relevant range of production, which is bounded by ridge lines; and (5) they are convex to the origin in the relevant range. The slope of an isoquant is called the marginal rate of technical substitution of labor for capital ($MRTS_{L:K}$). It can be shown that the $MRTS_{L:K} = MP_L/MP_K$.

Isocost curves show the various combinations of L and K that can be employed for a given cost C and a given set of per-unit factor costs, w and r, respectively. Isocost curves are linear with a negative slope, the absolute value of which is the factor cost ratio (w/r). Whether the objective of production is (1) to maximize output for a given cost or (2) to minimize the cost of producing a given level of output, the equilibrium condition is that

$$MRTS_{L:K} = \frac{w}{r}$$

$$\frac{MP_L}{MP_K} = \frac{w}{r}$$

$$\frac{MP_L}{w} = \frac{MP_K}{r}$$

That is, the marginal product per dollar should be equal for all inputs. This is true at the tangency of an isoquant curve with an isocost curve.

In the long run, all factors of production are variable. Thus the scale of production may be altered in the long run. If all inputs are increased by some percentage and output increases by a greater percentage, there are increasing returns to scale. If the percentages are equal, there are constant returns to scale. If the percentage increase in output is less than the percentage increase in all inputs, there are decreasing returns to scale.

When more than one product is being produced, the $MRTS_{L:K}$ should be equal in both types of production to have a Pareto optimal use of resources. Such points can be found using an Edgeworth box diagram.

They form a contract curve that contains the information necessary to construct a production possibilities curve. This curve (also called a product transformation curve) shows the alternative combinations of outputs that can be produced efficiently given a particular state of technology.

Selected Readings

Gallagher, Daniel G., and Edwin C. Hackleman. "Isoquants, Collective Bargaining, and Public School Resource Allocation." *Journal of Economics and Business* (Spring 1979), 160–165.

Mansfield, Edwin. *The Economics of Technical Change.* New York: Norton, 1968.

Pearl, D. J., and J. L. Enos. "Engineering Production Functions and Technological Progress." *Journal of Industrial Economics* (September 1975), 55–72.

Stigler, G. J. "The Division of Labor is Limited by the Extent of the Market." *Journal of Political Economy* (June 1951), 185–193.

QUESTIONS

1. Write a short explanation of the following terms or concepts that were used in this chapter:
   - (a) average product
   - (b) constant returns to scale
   - (c) decreasing returns to scale
   - (d) diminishing marginal product
   - (e) increasing returns to scale
   - (f) isocost curve
   - (g) isoquant curve
   - (h) law of variable proportions
   - (i) long run
   - (j) marginal product
   - (k) marginal rate of technical substitution
   - (l) production function
   - (m) ridge lines
   - (n) short run
   - (o) total product

2. Explain the "law of variable proportions." How would this concept be applicable to the production of corn? Would there be differences in the production of automobiles? Explain.

3. Suppose that you owned a small taco stand near campus. Explain what factors of production you would consider variable in the short run. Which ones would be variable only in the long run? In terms of time, how long would the short run cover for this operation (i.e., how long would it take to plan and operationalize long-run changes)? Contrast this situation with the length of time involved in the short run and the long run for electric power generation.

4. On page 119 the exponents for (a) capital and (b) labor are given for Cobb-Douglas type production functions in six industries. How would you interpret each of these exponents individually? Explain what these exponents mean in terms of returns to scale in each of those industries.

5. Fill in the values for average product and marginal product for the production function given in the table below. Then graph total product in one graph, and average and marginal product in a separate graph immediately below the total product graph.

Labor	Total Product	Average Product	Marginal Product
0	0		
2	35		
4	117		
6	216		
8	299		
10	333		
12	288		
14	131		

Does this function follow the "law of variable proportions"? Explain.

6. Use an isocost and isoquant diagram to *explain* how the optimum combination of inputs could be determined to maximize output for a given expenditure on inputs. Would the marginal product per dollar be equal for the inputs given your solution? Why?

7. What factors would contribute to the existence of increasing returns to scale in the manufacturing of major household appliances, such as refrigerators? Would these same factors be expected to operate in the same way and to the same degree in beef production? Explain.

8. Use an Edgeworth box diagram to illustrate optimum combinations of inputs to use in the production of two products from the same two inputs. Explain the condition that determines the points that compose the "contract curve." What is the relationship between the contract curve and a production possibilities curve?

9. As colleges and universities seek to deal with potentially declining enrollments throughout the 1980s they will have to take an ever more critical look at their operations. How would production concepts used in this chapter relate to higher education? Would you expect to observe the "law of variable proportions"? What about returns to scale?

APPENDIX TO CHAPTER 7: LINEAR PROGRAMMING

APPENDIX TO CHAPTER 7: LINEAR PROGRAMMING

INTRODUCTION AND ASSUMPTIONS

Linear programming is a widely used optimization technique. It has been applied to a great numer of economic/business decisions that include the determination of the best mix of products for a firm to produce, the allocation of an advertising budget among competing media, as well as the determination of the best production processes to be used, and others. Economic and business decisions often involve the allocation of limited resources (raw materials, time, space, money, people, etc.) among competing projects with the objective of maximizing some performance objective (output, sales, return on investment, market share, etc.) or minimizing some cost objective (dollar cost, waste, pollution, etc.). In many cases, decisions such as these can be analyzed using linear programming.

The following examples of situations in which linear programming has been used should provide some appreciation for the versatility of this technique.

This appendix is adapted from J. Holton Wilson and Steven G. Darr, *Managerial Economics* (New York: Harper & Row, 1979), chap. 3 and 7.

1. *Product mix problems.* The problem of deciding on the optimal mix of products to be produced with a company's limited supply of manpower, materials, and plant capacity can be analyzed using linear programming. This is a relatively common application. Consider, for example, a food processing firm that specializes in tomato products. Tomatoes may be used to produce the following products: chili sauce, tomato paste, stewed tomatoes, ketchup, tomato soup, tomato juice, or canned whole tomatoes. A given tomato processing plant can normally produce any or all of these products. The firm is usually limited by the available crop of tomatoes, time (since the crop is perishable), available labor, other material inputs such as sugar, the demand for each product, and so on. Each of the products is likely to have a different profit contribution, and thus management is faced with a complex decision regarding how much of each product should be produced. Furthermore, management may want to know how much they can afford to pay for additional units of the factors constraining their production. These questions, and others, can be answered with information provided by the linear programming technique.

2. *Diet problems.* In the production of animal feeds specific nutritional levels must be met. Feeds are prepared from a number of ingredients each of which contains a different content of various nutritional components (protein, vitamins, minerals, etc.) and each of which is likely to have a different cost. The firm would like to produce feeds that meet the nutritional requirements of their buyers (or the government) and to do so at the lowest cost. The firm may also be interested in evaluating how much the cost will increase when the nutritional level of the feed is increased. Linear programming is helpful in determining the best solution to these problems. This type of problem also arises in the pharmaceutical, fertilizer, lawn seed, and pet food industries.

3. *Distribution problems.* Many firms have multiple plants producing a given product and many warehouses in which the product is stored before being distributed to retail outlets. The distribution cost will vary depending on the route the product takes between the point of production and point of sale. The firm must determine how many units should go from each warehouse to each sales outlet. Determining the mix of shipments that will minimize shipping cost is a complex problem for which suboptimal solutions are likely without the aid of linear programming.

4. *The petroleum industry.* Any large petroleum firm has crude oil from several sources that must be transported to one of several refineries where it is made into a variety of products, each of which must be distributed for sale. The products are jointly produced in the cracking process, which can be manipulated (within limits) to vary the mix of outputs. Linear programming can be used to determine the optimum mix of prod-

ucts and the best method for allocating crude from various sources to the several refineries as well as to distribute the final products for sale. Thus the petroleum industry represents a case in which linear programming can be used at virtually every stage of the production process.

5. *Process selection.* A problem that is in some respects similar to number 2 (above) involves the production of a product that can be made using any one (or more) of several processes. The firm would prefer to produce the product using the process(es) that will combine inputs in such a manner as to minimize production costs. The application of linear programming to this situation is the principle focus of this appendix.

Although a wide variety of problem situations can be analyzed using linear programming, there are certain requirements or assumptions that must be fulfilled. *First,* some explicit objective must be involved, which the firm wants to maximize or minimize. Multiple objectives can be incorporated into the analysis, but it is necessary that all objectives be stated in a concrete operational form. Furthermore, *the algebraic representation of the objective(s) must be linear.*

Second, alternatives must be available to the firm. If there are no alternatives, there is no decision: the firm is faced with a single course of action. If there is only one advertising medium available, the firm need not allocate funds among media; if there is only one process by which a product can be produced, there is no decision with regard to which processes to use, and so on.

Third, optimization of the objective function must be subject to some type of restrictions. These restrictions may be related to limited supply of resources (materials, time, money, etc.), capacity of the firm's plant, legal considerations, contractual agreements, marketing quotas, or anything else that may impinge on the firm's attempt to optimize their objective. In linear programming, these restrictions are called "structural constraints." *The algebraic representation of these constraints must be either in the form of linear inequalities or linear equations.* It is important to stress that just as the objective function must be linear, each of the constraints must be a linear function. Fortunately, many economic and business relationships are linear in the relevant range of activity, or are close enough to being so, in order that linear approximations can be used. For example, in the application of linear programming to electric utility capacity planning, McNamara observes that "the fundamental technical and cost relationships in an electric utility can be approximated to a useful degree of accuracy by linear or piece-wise linear functions."[1]

---

[1] John R. McNamara, "A Linear Programming Model for Long-Range Capacity Planning in an Electric Utility," *Journal of Economics and Business* 28:3 (Spring–Summer 1976), 227.

Fourth, variables never take on negative values. This is called the "nonnegativity restriction," which means that all decision variables must have either a zero or positive value. This is quite reasonable and necessary in the business/economic setting. After all, what would it mean to hire −50 units of labor, or to ship −10 tons of coal, or produce −25 cars?

FORMULATING THE PROBLEM

Let us consider a product mix problem and evaluate how each of these requirements relates to that problem. The Lumin Company is a small manufacturer of specialty lamps. Their product line consists of two lamps, both of which are made out of a bronze sculpture. The standard lamp is less intricate than the deluxe model but is polished to a high gloss. The sculpture for the deluxe model is more complex with many more folds and undulations in the metal. Only the high points are polished on the deluxe lamps.

The casting is done on two machines, each of which provides just eight hours of usable time each day. The polishing is done by hand and 12 hours of labor are available each day for this purpose. Each standard lamp takes one hour to cast and an additional two hours to polish, while each deluxe lamp needs twice as much casting time but only one-third as much time to do the necessary polishing. The profit margin on standard lamps is $20 per unit, while the deluxe lamps have a profit margin of $30 each.

For this problem the objective function may be explicitly stated as follows: The Lumin Company wants to maximize their profit from the sale of standard and deluxe lamps. As long as the $20 and $30 contribution margins do not change, this objective is linear. Each additional standard lamp increases profit by $20, and each additional deluxe lamp increases profit by $30. Clearly, the firm has alternatives: It can make a profit by producing only standard lamps, only deluxe lamps, or some of each. Given the objective function stated above, the Lumin Company should select the alternative that yields the greatest profit.

In this problem the firm is restricted or constrained in its quest for maximum profits by the limited time available for casting and polishing the lamps. The constraints are linear because the time necessary to cast or polish a given lamp is constant. The nonnegativity assumption reinforces the commonsense conclusion that the number of each type of lamp produced must be greater than or equal to zero. For example, it would not make sense to talk about producing a negative quantity of either type of lamp.

The process of formulating the linear programming problem involves transforming the descriptive information about the situation into mathematical statements. One usually begins by constructing the objective function. For the Lumin Company this is a relatively simple task. If we let X_1 represent the number of standard lamps produced and X_2 represent the number of deluxe lamps produced, then profit equals $20X_1 + 30X_2$. By letting Z represent profit, we get the objective, which is

$$\text{Maximize } Z = 20X_1 + 30X_2$$

where 20 and 30 are the contribution margins for standard and deluxe lamps, respectively.

The next step in formulating the linear programming problem is to specify the constraints. This is most easily accomplished by first summarizing what is known about the relationships involved in the problem. This can be done by answering the following questions:

1. What activities or phenomena limit the objective function?
2. How do the variables in the objective function relate to these restrictions?

Let us see how these questions are answered for the Lumin Company.

The objective function is limited by two factors. There are only 12 hours of available polishing time each day, and only 16 hours of casting time can be used daily. The second question can be answered by recalling that each standard lamp (X_1) requires one hour of casting time and two hours of polishing time. Furthermore, from the general presentation of the Lumin case given above, we know that each deluxe lamp (X_2) takes two hours of casting time and 40 minutes ($\frac{2}{3}$ hour) of polishing time. It is often helpful to summarize this information in a table, such as Table 7A.1.

From this table, the constraint functions can be readily constructed. We see that one hour times the number of standard lamps produced plus two hours times the number of deluxe lamps produced must not exceed the 16 total casting hours available. That is, $X_1 + 2X_2 \leq 16$. Furthermore, two hours times the number of standard lamps, plus $\frac{2}{3}$ hour times the number of deluxe lamps must not be greater than the 12 total polishing hours available. That is, $2X_1 + \frac{2}{3}X_2 \leq 12$.

Table 7A.1 SUMMARY OF LUMIN COMPANY DATA

PRODUCT	CASTING HOURS	POLISHING HOURS
Standard lamps (X_1)	1	2
Deluxe lamps (X_2)	2	$\frac{2}{3}$
Total hours available	16	12

The complete linear programming problem can then be stated as follows:

$$\text{Maximize } Z = 20X_1 + 30X_2$$
$$\text{Subject to:} \quad X_1 + 2X_2 \leq 16$$
$$2X_1 + \tfrac{2}{3}X_2 \leq 12$$
$$X_1, X_2 \geq 0$$

In this form the problem is ready to be solved. If there are only two variables, as in this case, the problem can be solved by a simple graphic procedure. However, most problems have more variables and are analyzed using a computer program.

GRAPHIC SOLUTIONS: MAXIMIZATION

In this section we will evaluate the product mix problem discussed above, using the *graphic method* for solving linear programming problems. Although this approach is limited to problems that have just two variables, it does provide an excellent foundation for understanding more complex linear programming problems.

Having already formulated our product mix problem, we have all the necessary information represented in the form of an objective function and a set of constraints. There are just two decision variables in these functions: standard lamps (X_1) and deluxe lamps (X_2). These variables are measured along the vertical and horizontal axes of Figure 7A.1. The constraints are constructed graphically as follows: First, graph the line that represents the linear equality form of each constraint; and second, indicate the direction of the inequality with arrows. If a problem contains an equality constraint, no arrow is necessary for that constraint since the line itself represents the constraint (rather than the line plus the space above or below the line).

For our product mix problem the constraints are:

Casting:	$X_1 + 2X_2 \leq 16$	inequality form
	$X_1 + 2X_2 = 16$	equality form
Polishing:	$2X_1 + \tfrac{2}{3}X_2 \leq 12$	inequality form
	$2X_1 + \tfrac{2}{3}X_2 = 12$	equality form

The entire triangle *OBD* (perimeter and interior) represents possible combinations of standard and deluxe lamps that can be produced without violating the constraint imposed by the amount of casting time available. The entire triangle *OAE* contains combinations that satisfy the polishing constraint.

The intersection of these two triangles (*OBD* and *OAE*) forms the convex set of points that satisfy both of the restrictions imposed on the Lumin Company. In Figure 7A.1 this intersection is represented by the

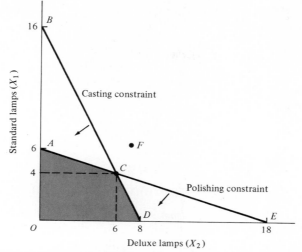

Figure 7A.1 Linear Production Constraints The casting constraint and the polishing constraint in the production of two types of lamps: standard lamps (X_1) and deluxe lamps (X_2). The shaded area, *OACD*, represents all feasible solutions, and points *O, A, C,* and *D* are basic feasible solutions.

shaded polyhedron *OACD*. That is, any combination of standard and deluxe lamps that lies either inside *OACD* or on the perimeter of *OACD* satisfies both the casting and polishing constraints. Any other point (such as *B, E,* or *F*) will violate one or both of the constraints and thus does not represent a possible level of production (the polyhedron *OACD* is similar to the production possibilities curve introduced in Figure 7.14). For this reason the points in *OACD* are called *feasible solutions* to the linear programming problem. Although defining the set of feasible solutions greatly reduces the number of solution points, there are still many alternatives available to the firm.

Given that the objective is to maximize or minimize some objective function, the viable alternatives can be even more significantly reduced. There is a fundamental theorem in linear programming that states that the objective function is optimized at an extreme point of the convex set of feasible solutions. This means that only the corner points of the polyhedron *OACD* need to be evaluated to determine the maximum profit for the Lumin Company. That is, the objective function will be maximized at either *O, A, C,* or *D*. These points are called *basic feasible solutions.*

We have now reduced the decision maker's problem to selecting one of four possible combinations of output. Given that each standard lamp (X_1) has a profit contribution of $20 and each deluxe lamp (X_2) has a profit contribution of $30, we can evaluate each of the four basic feasible solutions to determine the one that generates the greatest profit as follows:

1. At point O, $X_1 = 0$ and $X_2 = 0$; hence

$$Z = (20 \times 0) + (30 \times 0) = 0$$

2. At point A, $X_1 = 6$ and $X_2 = 0$; hence

$$Z = (20 \times 6) + (30 \times 0) = 120$$

3. At point C, $X_1 = 4$ and $X_2 = 6$; hence

$$Z = (20 \times 4) + (30 \times 6) = 260$$

4. At point D, $X_1 = 0$ and $X_2 = 8$; hence

$$Z = (20 \times 0) + (30 \times 8) = 240$$

Point C is called the *optimal basic feasible solution* since it is the basic feasible solution for which the objective function is optimized. We must conclude that if the Lumin Company wishes to maximize the profit from the sale of standard and deluxe lamps, they should allocate the casting and polishing time so that four standard lamps and six deluxe lamps are produced.

An alternative method for determining the optimal basic feasible solution is illustrated in Figure 7A.2. This diagram is identical to Figure 7A.1, except that three isoprofit lines have been added. An *isoprofit line* is a graphic representation of all possible combinations of the two products that yield the same level of profit. These are represented by dashed lines in Figure 7A.2.

All combinations of X_1 and X_2 along the isoprofit line I_1 yield a profit of $60. For example, if $X_1 = 3$ and $X_2 = 0$, profit is $60, and if $X_1 = 0$ and $X_2 = 2$, profit is again $60. Along I_2, profit equals $260, and I_3 identifies combinations of output that yield a profit of $340.

From Figure 7A.2 we can observe three important characteristics of the isoprofit functions: (1) They all have the same slope; that is, they are parallel[2]; (2) the farther an isoprofit function is from the origin, the greater the profit; and (3) an infinite number of isoprofit functions could be drawn, one for each level of profit (of course, many are not meaningful since they lie outside the set of feasible solutions). To determine the optimal basic feasible solution to the linear programming problem, we can draw one isoprofit function, such as I_1, and then slide the line outward parallel to I_1 until the isoprofit function is found, which is as far from the origin as possible, while still having at least one point in common with the set of feasible solutions. That point is the optimal basic feasible solution to the linear programming problem.

[2] The slope is equal to the negative of the ratio of the contribution margin for X_2 to the contribution margin for X_1, or $-30/20$.

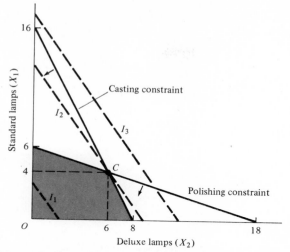

Figure 7A.2 Maximum Profit Given Production Constraints The lamp production problem as in Figure 7A.1 but with isoprofit lines ($I_1 = \$60$, $I_2 = \$260$, and $I_3 = \$340$) added. The highest profit is obtained by producing 6 deluxe lamps and 4 standard lamps as indicated at point C. This is the only point in the feasible set that would allow the firm to earn a \$260 profit from the lamps. Given the constraints, no higher profit is possible. Thus C is called the optimal basic feasible solution point.

In the present example we see that I_2 is the isoprofit function that is farthest from the origin while having only one point in common with the set of feasible solutions. The point C in Figure 7A.2 (corresponding to $X_1 = 4$, $X_2 = 6$) is the common point between I_2 and the feasible solutions. Therefore, the optimal basic feasible solution to this product mix problem is to produce four standard lamps and six deluxe lamps, yielding a profit of \$260.

GRAPHIC SOLUTIONS: MINIMIZATION

Before going on to analyze production process problems, let us briefly discuss the graphic method of solving a simple minimization problem. Assume that the problem has been formulated and that we have the following objective function and constraints:

$$\text{Minimize } Z = 15X + 15Y$$
$$\text{Subject to } A: \quad 4X + 2Y \geq 16$$
$$B: \quad X + 3Y \geq 9$$
$$X, Y \geq 0$$

The constraints, A and B, are graphed in Figure 7A.3 along with two

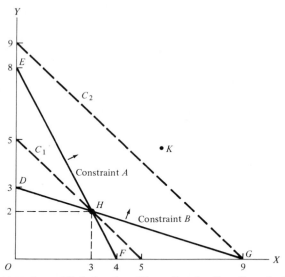

Figure 7A.3 Cost Minimization Given Production Constraints A cost minimization problem with two constraints, A and B. The set of feasible solutions extends upward and to the right of the line EHG. The basic feasible solutions are the corner points E, H, and G. The lowest cost consistent with the two constraints is C_1 (= $75) and, thus, H is the optimal basic feasible solution.

isocost functions (we will assume that the objective function Z represents the cost of producing X and Y). The isocost line C_1 illustrates combinations of X and Y that cost $75, while C_2 represents a cost of $135.

Feasible solutions to this problem are found in the region bounded by the line EHG, the vertical axis beyond E, and the horizontal axis beyond G. Thus, in this case, K is a feasible solution while D and F are not. The basic feasible solutions are again found at the corner points, E, H, and G. The cost Z at these points are $120, $75, and $135, respectively. Point H is therefore the optimal basic feasible solution to this minimization problem. We can see in Figure 7A.3 that C_1 is the lowest isocost function that has only one point in common with the set of feasible solutions. This common point is, of course, H, and the optimal basic feasible solution is to let $X = 3$ and $Y = 2$, with a minimum cost of $75.

PRODUCTION PROCESSES

We have generally discussed production under the assumption that firms can vary the level of output by changing one or more of the input factors in a continuous manner. That is, we have assumed smooth continuous production functions. These are quite satisfactory for some types of productive activity but may not be adequate for other situations, in which the technology limits production to certain combinations of inputs. As a consequence of this limitation, isoquants are not smooth functions and the production functions are not continuous.

Let us take a very simple case. Suppose that a product is produced in such a way that each unit of output requires 0.3 unit of labor input (L) and 0.3 unit of capital input (K). Isoquants representing 10, 20, and 30 units of output are graphed in Figure 7A.4. At point A, 10 units of output are produced using 3 units of labor and 3 units of capital. Point B represents 20 units of output (using $6L$ and $6K$) and point C represents 30 units of output (from $9L$ and $9K$). Note that with 3 units of labor input the isoquant, $Q(10)$, is vertical above point A, because additional capital will not increase output unless labor is increased as well. In this case, labor and capital cannot be substituted for one another in production and the isoquants are rectangular. Production requires that the inputs be combined in fixed proportions: $0.3L$ and $0.3K$ per unit of output.

The ray connecting A, B, and C illustrates this production *process*. The idea of a process is basic to many production situations and to the application of linear programming to such problems. A process is a method or technique of combining inputs to produce a product. The process defines the rate of use of each input necessary to produce a unit of output by that technique. Each process can be described by a set of technical coefficients $(a_1, a_2, \ldots, a_m)$ that represents the amount of each of the m inputs necessary to produce one unit of output by that process.

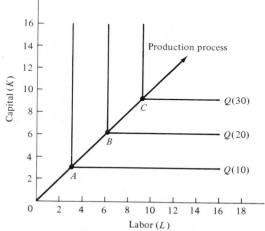

Figure 7A.4 A Single Production Process   Isoquants representing 10, 20, and 30 units of output, which must be produced using a process that requires 0.3 unit of labor and 0.3 unit of capital per unit of the product. The ray connecting A, B, and C represents the production process.

In many situations, firms will have more than one available process (although, at least in the short run, the number of processes is finite). Each process could be represented by a ray through the input space, and we would have a variable, X_i, representing the number of units of output produced by each process. Suppose that in addition to the process depicted in Figure 7A.4, our output could be produced by two additional processes: in one, 0.2 unit of labor and 0.4 unit of capital are necessary to produce each unit of output; and in the other, 0.6 unit of labor and 0.2 unit of capital are necessary per unit of output. The technical coefficients for each of these processes are summarized in Table 7A.2. These three processes are graphed in Figure 7A.5. (Process 2 corresponds to the process depicted in Figure 7A.4.)

We shall define the number of units of output produced with process 1 as X_1, the number of units produced with process 2 as X_2, and X_3 will represent the number of units of output produced using process 3. If we want to produce $Q = 10$ units of output with process 1 ($X_1 = 10$), we would have to use $2L$ and $4K$. This is point A in Figure 7A.5. Using process 2 to produce 10 units ($X_2 = 10$), we would use $3L$ and $3K$ at point A'. The same output could be produced at A'', using process 3 ($X_3 = 10$). The points labeled B, B', B'' represent $X_1 = 20$, $X_2 = 20$, and $X_3 = 20$, respectively, while C, C', C'' indicate $X_1 = 30$, $X_2 = 30$, and $X_3 = 30$.

The 20 units of output could be produced at B, B', or B''; as well as by using combinations of processes 1, 2, and 3 and the corresponding amounts of labor and capital represented by the points along the three line segments connecting these points. However, the combinations of inputs along the line BB'' are inefficient. This line represents combinations of processes 1 and 3 and the required labor and capital that will yield 20 units of output. At point D on that line segment, if the same amounts of the two inputs were used in process 2 (rather than split between 1 and 3), output would be greater than 20 (D lies farther from the origin along the ray for process 2 than does B'). We can conclude that for this example the only relevant combinations of processes lie along the lines connecting two adjacent processes at some given output level.

All points along the line segments running through points A, A', and A'' represent combinations of labor and capital that can be used to produce 10 units of output. Some combinations will use just one process

Table 7A.2 TECHNICAL COEFFICIENTS FOR EACH OF THREE PRODUCTION PROCESSES

	PROCESS 1	PROCESS 2	PROCESS 3
Labor required per unit of output	0.2	0.3	0.6
Capital required per unit of output	0.4	0.3	0.2

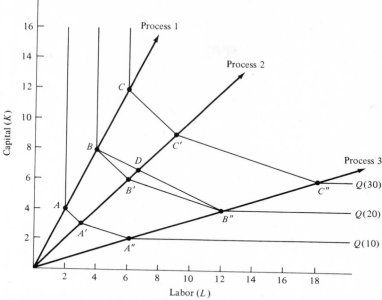

Figure 7A.5 Three Production Processes Isoquants for 10, 20,
and 30 units of a product that can be produced using three
alternative processes. In process 1, 0.2 unit of labor and 0.4 unit of
capital combine to produce 1 unit of output. In process 3, 0.6 unit
of labor and 0.2 unit of capital are necessary to produce each unit
of output. Process 2 is the same as the process in Figure 7A.4,
combining 0.3 unit of both labor and capital per unit of product.

($L = 2, K = 4; L = 3, K = 3;$ and $L = 6, K = 2$), and other combinations
would use a mix of two processes. That set of line segments thus corresponds to our earlier definition of an isoquant, and therefore we have
labeled it $Q(10)$. Other isoquants labeled $Q(20)$ and $Q(30)$ are also illustrated in Figure 7A.5. We could identify an isoquant for each level of
output in a similar manner. Note that these isoquants have a negative
slope and are convex like the ones depicted in earlier sections of this
chapter. The only difference is that the isoquants derived from a finite set
of production processes are a series of linear segments rather than being
smooth, continuous curves. As more and more different processes are
available, these isoquants become more like the smooth ones developed
earlier.

OUTPUT MAXIMIZATION WITH INPUT CONSTRAINTS

Having developed this method of specifying isoquants, we can use
them—along with a knowledge of linear programming—to answer a
number of interesting questions involving different decisions a firm must

make. We shall look at two types of questions that can be answered by using these isoquants and the linear programming optimization model. Further discussion of this topic is beyond the scope of this text but can be pursued in the works of Vandermeulen and Baumol.[3]

First, let us assume that the quantities of labor and capital available are limited to 15 and 7 units, respectively. What is the maximum output that can be produced, and how much of that output should be produced with each process? Output (Q) can be units produced with process 1 (X_1), process 2 (X_2), process 3 (X_3), or some combination of the three processes. That is,

$$Q = X_1 + X_2 + X_3$$

We want to maximize Q subject to the limitation that $L \leq 15$ and $K \leq 7$.

From the technical coefficients given in Table 7A.2, we can determine the following algebraic statement of the constraints in terms of the process variables X_1, X_2, and X_3.

$$0.2X_1 + 0.3X_2 + 0.6X_3 \leq 15$$
$$0.4X_1 + 0.3X_2 + 0.2X_3 \leq 7$$

Since our problem has just two inputs, we can solve this problem graphically. The production processes and isoquants shown in Figure 7A.5 are reproduced in Figure 7A.6, along with the constraints on labor and capital. The space bounded by the rectangle $OABC$ represents the set of feasible solutions. The highest isoquant within the set of feasible solutions is at point B, on $Q(30)$, which gives us only the maximum number of units of output possible. We still must determine how much should be produced with each process. Since B lies between process 2 and process 3, we know that the 30 units of output will be produced using those two processes.

The method of solution is not difficult. To determine the number of units to be produced by process 2, we draw a line parallel to process 3 connecting point B with process 2: line BD in Figure 7A.6. At point D, three units of both labor and capital are used in process 2. Since one unit of output can be produced with $0.3L$ and $0.3K$ using process 2, ten times as many units of each input would produce 10 units of output; that is, $X_2 = 10$.

To find the number of units produced with process 3, we draw a line parallel to process 2 connecting point B with process 3: line BE in Figure 7A.6. We see that at E, $12L$ and $4K$ are used in process 3. This is 20 times the requirement for each unit of production on process 3; thus $X_3 = 20$.

[3] For excellent extensions of the discussion presented here, see D. C. Vandermeulen, *Linear Economic Theory* (Englewood Cliffs, N.J.: Prentice-Hall, 1971), chap. 8, 9, 10, and 11; and W. J. Baumol, *Economic Theory and Operations Analysis*, 3d ed. (Englewood Cliffs, N.J.: Prentice-Hall, 1972), chap. 12.

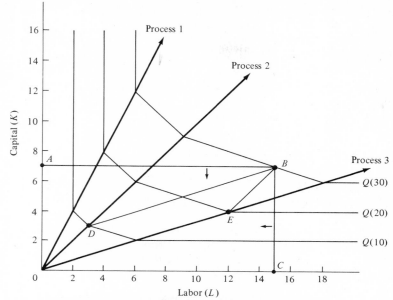

Figure 7A.6 Output Maximization with Input Constraints
Isoquants for 10, 20, and 30 units of output that can be produced
using any of three processes, along with constraints that no more
than 15 units of labor and 7 units of capital are available. The
objective is to maximize Q subject to those constraints. The
rectangle *OABC* is the set of feasible solutions and the points *O*,
A, B, and *C* are basic feasible solutions. At *B* production is
maximized, but *B* is not on one of the processes. Thus, the 30
units ($Q = 30$ at *B*) would be produced at points *D* and *E* on
processes 2 and 3, respectively. Ten units of output would be
made using process 2, whereas 20 units would be produced with
process 3. We see that between the two, all 15 units of labor and
all 7 units of capital are utilized.

Since $Q = X_1 + X_2 + X_3$ and $X_1 = 0$, $X_2 = 10$, and $X_3 = 20$, total output Q
must be 30, which checks with our original conclusion that the maximum
Q is at point B along $Q(30)$.

COST MINIMIZATION WITH AN OUTPUT CONSTRAINT

Let us now look at a second type of problem that can be investigated
using this methodology. Suppose that the firm wants to produce 20 units
of output at the lowest possible cost. If we assume that the firm pays $90
per unit of capital and $60 per unit of labor, their cost function may be
expressed as

$$C = 90K + 60L$$

or, in terms of output,[4]

$$C = 48X_1 + 45X_2 + 54X_3$$

Our objective is to minimize C, subject to $Q = 20$. From the above, it is clear that the least expensive way to produce $Q = 20$ is by process 2. This will use $6K$ and $6L$. Thus, using either expression for cost, we have

$$C = 90(6) + 60(6) = 900$$

and

$$C = 48(0) + 45(20) + 54(0) = 900$$

We can reach the same conclusion by graphic analysis but in such a simple case, it is not necessary. However, let us look at a more interesting case.

Suppose that we want to minimize the cost of producing $Q = 20$ but are further constrained by resource limitations of $L \le 12$ and $K \le 5$. The above solution with $L = 6, K = 6$ is no longer feasible. Our problem may now be stated as follows:

Minimize $C = 48X_1 + 45X_2 + 54X_3$
Subject to: $\quad\quad X_1 + X_2 + X_3 = 20$
$\quad\quad 0.2X_1 + 0.3X_2 + 0.6X_3 \le 12$
$\quad\quad 0.4X_1 + 0.3X_2 + 0.2X_3 \le 5$

where these equations are the output, labor, and capital constraints, respectively.

The problem is solved graphically in Figure 7A.7. The rectangle $OABC$ represents the set of feasible solutions as defined by just the input constraints. When we take into account the constraint that $Q = 20$, the feasible solution set is reduced to points along the line segment DE in the space $OABC$. The question is: Which of those points represents the lowest cost? We can incorporate isocost functions into Figure 7A.7. We know that there will be a whole family of parallel isocost functions, each with a slope of minus the ratio of unit labor cost to unit capital cost—that is, $-60/90$, or $-2/3$.

Three of these cost functions, $C_1 = 900, C_2 = 990$, and $C_3 = 1080$, are drawn on Figure 7A.7. We see that C_1 represents the least-cost solution to the simple problem posed above (i.e., minimize cost, subject to $Q = 20$) with the optimum at point F, using just process 2. But given the added

---

[4] The cost per unit of X_1 equals $0.4(90) + 0.2(60)$, where the 0.4 is the number of units of capital per unit of output and 0.2 is the number of units of labor per unit of output using process 1. In a similar manner, the cost per unit of X_2 equals $0.3(90) + 0.3(60)$ and the cost per unit of X_3 is equal to $0.2(90) + 0.6(60)$.

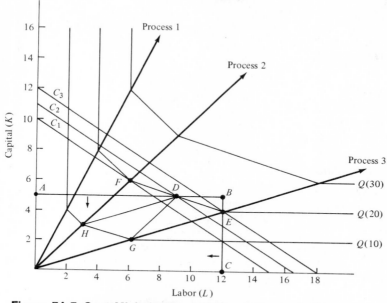

Figure 7A.7 Cost Minimization with Input Constraints and a Target Output Graphic solution to the problem of minimizing the cost of producing 20 units of output when just 12 units of labor and 5 units of capital are available. If it were not for the input constraints, 20 units could be produced at point F which is on the isocost C_1. With the input constraints, only points along the line segment DE satisfy all constraints. The cost at E (C_3) is greater than at D (C_2), so D is the optimal basic feasible solution. Since D is not on any process, the 20 units would be produced using processes 2 and 3 (at points H and G, respectively) with 10 units produced using each process. All 12 units of labor and all 5 units of capital will be employed.

constraints, there is no point along C_1 that satisfies all three conditions: $L \le 12, K \le 5,$ and $Q = 20$. We note that the lowest isocost curve that will satisfy these conditions is $C_2 = 990$ at point D. The question yet to be answered is: How much should be produced with each process?

Clearly, since D lies between process 2 and process 3, $X_1 = 0$, and we can solve for X_2 and X_3 in the same manner as in Figure 7A.6. Drawing the relevant parallelogram (see line segments DH and DG), we find that at point H along process 2, $L = 3$ and $K = 3$, so X_2 must be 10. Also at point G along process 3, $L = 6$ and $K = 2$, so X_3 must also equal 10. Thus

$$Q = 0 + 10 + 10 = 20$$
$$L = 3 + 6 = 9 \le 12$$
$$K = 3 + 2 = 5 \le 5$$

and from either expression for cost, we find that

$$C = 90K + 60L = 90(5) + 60(9) = 990$$

or

$$C = 48X_1 + 45X_2 + 54X_3 = 48(0) + 45(10) + 54(10) = 990$$

It should be evident in this example that, since all of the 12 available units of labor were not used, there is excess labor and thus capital represents the binding constraint.

Selected Readings

Baumol, William J. "Activity Analysis in One Lesson." *American Economic Review* 48 (December 1958), 837–873.

Dorfman, Robert. "Mathematical or 'Linear' Programming: A Nonmathematical Exposition." *American Economic Review* 43 (December 1953), 797–825.

Stimson, David H., and Ronald P. Thompson. "Linear Programming, Busing, and Educational Administration." *Socio-Economic Planning Sciences* 8 (August 1974), 195–206.

Thompson, Gerald E. "Linear Programming and Microeconomic Analysis." *Nebraska Journal of Economics and Business* (Autumn 1972), 25–36.

QUESTIONS

1. Write a short explanation of the following terms or concepts that were used in this appendix:
   (a) basic feasible solutions
   (b) constraints
   (c) feasible solutions
   (d) linear programming
   (e) objective function
   (f) optimal basic feasible solution
   (g) production process
2. Solve the following linear programming problem.

$$\text{Maximize } Q = 10X + 20Y$$
$$\text{Subject to:} \quad 20X + 10Y \le 80$$
$$0.625X + Y \le 5$$
$$X, Y \ge 0$$

Shade the area representing feasible solutions and circle all basic feasible solutions.

3. Solve the following linear programming problem

$$\text{Minimize } C = 12X + 3Y$$
$$\text{Subject to:} \quad 2X + Y \ge 10$$
$$2X + 3Y \ge 24$$
$$X, Y \ge 0$$

Shade the area representing feasible solutions and circle the basic feasible solutions.

4. A firm can produce their product using any of three processes. Process *A* uses 0.3 unit of labor and 0.6 unit of capital per unit of output. Process *B* uses 0.4 unit of each input per unit of output and process *C* uses 0.8 unit of labor and 0.3 unit of capital per unit of output. Graph the three processes and the isoquants for 10, 20, and 30 units of output.

5. Suppose that in Question 4 the amount of labor is limited to 60 and capital is limited to 80. What is the maximum possible level of production, and how many units should be produced with each process?

6. Suppose that the firm in Question 4 pays $100 per unit of capital and $50 per unit of labor. What is the least-cost combination of processes that will enable them to produce 200 units of output assuming there are no restrictions on the amount of labor and capital used? How would your answer change if only 80 units of capital could be used?

CHAPTER 8
COST

We continue our analysis of the supply side of the marketplace by building on the background provided by the study of production. The relationship between inputs and output described by the production function is paramount in determining how much it will cost to produce various levels of the good or service in question. Costs play a central role in virtually all economic decisions, so it is important to develop a good understanding of the various different definitions and concepts used in cost analysis.

THE NATURE OF COSTS

The manner by which costs are classified or defined depends to a significant degree on the way in which the information is to be used. It is not at all uncommon for us to hear of substantially different estimates of cost for such things as:

1. building a highway through a wilderness area
2. developing a new major for the college curriculum
3. supplying 100 kilowatthours of electric power to a household
4. adding women's soccer as an intercollegiate sport

5. providing a program of national health insurance
6. delivering a first-class letter from Bangor to Denver
7. putting a bank "money machine" in the student union

The list could go on and on. The important thing is to think about each of these activities in terms of how the cost estimate might vary from one person's perspective to another's. For some of these items, there would be less disagreement about the correct cost than for others. This may imply that there is no true definition of cost that can be universally applied. However, the differences are more in what one chooses to include and how they choose to count than in the substance of each issue. *Objective* economic evaluations of cost will yield surprisingly close estimates in each case.

One of the problems is that the data or information necessary are generally collected for purposes other than economic analysis and objective decision making. Cost data are usually compiled within the framework of some accounting system for the purpose of reporting financial behavior and position to management or a tax authority, rather than as the basis for economic decisions. Accountants and economists have long debated the proper interpretation and reporting of cost data and, though differences still exist, progress is being made as more accountants become trained in economics and as more economists learn the workings of accounting systems.

An area of substantial difference involves the use of the *opportunity cost* concept. Economists rely heavily on this concept, which can be summarized as follows: The opportunity cost of a resource is the value of the resource in its next best use; that is, if it were not being used for the present purpose, the benefit from using it in the most attractive alternative is the opportunity cost. Consider, for example, the true cost of attending graduate school to study for an MBA on a full-time basis. Assume that in these days of tight budgets for graduate assistantships no financial aid is available. If the program of study can be completed in one calendar year (four academic quarters), the cost might be estimated as follows:

Tuition @ $800/quarter	=	$3200
Room and Board @ $750/quarter	=	3000
Books and other supplies	=	400
Miscellaneous expenses	=	500
Total MBA Cost	=	$7100

But this figure is much too low if one considers that a salary of some amount (say $17,000) is forgone by allocating the time and effort to graduate school rather than a job. The true cost of the MBA is then the explicit cost of $7100 plus an opportunity cost of $17,000, or $24,100. Thus, the decision of whether to undertake graduate study or not may be heavily dependent on one's perception of the costs involved.

This leads to another but related distinction to be made in the analysis of costs. Some costs are easily determined because they are written down in some form of account as a payment or an expense. These are called *explicit costs* and represent an actual money transfer (such as the $7100 above). Economists also include implicit or imputed costs in evaluating a given problem. The opportunity cost of the MBA program (above) is an imputed cost. There is no accounting record of the cost, but nonetheless it is a very real and important part of the true cost of the MBA degree.

Failure to include opportunity costs and imputed costs generally make accounting costs appear lower than are appropriate. This, in turn, results in overstating profit. Consider, for example, two firms with identical explicit operating costs and identical revenue. Assume that Firm 1 raised the money to begin operations by selling common stock, while Firm 2 obtained the same sum of money by selling bonds. An accounting report would show Firm 2 with less profit than Firm 1. They would correctly report Firm 2's cost because the interest on bonds would be deducted as an expense. But for Firm 1 the cost of capital would appear to be zero since dividends on common stock are not treated as an expense. Thus, accounting records would understate the cost and overstate the profit for Firm 1. An economist would include the dividends as a cost, even if they were not paid out but kept in retained earnings; or even if the firm didn't pay them because revenue and explicit production cost were equal, leaving no money for dividends. In the latter case, an accountant would say the firm "broke even," while the economist's view would recognize that not all resources (risk capital) had received their return. Clearly, the money investors have in common stock has an opportunity cost equal to the return available from alternative uses. This should then be an imputed cost of doing business.

Since costs are generally evaluated in the accounting process, we see that some important and very real costs of running a business enterprise are not fully recognized. In economics we attempt to make a more complete identification of all necessary costs, and therefore the term *economic profit* differs from the more common usage of "profit" as determined by standard accounting practices. At least part of what accountants recognize as profit is indeed a cost. Economists include a "normal profit" as a cost of doing business; for example, the return to entrepreneurship is viewed as a necessary cost. Thus in cost functions used in this text a "normal profit" is included as part of cost. If revenue exceeds cost (including normal profits) we would say that there is an "economic profit" (the terms *real profit* or *pure profit* are sometimes used synonymously with economic profit).

A study of the cost of producing corn and soybeans by Mueller and Hinton provides an illustration of some types of explicit and imputed costs. Their breakdown is as follows[1]:

Cash Costs (Explicit)	*Noncash and Imputed Costs*
Soil fertility	Labor, unpaid charges
Seed and crop expense	Machinery depreciation
Labor costs	Building depreciation
Machinery repairs, fuel, and higher taxes	Land charges
Building repairs	Interest on other capital
Cash overhead expenses	Machinery investment
	Building investment
	Stored grain inventory
	Operating capital

Not only are there three more line items in the right-hand column, but also more than 50 percent of the cost per bushel originates in those categories.

A further distinction that confounds many discussions of costs, particularly in the public sector, is that between private and social costs. *Private costs* are those that accrue directly to the individual(s) engaged in the relevant activity. External costs, on the other hand, are passed on to persons not involved in the activity in any direct way (i.e., they are passed on to society at large). Consider the classic case of a manufacturer located on the edge of a lake or river who dumps waste into the water rather than disposing of it in some other manner. The private cost to the firm of dumping is zero. If the waste were hauled away to a land fill, or otherwise treated, there would be some explicit private cost involved. Production costs thus appear lower than they really are. Third parties located downcurrent are adversely affected by the waste and incur higher costs in terms of treating the water for their use, having to travel to alternative recreation facilities, and so on. If these external costs were included in the production costs of the producing firm, a truer picture of real or *social costs* of the output would be obtained. Ignoring external costs may lead to an inefficient and undesirable allocation of resources.

TOTAL COST IN THE SHORT RUN

In Chapter 7 we defined the short run as the period during which the firm has some inputs (factors of production) that are variable while others are available in a fixed amount. This leads to a distinction in short-run cost

---

[1] A. G. Mueller and R. A. Hinton, "Farmers' Production Cost for Corn and Soybeans by Unit Size," *American Journal of Agricultural Economics* 57 (December 1975), 934–939.

analysis between fixed costs (*FC*) and variable costs (*VC*) associated with the fixed and variable factors, respectively. The total cost (*TC*) to the firm in the short run is thus

$$TC = FC + VC$$

The variable cost portion of total cost is derived directly from the firm's short-run production function. The production function presented in Table 7.1 and Figure 7.1 is reproduced in the right-hand portion of Figure 8.1. It is drawn as a solid line only up to 10 units of the labor input since beyond that point total product diminishes (marginal product is negative). Each of the ten points used to plot the production function is labeled with a letter (*A* through *J*).

Now assume that each unit of labor costs $160 (e.g., a unit equals one eight-hour day at $20/hour including fringe benefits, social security, etc.). Then one labor unit, or 8.4 units of output (point *A*) would represent a variable cost of $160. Two labor units, or 31.2 units of output (point *B*), would have a variable cost of $320. Production of 150 units of output (point *E*) would involve 5 units of labor (or $800 of variable cost). Thus for each point on the production function there is some corresponding variable cost. These points are graphed in the left-hand part of Figure 8.1 as points *A'* through *J'*. We usually think of variable cost as a function of

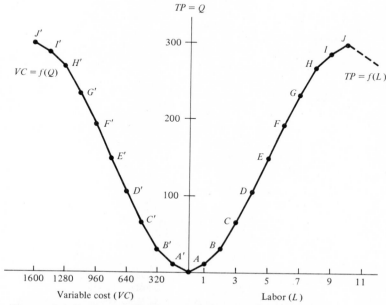

Figure 8.1 Derivation of Variable Cost Derivation of the variable-cost curve from the production function given in Figure 7.1, with a labor cost of $160 per unit.

the level of output. Therefore, to see the general shape of a variable-cost curve the diagram should be turned clockwise 90° so that the quantity $(TP = Q)$ axis becomes the horizontal and the variable cost axis is vertical.

Doing this, we see that VC intersects at the origin because zero output results when no labor is used, and if no labor is used there is no labor cost (here labor is the only variable factor). We also see that variable cost increases at first at a decreasing rate (the slope becomes less steep), then eventually it increases at an increasing rate (the slope becomes more steep). Remember that we are considering the quantity axis as the horizontal, so the slope is measured as $\Delta VC/\Delta Q$.

The fixed-cost function is a horizontal line (slope = 0) at the level of fixed cost. This is illustrated in part a of Figure 8.2. Regardless of the level of output, fixed costs are constant at $200. A variable-cost function with the same characteristics as discussed above is graphed in Figure 8.2(b). We see, for example, the $VC = 0$ for $Q = 0$, $VC = 200$ for $Q = 2$,

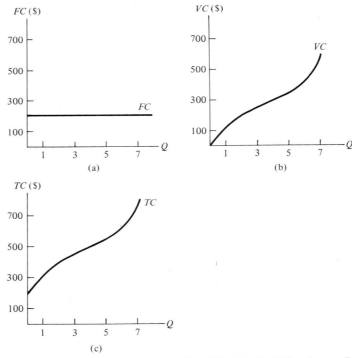

Figure 8.2 Fixed, Variable, and Total Costs (a) Fixed cost FC, (b) variable cost VC, and (c) total cost TC graphed as functions of the level of output Q, given that production follows the law of variable proportions.

$VC = 300$ for $Q = 4$, and $VC = 600$ for $Q = 7$. As defined above, total cost equals the sum of the variable and fixed costs. This is depicted in Figure 8.2(c), where $TC = 200$ for $Q = 0$, $TC = 400$ for $Q = 2$, $TC = 500$ for $Q = 4$, and $TC = 800$ for $Q = 7$. That is, for each level of output total cost is exactly \$200 ($= FC$) greater than variable cost.

Before leaving our discussion of total cost, it is important to emphasize the relationship between the production and cost functions. The reason that the variable- and total-cost functions have the shapes depicted in Figure 8.2 is because production is subject to the law of variable proportions (see page 119) in the short run.

UNIT COSTS IN THE SHORT RUN

Having developed an understanding of fixed, variable, and total costs, we can now investigate unit costs (costs per unit of output), which are much more important in making economic decisions. We begin by defining four short-run unit cost concepts: average fixed cost (AFC), average variable cost (AVC), average total cost (AC), and marginal cost (MC).

$$AFC = \frac{FC}{Q}$$

$$AVC = \frac{VC}{Q}$$

$$AC = \frac{TC}{Q} = \frac{FC + VC}{Q} = AFC + AVC$$

$$MC = \frac{\Delta TC}{Q} = \frac{\Delta VC}{Q}$$

Each of these will be discussed in terms of the cost function underlying the diagrams in Figure 8.2, as given in schedule form in Table 8.1.

We see that average fixed cost declines throughout the cost schedule as the given fixed cost (\$200) is spread over more and more units of output. In Figure 8.3(d), AFC is illustrated graphically below the graph of FC in part (a). Note that the slope of the lines OA and OB in Figure 8.3(a) measure the AFC at points A and B, respectively. At A, the slope of OA is 100 ($= 200/2$), which corresponds to point A' along the average fixed cost curve.

Figure 8.3(e) illustrates the average variable cost and the marginal cost for the data in Table 8.1. Let us consider AVC first. The value of AVC at any level of output can be determined from the table or from the slope of a line from the origin to the variable-cost curve at that level of output. For example, the line OC in Figure 8.3(b) has a slope of 100 ($= 200/2$), which is the AVC at $Q = 2$. The slope of lines from the origin to the

Table 8.1 COST DATA FOR THE FUNCTIONS IN FIGURES 8.2 AND 8.3

OUTPUT (Q)	FIXED COST (FC)	VARIABLE COST (VC)	TOTAL COST (TC)	AVERAGE FIXED COST (AFC)	AVERAGE VARIABLE COST (AVC)	AVERAGE COST (AC)	MARGINAL COST (MC)
0	200	0	200	—	—	—	
1	200	110	310	200	110	310	110
2	200	200	400	100	100	200	90
3	200	245	445	66.7	81.7	148.3	45
4	200	300	500	50	75	125	55
5	200	360	560	40	72	112	60
6	200	430	630	33.3	71.7	105	70
7	200	600	800	28.6	85.7	114.3	170

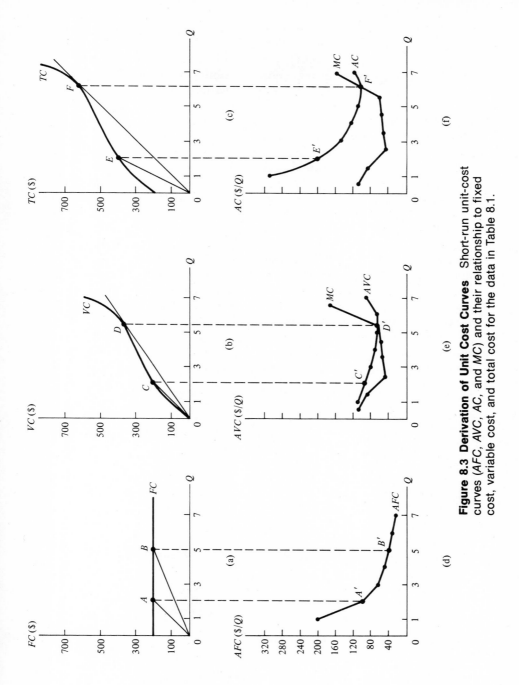

Figure 8.3 Derivation of Unit Cost Curves Short-run unit-cost curves (*AFC*, *AVC*, *AC*, and *MC*) and their relationship to fixed cost, variable cost, and total cost for the data in Table 8.1.

variable-cost function decrease out to point D (roughly 5.5 units) and then increase beyond that level of output. Thus, AVC will at first decline, reach a minimum (at about $Q = 5.5$), and then increase.[2]

The marginal-cost curve, shown in both Figure 8.3(e) and 8.3(f), is a measure of the rate of change in either variable cost or total cost. This is true since the only part of TC that can change is VC. At any level of output MC may be determined by measuring the slope of TC or VC. The slope of OD in Figure 8.3(b) is 70 (= 385/5.5) and the slope of OF in Figure 8.3(c) is 100 (= 610/6.1). The corresponding points on MC are D' and F'. We see that marginal cost at first declines, reaches a minimum, and then increases (as do the slopes of VC and TC).[3]

Finally, let us look at average cost (we usually use the shorter term "average cost" rather than "average total cost"). The AC curve for the data in Table 8.1 is illustrated in Figure 8.3(f). Once more it may be derived by measuring the slope of lines from the origin to the respective total curve (TC). For example, the slope of OE, in Figure 8.3(c), is 200 (= 400/2), which is indicated as point E' on the AC curve. The average-cost curve could also be obtained by adding the AFC and AVC curves vertically (i.e., AC lies above AVC by the amount of AFC). Note that at their respective minimum points both AC and AVC equal MC.

The three cost functions that will ultimately be seen as most important in making economic decisions are average cost (AC), average variable cost (AVC), and marginal cost (MC). Generalized curves for each of

---

[2] The relationship between AVC and average product (AP) can be shown rather simply:

$$AP = \frac{TP}{L} = \frac{Q}{L}$$

$$VC = wL$$

$$AVC = \frac{wL}{Q} = w\left(\frac{L}{Q}\right)$$

$$AVC = \frac{w}{AP}$$

where w is the cost per unit of labor. Thus when AP is increasing, AVC is decreasing, and vice versa.

[3] The relationship between MC and marginal product (MP) can also be shown easily.

$$MP = \frac{\Delta TP}{\Delta L} = \frac{\Delta Q}{\Delta L}$$

$$MC = \frac{\Delta TC}{\Delta Q} = \frac{\Delta VC}{\Delta Q} = w\Delta L/\Delta Q$$

$$MC = w(\Delta L/\Delta Q)$$

$$MC = w/MP$$

where w is the cost per unit of the variable input labor. Thus when MP increases, MC declines, and when MP decreases, MC increases.

these are graphed in Figure 8.4. Recall that each of these curves at first declines, reaches a minimum, and then increases. For this reason we say they are "U-shaped" cost curves. They are not drawn with these shapes arbitrarily. It is the fact that they are based on production relationships which are subject to the law of variable proportions that determines this U-shape for *AC, AVC,* and *MC* curves.

TOTAL COST IN THE LONG RUN

Most decisions involve short-run cost concepts because they are made in a context in which some fixed inputs exist. However, long-range plans and decisions are made based on the ability to change the level of use of all inputs. Thus all short-run decisions are made within the framework of having certain fixed factors, the level of which were determined by an earlier long-run plan or decision. For this reason the long-run cost curves are often used to depict the firm's planning horizon.

The long-run total-cost curve is derived from the long-run production function in which all inputs are variable. Such a production function is represented by the five isoquant curves in Figure 8.5. Although the respective isoquants appear to be the same distance apart, the change in the level of output between successive ones is not constant. As we move from Q_1 to Q_2, output increases by 150 units (= 250 − 100); from Q_2 to Q_3, output increases by 250 units (= 500 − 250); from Q_3 to Q_4, output increases by 100 units (= 600 − 500); and from Q_4 to Q_5, output increases by 50 units (= 650 − 600).

The five isocost curves tangent to these isoquants at the points *A, B, C, D,* and *E* represent expenditures of resources (total costs) of 300, 400, 500, 600, and 700 dollars, respectively. Since the costs per unit of capital

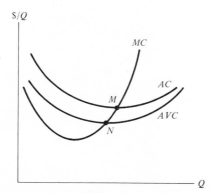

Figure 8.4 U-Shaped Unit Costs The general relationship between *AC, AVC,* and *MC.* The *MC* curve intersects both *AC* and *AVC* at their minimum points (*M* and *N,* respectively).

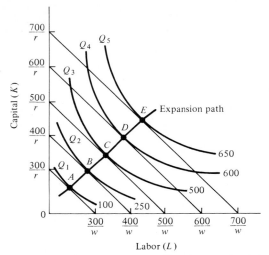

Figure 8.5 The Expansion Path and Returns to Scale Isoquant
and isocost curves for a production function that at first has
increasing returns to scale (*A* to *C*), then constant returns to scale
(*C* to *D*), and finally decreasing returns to scale (*D* to *E*). Points *A*,
B, *C*, *D*, and *E* form the expansion path. The vertical and horizontal
intercepts equal total cost divided by the cost per unit of capital (*r*)
and the cost per unit of labor (*w*), respectively. Isoquants are
labeled according to the number of units of output each
represents.

r and labor *w* are assumed to be constant, these five isocost curves are parallel to one another and the distance between them is constant along the
expansion path traced out by *A, B, C, D,* and *E*.

By comparing the relative change in resources to the relative change
in output we can determine whether or not there are economies of scale
over any interval. Since *r* and *w* are constant, the percentage change in
cost will equal the percentage change in resources employed. The percentage changes are as follows:

Region	% Δ Total Cost		% Δ Output
AB	33	<	150
BC	25	<	100
CD	20	=	20
DE	17	>	8

Thus this production function is characterized by increasing returns to
scale over the range from *A* to *C*, constant returns to scale from *C* to *D*,
and decreasing returns to scale from *D* to *E*.

Taking the values for total cost and output from the expansion path of Figure 8.5, we can construct the following table for total cost and output:

Output (Q)	Long-Run Total Cost (LRTC)
100	300
250	400
500	500
600	600
650	700

These points are graphed in Figure 8.6 as the long-run total-cost (*LRTC*) curve. The points A', B', C', D', and E' correspond to the equilibrium points in Figure 8.5 ($A, B, C, D,$ and E, respectively). Note that the *LRTC* curve at first increases at a decreasing rate, then at a constant rate, and finally at an increasing rate (once more indicating the existence of increasing, constant, and decreasing returns to scale, respectively).

The graph of *LRTC* is extended from A' to the origin since in the long run all costs are variable and if nothing is produced no resources will be used (i.e., the firm will leave the industry entirely). Thus the *LRTC* curve is analogous to the short-run *VC* curve. But the similarity is really only skin deep. Although these two curves have the same general shape, the reason they do is quite different. The shape of *VC* is caused by produc-

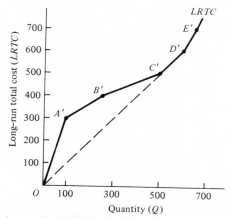

Figure 8.6 The Long-Run Total-Cost Curve The long-run total-cost (*LRTC*) curve derived from the expansion path of Figure 8.5. The *LRTC* curve increases at a decreasing rate (*O* through *C'*), then at a constant rate (*C'* to *D'*), and then at an increasing rate (beyond *D'*), representing the stages of increasing, constant, and decreasing returns to scale, respectively.

tion being subject to the law of variable proportions in the short run. In the long run, however, it is the existence of increasing, constant, and decreasing returns to scale that accounts for the shape of *LRTC*.

UNIT COSTS IN THE LONG RUN

In the long run costs are not dichotomized into fixed and variable components (all costs are variable). Thus the only long-run unit-cost functions of interest are long-run average cost (*LRAC*) and long-run marginal cost (*LRMC*). These are defined as follows:

$$LRAC = \frac{LRTC}{Q}$$

$$LRMC = \frac{\Delta LRTC}{\Delta Q}$$

For the long-run total cost given in Figure 8.6, these unit costs can be presented in tubular form as follows:

Output (Q)	Long-Run Total Cost (LRTC)	Long-Run Average Cost (LRAC)	Long-Run Marginal Cost (LRMC)
0	0	—	
			3.00
100	300	3.00	
			.67
250	400	1.60	
			.67
500	500	1.00	
			1.00
600	600	1.00	
			2.00
650	700	1.08	

These *LRAC* and *LRMC* values are graphed in Figure 8.7. We see, both in the table above and in the graph, that *LRAC* and *LRMC* are U-shaped and that they are equal at the minimum of *LRAC*. The values of *LRMC* are graphed at the midpoints of the output intervals they represent.

The values for *LRMC* could be obtained from the table above or alternatively from the *LRTC* function in Figure 8.6. *LRAC* can also be determined from Figure 8.6. For example, the *LRAC* of producing 100 units is the slope of *OA'* (= 300/100), and the *LRAC* of producing 500 units is the slope of the dashed line *OC'* (= 500/500 = 1).

The long-run average-cost curve is sometimes shown as the envelope curve of a series of all the possible short-run average-cost curves.

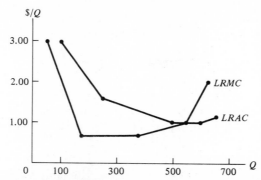

Figure 8.7 Long-Run Unit-Cost Curves Long-run marginal cost
(*LRMC*) and long-run average cost (*LRAC*) for the *LRTC* function
graphed in Figure 8.6. *LRMC* equals *LRAC* at the minimum of
LRAC.

This is done in Figure 8.8. Five short-run average-cost curves, each representing a different-size plant (set of fixed factors) are illustrated, although many more may exist. For any given rate of output there is one plant size that will accommodate that level of production at the lowest

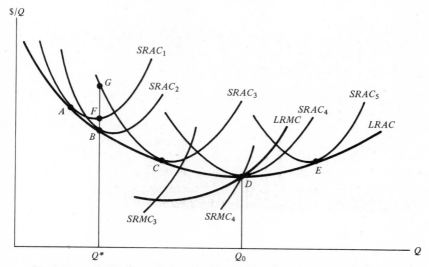

Figure 8.8 Long-Run Average Cost as an Envelope Curve The
LRAC curve as the envelope curve of a series of *SRAC* curves,
each representing a different size of plant. The minimum possible
cost of producing each level of output (such as points *A, B, C, D,*
and *E*) determine *LRAC*. Economies of scale exist up to Q_0, and
diseconomies of scale are evident beyond that level. The *LRMC* is
composed of a single point from each *SRMC* and intersects *LRAC*
at its minimum (*D*).

possible unit cost. Interestingly, the lowest cost of producing some rate of output will not generally be at the minimum point of a short-run average-cost curve.

Consider, for example, the production of Q^* units in Figure 8.8. That level of output could be produced with the plant size represented by $SRAC_1$, $SRAC_2$, or $SRAC_3$. It represents the *optimum rate of output* for the size plant represented by $SRAC_1$ (i.e., it is at the minimum point of $SRAC_1$). However, if the firm expects to produce at that rate, the best size of plant is the one related to $SRAC_2$. The Q^* units could be produced at a cost savings of FB per unit over $SRAC_1$. However, if the firm expanded too much, say to the plant with $SRAC_3$, the unit cost would be even higher (at point G) than with $SRAC_1$. The series of points such as A, B, C, D, and E that represent the lowest possible cost of producing each rate of output trace out the $LRAC$ curve. Each of these points represents a tangency of a $SRAC$ with the $LRAC$ envelope curve.

The plant size associated with $SRAC_4$ is the *optimum size of plant* because its minimum point is the lowest of all possible unit costs. Given the $LRAC$ in Figure 8.8, we can say that there are increasing returns to scale (or economies of scale) up to Q_0 and decreasing returns to scale (or diseconomies of scale) beyond Q_0.[4]

The long-run marginal cost ($LRMC$) is composed of a single point from each $SRMC$ curve as shown in Figure 8.8. Just two representative short-run marginal-cost curves are illustrated ($SRMC_3$ and $SRMC_4$).

ECONOMIES OF SCALE: SOME EVIDENCE

Whether any particular industry has economies of scale or not, and if so over what range, is an empirical question. It may be that for many activities the long-run average-cost function is more L-shaped than U-shaped. An L-shaped $LRAC$, such as illustrated in Figure 8.9, is likely to result when marginal costs are relatively low and relatively constant. In this case there may be initial economies of scale, followed by a leveling of the $LRAC$ and no observable diseconomies of scale.

One of the most comprehensive studies involving economies of scale among a wide range of industries is Gupta's analysis of manufacturing industries in India.[5] The shapes of the 29 cost functions he estimated are

---

[4] We have used the terms *increasing returns to scale* and *economies of scale* (or *decreasing returns* and *diseconomies*) interchangeably. Strictly speaking, this is not correct. Returns to scale are determined by production and technological factors. Economies of scale (or diseconomies) may also result from monetary effects alone such as a larger firm being able to purchase large lots of inputs at a reduced cost. However, as they relate to $LRAC$, it does little harm to think of these as the same concept.

[5] Vinod K. Gupta, "Cost Functions, Concentration, and Barriers to Entry in Twenty-Nine Manufacturing Industries of India," *Journal of Industrial Economics* 17:1 (November 1968), 57–72.

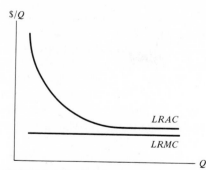

Figure 8.9 L-Shaped LRAC Curve An L-shaped long-run
average-cost curve and the associated long-run marginal-cost
curve. If long-run marginal cost is constant the long-run
average-cost curve approaches the long-run marginal cost.

summarized in Table 8.2. We see that the majority of the industries studied exhibited some economies of scale and just a few showed a tendency
for diseconomies of scale to develop at higher levels of production.

Christensen and Greene have reported on the study of economies of

Table 8.2 CLASSIFICATION OF 29 INDUSTRIES IN INDIA BASED ON THE
SHAPE OF THE LONG-RUN AVERAGE-COST FUNCTION

U-SHAPED	L-SHAPED	ESSENTIALLY FLAT
1. Starch	1. Sewing machines	1. Iron and steel
2. Matches	2. Electric lamps	2. Paints and varnishes
3. Cement	3. Electric fans	3. Vegetable oils
4. Distilleries and	4. Soap	(not edible)
breweries	5. Woolen textiles	4. Aluminum, copper, and
5. Rice milling	6. Bicycles	brass
	7. Paper and paperboard	5. Chemicals
	8. Fruit and vegetable	6. Jute textiles
	processing	
	9. Ceramics	
	10. Biscuit making	
	11. Plywood and tea chests	
	12. Vegetable oil (edible)	
	13. Glass and glassware	
	14. Tanning	
	15. Wheat flour	
	16. Cotton textiles	
	17. General and electrical	
	engineering	
	18. Sugar	

SOURCE: Adapted from Vinod K. Gupta, "Cost Functions, Concentration, and Barriers to
Entry in Twenty-Nine Manufacturing Industries of India," *Journal of Industrial Economics* 17:1 (November 1968), 59–60.

scale in electric power generation.[6] The long-run average-cost curve they estimated is reproduced in Figure 8.10. We see that there are substantial economies of scale up to nearly 20 billion kilowatthours of output, then essentially constant *LRAC* out to about 67 billion kWh. They estimated that statistically significant diseconomies exist above that level. Only one firm in their sample of 114 was above that level (but accounted for 6.7 percent of industry output). Ninety-seven of the firms (accounting for 48.7 percent of industry output) fell in the initial phase of significant scale economies.

The author's own research on economies of scale in the savings and loan industry for the Twelfth Federal Home Loan Bank District shows results that are somewhat similar. The data for *LRAC* can be represented by the following eight observations:

Total Assets *(Millions of Dollars)*	*Average Operating Costs* *(Costs)*
1.1	14.6
2.5	3.8
5.8	2.2
16.3	0.8
178.0	0.7
354.6	1.0
740.4	1.5
1137.9	2.1

These observations represent points along the "frontier frame" of the *LRAC* curve and thus give a pretty good idea of what the entire set of data would look like. We can see that a relatively small savings and loan association has much higher average operating costs than larger ones. The major economies of scale are reached by the $16 million asset level and slight diseconomies of scale appear to exist for savings and loan associations that are above approximately $350 million in assets.

ALLOCATING OUTPUT FOR THE MULTIPLANT FIRM

Let us now turn to a problem faced by firms that produce a given product in more than one plant. For purposes of exposition the two-plant case will be considered, although the analysis can be generalized to any number of plants. The problem is to determine how much of the product to produce at each plant. We will assume that the total level of output desired has already been determined (this question will be addressed in Chapters 9 through 12).

[6] L. R. Christensen and W. H. Greene, "Economies of Scale in U.S. Electric Power Generation," *Journal of Political Economy* 84:4, part 1 (August 1976), 655–676.

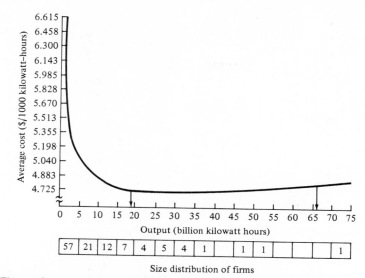

Figure 8.10 LRAC for the Electric Power Industry The *LRAC* curve for U.S. electric power generation, showing an initial stage of substantial economies of scale. (Source: L. R. Christensen and W. H. Greene, "Economies of Scale in U.S. Electric Power Generation," *Journal of Political Economy* 84:4 (August 1976), 674. Reprinted by permission of the University of Chicago Press.)

The marginal-cost functions for the two plants (MC_1 and MC_2) are both graphed in Figure 8.11. We see that the marginal cost of production is higher in Plant 2 for all levels of production. This may be because Plant 2 is an older facility or is located in an area with higher labor cost, among other things that could cause marginal cost to be greater.

Suppose that it has been decided that the firm should produce 170 units of output. One might at first suggest that all 170 should be produced in Plant 1 since for all levels the marginal cost is lower in that plant. Suppose that the firm was producing all 170 in Plant 1 and asked for advice on cutting costs. We could tell them that if 10 fewer units were produced in Plant 1, the marginal cost of the 160th unit would fall to about $5 (whereas the current marginal cost of 170 is roughly $6.50). If those 10 units were produced in Plant 2, the marginal cost of each of the 10 units would be roughly $2.10. Considerable savings would result. The decrease in cost by moving from 170 to 160 along MC_1 (call it A) is the area under MC_1 over that interval (the shaded area at the right edge of Figure 8.11). The added cost by increasing production in Plant 2 from 0 to 10 (call it B) is the area under MC_2 over that range (the shaded part at the left edge of Figure 8.11). The net savings is A minus B, or roughly $55 − $21 = $34.

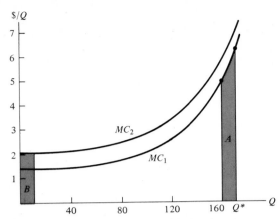

Figure 8.11 Marginal-Cost Curves for Two Plants
Marginal-cost curves for each of two plants (MC_1 and MC_2). The
marginal cost of production is higher for Plant 2 at all levels of
output ($MC_1 < MC_2$ for all Q). If Q^* (=170) is the predetermined
rate of output desired by the firm, producing 160 in plant 2 and 10
in plant 1 is less costly than producing all 170 in plant 2 since area
A is greater than area B.

Just how many units should be produced in Plant 1 and how many in
Plant 2 can be determined using Figure 8.12. In this figure the two
marginal cost curves from Figure 8.11 are reproduced with MC_1 increasing from left to right, as in the original, but MC_2 increases from right to
left. That is, the origin for Plant 2's marginal cost is at the lower right
corner of the diagram (at O_2). Each additional unit should be produced in
the plant with the lowest MC for that unit. Production will thus begin in
Plant 1 and continue until it becomes less expensive at the margin to
produce the next unit in Plant 2. This will lead to allocating production
between plants such that the marginal cost is equal for both. This is
shown as point E in Figure 8.12, which corresponds to 113 units in Plant
1 and, reading from right to left, 57 units in Plant 2 (57 = 170 − 113).

BREAK-EVEN ANALYSIS

Break-even analysis represents one of the simplest, yet most useful,
techniques of all economic analyses. In this section we present only the
fundamental model and a sample of variations that may be developed.
The break-even graph is the most frequent mode of using this form of the
analysis. Such a graph is presented in Figure 8.13. It is common to use
linear revenue and cost functions, in using break-even analysis. For many
practical applications this is often satisfactory because these functions are
either linear or very nearly linear in the relevant range of output being

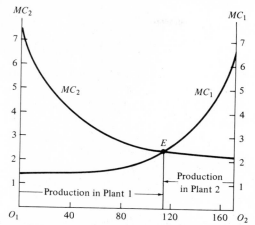

**Figure 8.12 Optimum Allocation of Production Between
Plants** Determination of how many units of output to produce in
each of two plants, given their marginal cost curves (MC_1 and
MC_2) and that 170 units are to be produced in total. Production
should be allocated such that $MC_1 = MC_2$. This results in 113 units
produced in Plant 1 and 57 units in Plant 2.

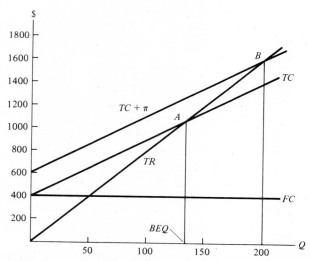

Figure 8.13 Break-Even Analysis Graphic determination of the
break-even level of output (BEQ), given fixed costs of $400,
average variable cost of $5 per unit, and a price of $8 per unit. The
break-even point is at A, where $BEQ = 133$. For a target profit of
$200, the level of output necessary is determined at B, or 200
units.

considered. Nonlinear functions can be used if it is determined that the use of linear approximations is accompanied by unacceptable errors.

Several facts should be readily apparent from Figure 8.13. First, the vertical distance between the total-cost line and the horizontal fixed-cost line represents the variable cost of alternative levels of output. Second, since total revenue (TR) is linear, price (P) must be constant over the relevant range of output. Furthermore, unit variable costs (AVC) must also be constant over this range in order for total cost (TC) to be linear. Finally, note that the break-even level of output (BEQ) is at the point on the horizontal axis directly below the intersection of TR and TC (this intersection is the break-even point).

This graphic model may be expressed in algebraic forms as well. By definition, profit (π) equals total revenue minus total cost.

$$\pi = TR - TC$$

and

$$TR = P \cdot Q$$
$$TC = FC + VC$$
$$TC = FC + AVC \cdot Q$$

Furthermore, by definition, profit is zero if the firm breaks even. Thus for the break-even quantity, we have

$$O = P \cdot Q - FC - AVC \cdot Q$$

$$FC = (P - AVC)Q$$

$$Q = \frac{FC}{P - AVC} = BEQ$$

In this form the denominator $(P - AVC)$ is often referred to as the contribution margin per unit because that value represents the portion of selling price that contributes to paying the fixed costs and to profit.

If the only use of break-even analysis was to determine the level of sales at which the firm would break even, given price and costs, the technique would not be so widely adopted. A single break-even graph also shows how much profit (for $Q > BEQ$) or loss (for $Q < BEQ$) the firm will make at each level of output. Suppose that the firm has a target profit of π dollars. By adding that to fixed costs, we can use the break-even analysis to determine how great a sales volume will be necessary to achieve that rate of profit. In addition, suppose that the firm has econometric or marketing studies that indicated expected sales at each of three different prices. By plotting the total revenue line representing each price, the firm can quickly determine which price and corresponding level of sales will be most profitable. These are just examples of the types of situations in which break-even analysis can be used.

First, suppose that a firm has fixed costs of $400 and average variable costs of $5, and sells their product for $8. The break-even level of sales is calculated as

$$BEQ = \frac{400}{8 - 5}$$

$$BEQ = \frac{400}{3}$$

$$BEQ = 133$$

This result can also be seen by examining Figure 8.13 for the intersection of total revenue (TR) and total cost (TC) at point A. Now if the firm decided that they would set a target rate of profit (π) of $200, how many units must be sold to achieve that objective? If the contribution margin is $3 per unit, then we should expect them to have to sell 67 more units to get the desired profit. This can be seen by adding $\pi = 200$ to fixed costs in either graphic or algebraic forms. For the latter we simply calculate

$$Q = \frac{FC + \pi}{P - AVC}$$

$$Q = \frac{400 + 200}{8 - 5} = 200$$

The result is determined at point B in Figure 8.13.

SUMMARY

Cost analysis is central to most economic decisions and thus it is important to understand the alternative ways of looking at and evaluating costs. Economists rely heavily on the opportunity cost concept: The *opportunity cost* of a resource is the value forgone by not using that resource in its next most attractive alternative use.

Often only *explicit costs* (actual money transfers) are included in cost analysis because they are readily available in various accounting documents. However, this has the effect of making costs appear lower than they should. It is frequently necessary to add *imputed costs* (or *implicit cost*), such as the money value of a rancher's time, to arrive at a more appropriate measure of the cost of production.

Costs may also be understated in many cases because *private costs* (those that accrue to a particular person or firm) do not reflect the true *social cost* of production (including those costs that are passed on to third parties). If a firm emits smoke (that causes neighboring houses to need more frequent painting) rather than cleaning its air effluent, part of the cost of production is passed on to local residents.

In the short run total costs can be dichotomized into *fixed costs* and *variable costs.* Since fixed costs are constant, total cost and variable cost behave in a similar manner: at first increasing at a decreasing rate and ultimately increasing at an increasing rate. As illustrated in Figure 8.1 the shape of these cost functions is determined by the shape of the total product curve.

In the long run all costs are variable. The long-run total-cost curve is derived from points along the firm's expansion path and thus has a shape that is dependent upon the type of returns to scale reflected in the production function. The long-run average-cost curves will be U-shaped if production exhibits increasing returns to scale at first and ultimately has decreasing returns to scale. Many long-run average-cost curves may appear L-shaped, either because decreasing returns to scale do not exist for that industry, or because a large enough level of output has not been reached to allow such diseconomies to become evident.

When a firm produces the same product in more than one plant, a question arises concerning how the total production should be distributed among plants. A simple rule can be shown to minimize the total production cost. It is, *production should be allocated such that the marginal cost of the last unit produced in each plant is equal.*

In many practical applications of cost analysis the cost and revenue functions are linear or can be reasonably approximated by linear functions. In such cases *break-even analysis* becomes a useful tool for evaluating how the rate of output affects the firm's profitability.

At the beginning of this chapter we listed seven situations in which different cost estimates would be likely depending on the perspective of the person making the estimate. It would be worthwhile at this point to go back and review each of those situations to see how the various cost concepts discussed in the chapter may influence the cost estimates. How would a long-run versus a short-run view of cost affect each? Are imputed costs and social costs important?

Selected Readings

Dean, Joel. "Statistical Cost Curves." *Journal of the American Statistical Association* (March 1937), 83–89.

Rakowski, James P. "Economies of Scale in U.S. Trucking." *Journal of Economics and Business* (Spring/Summer 1978), 166–176.

Roth, Timothy P. "Empirical Cost Curves and the Production-Theoretic Short Run: A Reconciliation." *Quarterly Review of Economics and Business* (Autumn 1979), 35–47.

Walters, A. A. "Production and Cost Functions." *Econometrica* (January–April 1963), 1–66.

QUESTIONS

1. Write a short explanation of the following terms or concepts that were used in this chapter:
   (a) average fixed cost
   (b) average variable cost
   (c) average (total) cost
   (d) break-even analysis
   (e) economies of scale
   (f) expansion path
   (g) fixed cost
   (h) imputed costs
   (i) long-run costs
   (j) marginal costs
   (k) normal profit
   (l) opportunity costs
   (m) optimum size of plant
   (n) private costs
   (o) total cost
   (p) variable cost

2. A firm has fixed costs of $1000 and average variable costs of $21 per unit. Its product sells for $25. At what level of sales will the firm break even? Suppose management wanted to earn a profit of $500 rather than just break even. Then how many units would the firm need to sell?

3. Suppose that a firm recognized that the demand for the product they sell is quite inelastic and that they want to earn a profit equal to 200 percent of their fixed cost, which is $1 million. The firm is confident that 250,000 units can be sold at any price between $45 and $57. Which price should be charged to meet this profit objective? The AVC of production is $40.

4. For the total-cost functions shown, graph the average-cost and marginal-cost functions in the space provided immediately below each total-cost graph.

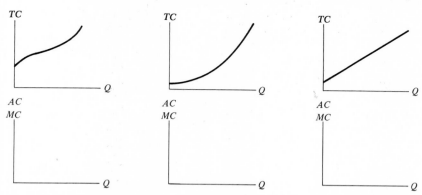

5. Explain why the average cost, average variable cost, and marginal cost curves will be U-shaped if the short-run production function is of the shape

illustrated. What is the relationship between the average-product curve and the marginal-product curve derived from this total-product curve and the average-, variable-, and marginal-cost curves, respectively?

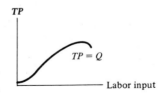

6. Explain factors that you think would contribute to the existence of economies of scale in higher education. Do you think such factors would continue to operate at all levels of "output"? Why or why not? Might there be a range of diseconomies of scale?
7. A firm produces a single product in two separate plants. In Plant 1 the marginal cost is given by the equation $MC = + 1.5Q$. In Plant 2 the marginal cost is given by the equation $MC = 100 + Q$. At what level of output would the firm find it desirable to begin using Plant 2? If the firm wishes to produce 100 units, how many should be produced in each plant?
8. In the spaces provided derive expansion paths for the following three cases: (a) increasing returns to scale, (b) constant returns to scale, and (c) decreasing returns to scale. Explain each graph carefully.

9. A firm's total cost function is given in the first two columns of the table shown. From that information find the values necessary to complete the table.

Q	TC	FC	VC	AC	AFC	AVC	MC
0	100			—	—	—	
2	138						
4	173						
6	206						
8	238						
10	270						
12	303						
14	337						
16	374						
18	415						
20	460						

10. Graph each of the cost functions represented in the table you have completed in Question 9. Use two separate graphs with TC, FC, and VC in one, and AC, AFC, AVC, and MC in the other. Explain the relationship you observe between marginal cost and both average cost and average variable cost.

11. List and explain the opportunity costs involved in each of the following personal decisions made by a college senior:
    (a) Decision to go to Aspen to ski over the Christmas break.
    (b) Decision to buy a new motorcycle.
    (c) Decision to take a part-time job at a local bar.
    (d) Decision to attend graduate school and take a master's degree in chemistry.
    (e) Decision to play on the school's tennis team.

CHAPTER 9
PERFECT COMPETITION

We have developed a background understanding of the forces determining the demand for goods and services as well as the factors influencing their production and the cost of production. Now we can begin to bring these two sides of the market, demand and supply, together to analyze the determination of price and output for individual firms.

As we shall see, this determination is dependent on the type of market structure that characterizes an industry. Market structure refers to the organization of participants in the market relative to the entire market. The organization of both buyers and sellers is important, but our emphasis will be on the seller's side. The most important classifications of market structures are perfect competition, monopoly, monopolistic competition, and oligopoly. A complete chapter will be devoted to the process of price and output determination in each of these forms of market organization. The insights developed will be a valuable aid in understanding much of the behavior within the business community as well as in the public sector of the economy.

CHARACTERISTICS OF PERFECT COMPETITION

There are four characteristics we shall use to distinguish among the various forms of market structure and so we will begin our discussion of each market structure by reviewing these characteristics. They are: the number of buyers and sellers; the variation in the type of output from firm to firm; the ease of exit and entry (or contraction and expansion) within the industry; and the extent of each firm's knowledge about important factors affecting the industry.

In perfectly competitive markets there is a very large number of buyers and sellers in the industry. Each one is quite small relative to the total market and thus the actions of any one will have zero (or negligible) effect on price and output for the entire industry. For example, consider the effect that one wheat farmer has on the total wheat market.

Second, *the output of one firm in a perfectly competitive industry is precisely the same as the output of every other firm in that industry.* We say that the products are *homogeneous.* This is an important characteristic and is more encompassing than one might at first think. For output to be homogeneous, it must not only be the same product (e.g., wheat), but, further, one firm's product must be completely indistinguishable (in the eyes of the buyer) from that of another producer. For example, a bushel of a certain grade of hard red winter wheat from a Montana grower is the same to the purchasing agent for a major food producer such as General Mills as a bushel of the same grade of hard red winter wheat from North Dakota. The wheat grower does not put a brand or other distinguishing mark on the product, nor is there any incentive to do so.

Next, *in a perfectly competitive industry, resources may move freely into or out of the production of the particular good or service.* This means that given the proper economic incentive (to be discussed in more detail shortly) additional factors of production may flow into a perfectly competitive industry. This can take the form of new firms entering the industry or existing firms expanding production. Of course, the movement of resources may be out of the industry as well, in which case firms may leave the industry entirely or they may simply cut back production. We refer to this as the *complete mobility of resources.*[1]

Finally, in *perfectly competitive markets each participant has complete knowledge about factors affecting the operation of that market.* This means that each firm knows the prices that other firms pay for all the inputs for the production process. All producers are aware of the same

---

[1] It is important to think of resource mobility in terms of use rather than geographic location. Human resources are very mobile in both contexts. We can move from Tulsa to Seattle or we can move from being a public school teacher to an insurance sales agent within the same community. Land that is geographically fixed may also be mobile in terms of economic use. Farm land in Illinois may be switched from corn to soybeans, a ball field in Pittsburgh (old Forbes Field) may be altered for use as an educational facility for the University of Pittsburgh, and so on. Buildings are much the same in terms of mobility. Some are more mobile than others, dependent largely on the degree of specialization or use for which they were constructed. Look around almost any campus and you'll find a library turned to office or classroom space, and apartments or houses turned to dormitory living quarters, and perhaps back again.

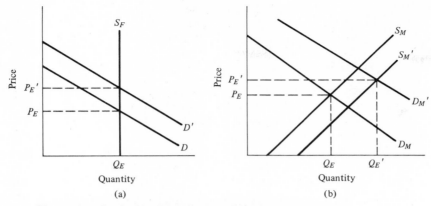

Figure 9.1 Perfectly Competitive Market Equilibrium
Determination of the equilibrium price in a perfectly competitive
industry. (a) The case of the very short-run, or market, period
(supply is fixed at S_F) in which price is determined by the level of
demand. (b) The case in which both market supply and demand
changes affect price.

technological information and have access to its use. Every producer
knows as much as any other about the market demand for their product.
In short, there are no industry secrets.

   The combination of these characteristics leads to an important out-
come for individual firms in perfectly competitive markets. *No one firm
has any control over price.* Each firm is a *price taker.* If the firms do not
determine price, how then is it determined? As we saw in Chapter 2, in a
perfectly competitive market, price is determined by the interaction of
market demand and market supply. In Chapter 4 (pages 69–71) we saw
how market demand is determined, and that a market demand curve will
have a negative slope. Thus far we have not determined a market supply
curve (although we will do so later in this chapter), but we will continue
with our earlier assumption that the market supply curve will generally
be a positively sloped function. Market supply and demand functions are
illustrated in Figure 9.1. In the *very* short run, a period during which the
level of output is absolutely fixed, the supply curve is a vertical line (S_F)
as indicated in the left-hand part of the figure.[2] When this is true, the
equilibrium price for the industry is determined by the level of demand.
A higher demand (D') establishes a higher equilibrium price (P_E').

   In the short run, or in the long run, the equilibrium price is determined by the interaction of changes in supply and demand, as illustrated
in Figure 9.1(b). In the case shown here, the increase in demand from D_M
to D_M' and the increase in supply from S_M to S_M' results in both a higher
price, P_E', and a greater quantity produced, Q_E'. This need not be the

[2] This very short-run period is often called the "market period" as well.

case, as we shall see on page 203. The important thing to note here is that price is determined by market forces.

SHORT-RUN EQUILIBRIUM FOR THE FIRM

Since the price in a perfectly competitive industry is determined by supply and demand, each individual firm takes that price as given and sells whatever level of output is produced at that price. For example, overall market conditions determine the wheat price on any given day, and the farmer who takes wheat to market on that day accepts the market price or does not sell the wheat.

This means that the demand curve for the individual perfectly competitive firm is a horizontal line at the market price, as illustrated in Figure 9.2. The firm has no incentive to lower price below $P_f (= P_E)$ since the entire amount of output can be sold at that price. Thus, lowering price would simply reduce revenue to the firm without any compensating reduction in cost. If the firm tries to obtain a higher price, no one will purchase its goods since an identical product is available from other sellers at P_f, (recall the importance of the homogeneity assumption regarding the product in a perfectly competitive industry).

While price is determined outside the control of the firm, the rate or level of production is not. The firm must make that decision in the context of the given operating objective(s), which we shall assume to be profit maximization. Given that the firm is a price taker, total revenue (TR) will be a linear function of the level of output beginning at the origin. The slope of TR is equal to the price (P). Such a function is graphed in Figure 9.3 along with a representative total-cost curve (TC).

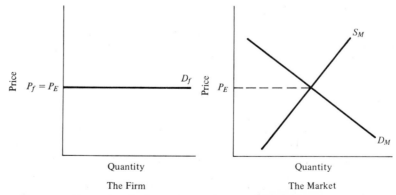

Figure 9.2 Determination of the Perfectly Competitive Firm's Demand Function The interaction of market supply (S_M) and market demand (D_M) determines the equilibrium price (P_E), which in turn determines the firm's demand curve (D_f) and price $P_f = P_E$.

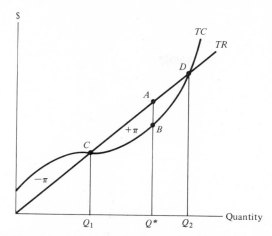

Figure 9.3 Total Revenue, Total Cost, and Profit Total-revenue
(*TR*) and total-cost (*TC*) curves for a perfectly competitive firm
showing the profit-maximizing level of output *Q**. The dollar
amount of profit is the distance *AB* at the *Q** level of output.

Since profit (π) is defined as the difference between total revenue
and total cost ($\pi = TR - TC$), the firm's objective is to produce the level
of output that maximizes the vertical distance between *TR* and *TC* (for
$TR > TC$). This is the level denoted Q^* in Figure 9.3 (we shall generally
use Q^* to represent the profit-maximizing level of output). As we move
from the origin toward Q^*, $TC > TR$ up to Q_1 units of output. The firm,
therefore, makes an economic loss in that interval. Moving beyond Q_1,
we see that $TR > TC$ and a positive economic profit exists up to Q_2.
Above Q_2 the firm would again have an economic loss.

Starting at point *C* on the total-cost curve (corresponding to output
Q_1) and going to the right, we see that the slope of *TC* is less than the
slope of *TR*, but is increasing. Between *C* and *B* the slope of *TC* is less
than the slope of *TR*. This means that as quantity increases, total revenue
is increasing at a more rapid rate than total cost, and thus profit must be
increasing. Beyond point *B* total cost is increasing faster than total revenue, so profit must be decreasing in that range. Thus profit is maximized
at Q^*, where the slopes of total revenue and total cost are equal. The
dollar amount of profit is the distance *AB*.

Recall that marginal revenue (*MR*) is the slope of total revenue, and
marginal cost (*MC*) is the slope of total cost. Therefore, if we graph these
functions (*MR* and *MC*) they must intersect (be equal) at the profit-
maximizing level of output Q^*. This is done in Figure 9.4. Note that,
because the perfectly competitive firm is a price taker, total revenue is
linear through the origin, and thus its slope may be represented as either

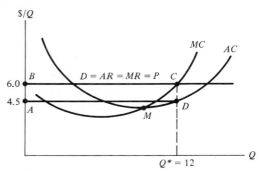

Figure 9.4 Perfectly Competitive Firm with Positive Profit A perfectly competitive firm making a positive economic profit of $18 (= $1.50/unit × 12 units). Profit is represented by the area of the rectangle *ABCD*. The profit-maximizing level of output is *Q** (= 12) where *MR* = *MC*. Profit (π) is seen to equal *Q** times price minus average cost; that is, in general, π = *Q*(P − AC)*.

P or *MR*. The graphic depiction of these functions is represented by the same line in Figure 9.4. This line also corresponds to the firm's demand curve and to the graph of average revenue (*AR*), since *P = AR* by the manner in which the terms are defined.

The average-cost curve (*AC*) in Figure 9.4 has the typical U-shape resulting from the law of variable proportions in production. The marginal-cost curve (*MC*) also has this typical U-shape, for the same reason, and intersects *AC* and the minimum point on the *AC* curve (point *M*).

The profit-maximizing level of output is 12 because *MR = MC* at that level. At output levels below *Q** (= 12) marginal revenue is greater than marginal cost. Producing and selling each of those units increases profit by the amount that *MR > MC*. If the level of production and sales is expanded beyond *Q**, *MR < MC* and profit would be diminished.

The amount of profit per unit at *Q** is $1.5, or the distance *CD*. Total profit (π) is the area of the rectangle *ABCD*, or 12 units times $1.5 per unit ($18). The distance *CD* (i.e., $1.5) is the profit margin per unit and is equal to price minus average cost. Multiplying the profit margin per unit times the number of units gives us total profit. This follows from our definition of profit; that is,

$$\pi = TR - TC$$
$$TR = P \cdot Q^*$$
$$TC = AC \cdot Q^*$$
$$\pi = P \cdot Q^* - AC \cdot Q^*$$
$$\pi = Q^*(P - AC)$$

The quantity *Q** times (*P − AC*) is the area of the rectangle *ABCD*. This area corresponds to the distance *AB* in Figure 9.3 showing π, *TR*, and *TC*.

The situation illustrated in Figure 9.4 shows the relationship between various cost and revenue functions for a perfectly competitive firm that enjoys a positive economic profit. But this situation may not necessarily exist. It is entirely possible that the best that a perfectly competitive firm can do in the short run is just break even, or operate at a loss. These cases are depicted in Figure 9.5.

In Figure 9.5(a) we see that the firm makes a negative economic profit since at the profit-maximizing level of output (Q^* at $MR = MC$) average cost is greater than price or average revenue. That is,

$$\pi = Q^*(P - AC)$$
$$AC > P$$
$$\therefore \pi < 0$$

Note that up to Q^*, marginal revenue exceeds marginal cost, so it increases profit (reduces loss) for the firm to expand to that point. The area of the rectangle $ABCD$ now represents the total amount of economic loss (negative profit), and the distance CD represents the loss per unit.

Figure 9.5(b) shows the case in which the perfectly competitive firm makes a zero economic profit. At the level of output (Q^*) where $MR = MC$ we see that price also equals average cost. That is,

$$\pi = Q^*(P - AC)$$
$$P = AC$$
$$0 = P - AC$$
$$\therefore \pi = 0$$

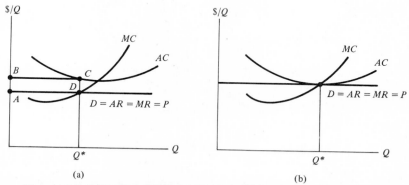

(a)   (b)

Figure 9.5 Perfectly Competitive Firms with Negative and Zero Profit (a) A perfectly competitive firm with a negative profit equilibrium. (b) One with a zero profit equilibrium. In both, the profit-maximizing output is Q^*, where $MR = MC$. However, in (a) this corresponds to a point where $AC > P$ such that the profit margin CD is negative, as is total profit (the area of the rectangle $ABCD$).

Even though economic profit is zero, all factors of production (all inputs) are receiving the appropriate opportunity cost return according to the way we have defined costs in Chapter 8.

From this discussion we see that the short-run equilibrium condition for the perfectly competitive firm is to produce that level of output (Q^*) at which marginal revenue is equal to marginal cost. As we shall see in the next section, there is one qualification to this principle. It is that production must be beyond what we defined as "Stage 1" in Chapter 7.

THE SUPPLY CURVE

We have now developed all of the concepts that are necessary to show how the firm's supply curve is determined and why we generally draw supply curves to have a positive slope. In Figure 9.6 we have indicated five (of many) possible price/quantity configurations. In each case the appropriate level of output is determined according to the $MR = MC$ rule.

Let us first focus attention on the point labeled SDP for "shutdown point." SDP is the point where the $P_1 = MR_1$ demand line is just tangent to the AVC curve. Since the P_1 line is horizontal, this must be where AVC has a zero slope, or the minimum of AVC. In Chapter 8 we have shown that average variable cost reaches a minimum where average product is a

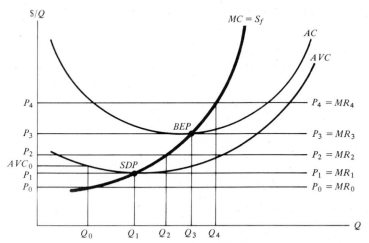

Figure 9.6 Determination of the Firm's Supply Curve Derivation of the firm's supply curve (S_f). As price increases from P_1 to P_2 to P_3 to P_4, the profit-maximizing level of output increases from Q_1 to Q_2 to Q_3 to Q_4, respectively. For any price below P_1, the profit-maximizing output would be such that $P < AVC$, and the firm would not even cover variable cost. Therefore, the price/quantity configuration P_1/Q_1 is called the shutdown point (SDP).

maximum. We have also shown, in Chapter 7, that the relevant range of production begins at the level where average product is a maximum. Thus, it follows that the relevant range of production begins at SDP where AVC is a minimum.

Another, and perhaps better, way to look at this is to ask what would happen if the firm produced the profit-maximizing level of output (where $MR = MC$) for any price less than P_1. If price were less than P_1, marginal revenue would equal marginal cost at a quantity for which price would be less than average variable cost. Such a case is illustrated for P_0, Q_0, and AVC_0. Variable cost (VC) and total revenue (TR) would be:

$$VC = Q_0(AVC_0)$$
$$TR = Q_0(P_0)$$

Since $P_0 < AVC_0$ at Q_0, total revenue would be less than variable cost. By operating at P_0 and Q_0, the firm would not only lose all of the fixed cost but also would fail to generate enough revenue to even cover the cost of variable inputs. By shutting down, the most that would be lost is the fixed cost. Therefore, SDP represents the "shutdown point" for the firm in the short run.

Above SDP, but below BEP, the firm covers the variable cost of production (P is greater than AVC) and has some revenue left to allocate to fixed costs, even though the result is an economic loss ($P < AC$). BEP represents the "break-even point" for the firm, since at that price/quantity configuration $P = AC$ and thus $TR = TC$ ($\pi = 0$).

We see that following profit-maximizing behavior the firm will produce the quantities Q_1, Q_2, Q_3, and Q_4 at the prices P_1, P_2, P_3, and P_4, respectively, along the marginal-cost curve. *Since we define supply to be the quantities a firm is willing and able to offer for sale at various prices, the marginal-cost curve above SDP is the firm's supply curve S_f.*

The market supply curve is determined by adding together the quantities that each individual firm would supply at each price. This is illustrated in Figure 9.7 for the case of just two firms. Firm A's marginal-cost curve (MC_A) is added horizontally to the marginal-cost curve for Firm B (MC_B) to arrive at the market supply curve (S_M). At a price of $5, Firm A produces 10 units while Firm B produces 50 units. When price rises to $10, their respective outputs increase to 40 and 100 units. Thus, the quantity supplied in the market increases from 60 to 140 as price increases from $5 to $10.

Note that at low prices (less than about $3.30), Firm A does not produce at all. Thus, up to point E (at $3.30) the market supply (S_M) coincides with Firm B's supply ($MC_B = S_B$). Beyond that point the horizontal sum of S_A and S_B equals S_M. We should note that determining the market supply curve in this way assumes that input prices are constant as the industry expands.

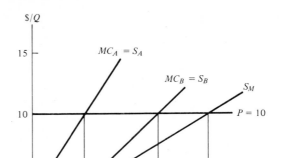

Figure 9.7 The Market Supply Curve Determination of the market supply curve (S_M) as the horizontal sum of the marginal cost (or supply) curves for each firm in the industry (only two are used for illustrative purposes). For example, at a price of $5, Firm A produces 10 units while Firm B produces 50 units, yielding a market supply of 60 units at that price. Other points along S_M can be determined in a like manner.

LONG-RUN ADJUSTMENTS

If economic profit exists in a perfectly competitive industry, we can expect additional resources to flow into that industry. It is important once more to keep in mind that the existence of economic profit $(P > AC)$ implies that all resources are being compensated according to their opportunity cost, and some (perhaps the entrepreneurial factor) have an excess return. This above-normal return serves as incentive for new firms to enter the industry or existing ones to expand production (recall that all firms produce a homogeneous product, there is completely free mobility of resources, and there is perfect knowledge—i.e., no industry secrets).

The adjustment process is illustrated in Figure 9.8. The right-hand portion of that figure shows an initial set of market conditions (D_M and S_M) that determine the price P. At this price the firm depicted in the left-hand part of the figure earns a positive economic profit by producing Q_f units. This profit acts as the stimulus for new resources to enter the industry which shifts the market supply curve to $S_M{'}$. This in turn lowers the market price to P'. The firm, faced with this lower price, produces $Q_f{'}$ units and has a zero economic profit. We can generalize to say that if the market price P is greater than the zero-profit price P', new resources will enter the industry until a zero-profit equilibrium is obtained.

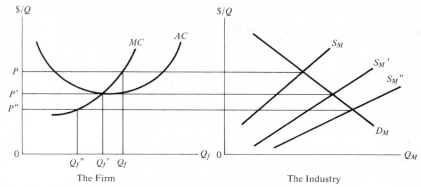

The Firm   The Industry

Figure 9.8 Adjustment to a Zero-Profit Equilibrium   The
adjustment to a zero-profit equilibrium in a perfectly competitive
industry through changes in the market supply. With market
supply S_M, the equilibrium price is P, at which the firm produces Q_f
units and earns a positive economic profit. As additional
resources enter the industry, market supply shifts to S_M' and price
falls to P'. The firm produces Q_f' units with zero economic profit. If
the market supply were S_M'', price would be P'', the firm would
produce Q_f'' units and incur an economic loss. Resources would
leave shifting supply to S_M' with the resulting price P' and the firm
operating at a zero economic profit, producing Q_f' units.

If too many new resources flow into this industry such that the market supply shifts to S_M'', or if S_M'' represents an initial condition, we can
expect some firms to leave the industry. With market supply at S_M'', the
price will be P'' at which firms are faced with economic losses. In such a
case, some firms will be forced out of the industry until the market supply
shifts to S_M' and the zero-profit long-run equilibrium price is established
at P'.

Although we have couched this discussion in terms of new firms
entering or existing firms leaving the industry, the adjustments may also
take place, in part or in whole, by expansion or contraction of existing
firms. When this happens, the average-cost curve for the firm may not be
static as in accordance with the concepts discussed in Chapter 8. More
will be said in this regard in the next section.

Regardless of the adjustment process the result is that, for the
long-run perfectly competitive industry, $P = MR = SRAC = SRMC =
LRAC = LRMC$. Thus, for perfectly competitive industries, firms will
be led by natural economic forces to produce the optimum level of production in plants of the optimum size.

Barring certain types of market failures, to be discussed later in the
text, we can now reach three important conclusions about perfect competition. First, since products are produced at the lowest possible cost (min-

imum average cost), we can say that perfect competition leads to technologically efficient production. Second, excess returns (economic profit) will be eliminated as price is driven to the level equal to minimum average cost. Finally, the perfectly competitive market leads to an efficient allocation of resources because price will also equal marginal cost.[3] These results have had, and are likely to continue to have, important influence on a wide variety of public policies aimed at promoting competition.

INDUSTRIES WITH CONSTANT, DECREASING, AND INCREASING COSTS

In discussing the adjustment process for perfectly competitive firms in the long run in the preceding section we restricted ourselves to a fixed level of market demand and a given $SRAC$ for all firms. Suppose now that demand does increase, causing an initial increase in price that stimulates expanded production. If the expansion takes place such that the average-cost curves for firms remain at the same level, the result will be a horizontal long-run supply (S_L), as shown in Figure 9.9(a). This is then called a constant-cost industry.

However, it may be that internal economies of scale result in lower short-run average-cost curves as firms expand the scale of operation. In addition, external economies of scale may result in lower $SRAC$ curves. An example of such an external economy would be the ability to purchase certain manufactured inputs at a lower cost because of economies of scale in their production. Such factors may cause the long-run supply curve to have a negative slope, in which case the industry is classified as a *decreasing-cost industry*, as shown in Figure 9.9(b).

These two cases are clearly not exhaustive. It may be that as an industry expands, internal and/or external diseconomies may result. We have already discussed the former. The latter would result if, as the industry expands, the price of an important raw material is bid up due to relative shortages. This in turn would cause the average-cost curve for each firm to shift upward. The result would be an *increasing-cost industry* as illustrated in Figure 9.9(c).

COBWEB PHENOMENA

In many economic relationships there is a considerable time lag between production planning and product sales. The agricultural sector of the economy provides some of the most striking examples. Corn prices in

---

[3] This assumes that price is a measure of the marginal social benefit of the last unit of the good that is produced, and that marginal cost truly represents the social cost of that last unit in terms of resource use.

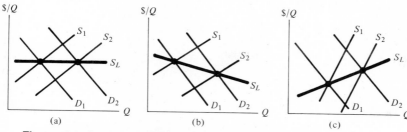

Figure 9.9 Constant, Decreasing, and Increasing Cost Industries Supply and demand shifts for (a) a constant-cost industry, (b) a decreasing-cost industry, and (c) an increasing-cost industry. Successive equilibrium points determine the long-run supply curve (S_L).

one harvest year are influential in determining how many acres of land will be planted in corn for the next year, and thus the level of corn production in that later year. In this case, the relevant time period is one year. It could be shorter or longer, depending on the lag between production planning and the availability of output for sale.

The cobweb theorem (so named because of the appearance of the graphic models) provides a method for the analysis of this type of dynamics in the marketplace. Simply stated, this model says that the quantity of a good produced in one time period is a function of the price in the previous time period. In algebraic terms,

$$Q_{t+1} = f(P_t)$$

Each firm behaves as though the present price (P_t) will remain stable and expand or contract output along the marginal-cost curve accordingly. This simultaneous, independently determined, behavior of the many small producers can cause a cyclical type of fluctuation in both prices and output. This cyclical pattern may have constant, convergent, or divergent oscillations, depending on the relative slopes of the demand and supply curves. Each of these cases is illustrated in Figure 9.10. For each case the demand curves are drawn to be identical with the slope of the supply curve varying from top to bottom.

Let us first consider the general behavior pattern characteristic of the cobweb phenomena as diagramed in Figure 9.10. The equilibrium price and quantity are labeled P_E and Q_E, respectively. Now suppose that a period of unfavorable weather caused a shortfall in production to Q' rather than Q_E. From the demand curve (point A), we can tell that this quantity can fetch a higher price in the marketplace so that in period one the price rises. This stimulates a high rate of production along the supply curve (point B) that can only be sold at the relatively low price determined from the demand curve (point C). At this low price producers plan less production (point F on the supply curve).

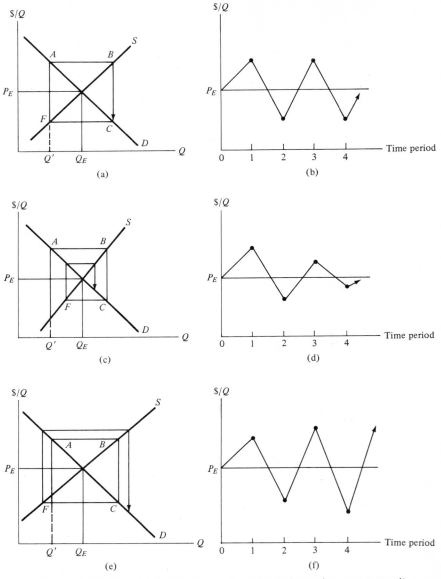

Figure 9.10 Economic "Cobwebs" Oscillating prices may result due to time lags between production planning and actual sales. From top to bottom each pair of diagrams represent constant oscillation, convergent oscillation, and divergent oscillation, respectively. These are called "cobweb" phenomena because of the appearance of the graphic representation of the models.

If the absolute value of the slopes of the demand and supply curves are equal, the fluctuations will continue with constant amplitude from period to period. This is illustrated in the supply and demand graph of Figure 9.10(a) as well as the time trend shown in part (b) of that figure (time period 0 represents the equilibrium position prior to the assumed shortfall in production to Q').

When the absolute value of the slope of the demand curve is less than the slope of the supply curve, the oscillations will be convergent. Such a case is depicted in Figure 9.10(c) and (d). The initial shortfall is assumed to be of the same amount; and since the demand function is also the same, the first price change (increase) is equal to the constant-oscillation case. However, in subsequent time periods the fluctuations become less and converge to the original equilibrium at P_E and Q_E. This represents an example of a *stable equilibrium* since once it is disturbed natural forces will restore the original equilibrium position.

The third case diagramed in Figure 9.10(e) and (f) represents *divergent oscillations because the absolute value of the slope of the demand curve is greater than the slope of the supply curve.* As shown in part (f), the fluctuations become increasingly distant from the equilibrium price. This (as well as the constant-oscillation case) represents an *unstable equilibrium* because an initial disturbance from the equilibrium stimulates a series of actions that will not result in returning to that original equilibrium position.

When such unstable equilibrium cobwebs are likely, some form of government action may help to offset the fluctuations. For example, a shortfall in production could be made up by the government selling surplus stocks of the product it has stored to keep price down. Or if the problem is recognized in a period of high prices and resulting surplus production, the government could purchase the surplus to keep it off the market. Another, and perhaps more desirable, form of government program would be to provide a better flow of information concerning price fluctuations such that producers have a more accurate picture of price expectations upon which to base decisions involving the level of production for the next time period.

SUMMARY

Perfect competition represents one of four primary market structures (the others are monopoly, monopolistic competition, and oligopoly). This form of market structure is characterized by: (a) the existence of many buyers and sellers; (b) production of identical (homogeneous) products by each firm; (c) complete freedom of resources to flow into and out of the industry; and (d) perfect knowledge about the industry by all participants. Some people would add a fifth characteristic that there are no artificial restraints in the industry (such as government regulation or control of a critical natural resource by one or more firms). These characteristics, taken together, determine that perfectly competitive firms are "price takers." The price is determined outside of the firm by the natural forces of supply and demand.

The demand curve for the perfectly competitive firm is a horizontal line at the market price. Thus price, average revenue, and marginal revenue are all equal (and are represented graphically by the same horizontal line as the firm's demand). The unit-cost curves for perfectly competitive firms have the typical U-shape. The firm maximizes profit by producing the level of output at which marginal revenue equals marginal cost. If this level of output results in a positive economic profit, resources will enter the industry until those profits are eliminated. On the other hand, if economic profit is negative $(P < AC)$, resources will leave the industry until a zero-profit equilibrium is determined.

In the short run the firm breaks even when price is such that production takes place at the minimum point of the average-cost curve. The firm may produce below this level in the short run as long as price is at least equal to the minimum point on the average variable cost curve (the "shutdown point").

In the long run, exit and/or entry of resources in a perfectly competitive industry assure that $P = AR = MR = SRAC = SRMC = LRAC = LRMC$. This has important social consequences: There are no abnormal or economic profits; products are produced at the technically efficient level—lowest AC; and there is an optimal allocation of resources because $P = MC$.

If long-run expansion in an industry leads to a horizontal long-run supply curve, it is called a constant-cost industry. If the long-run supply curve has a positive slope, it is an increasing-cost industry, and if the long-run supply curve declines, it is a decreasing-cost industry.

The perfectly competitive market model allows us to get an introductory look at economic dynamics when there is a significant time lag between production planning and the time when the product is ready for sale. The time lag may be of various duration, but often a year is used because of the application of the resulting cobweb model to agricultural production. The important aspect of the model is that the level of output planned for the next time period is dependent on the level of price in the current time period. Whether the oscillations that result are constant or divergent (unstable equilibrium cases) or are convergent (stable equilibrium case) depends on the relative slopes of the demand and supply curves.

An understanding of the perfectly competitive market model will be a valuable aid in evaluating the other market structures to be discussed in Chapters 10, 11, and 12, as well as in understanding many public policies and regulations.

Selected Readings

Eckert, Ross D., and George W. Hilton. "The Jitneys." *Journal of Law and Economics* 15 (October 1972), 293–325.

Harlow, A. A. "The Hog Cycle and the Cobweb Theorem." *Journal of Farm Economics* 42 (November 1960), 842–853.

McCallum, B. T. "Competitive Price Adjustments: An Empirical Study." *American Economic Review* 64 (March 1974), 56–65.

Scitovsky, Tibor. "Two Concepts of External Economies." *Journal of Political Economy* 17 (April 1954), 143–151.

QUESTIONS

1. Write a short explanation of the following terms or concepts that were used in this chapter:
   - (a) average fixed cost
   - (b) cobweb theorem
   - (c) constant-cost industry
   - (d) decreasing-cost industry
   - (e) homogeneous product
   - (f) increasing-cost industry
   - (g) market supply curve
   - (h) perfect competition
   - (i) profit
   - (j) price taker
   - (k) resource mobility
   - (l) shutdown point
   - (m) supply curve (for the firm)
2. Suppose that in a perfectly competitive industry each firm has the following marginal cost schedule:

Quantity	Marginal Cost
1	1.20
2	1.40
3	1.60
4	1.80
5	2.00
6	2.20
7	2.40
8	2.60
9	2.80
10	3.00

   - (a) If the market forces of supply and demand interact such that the market price is $2.10, how many units would each firm produce?
   - (b) What if, due to decreased demand, the market price fell to $2.00?
   - (c) If there are 2000 firms in the industry what would be the "quantity supplied" at a price of $2.60?

3. For the industry represented above, the supply curve for each firm is:

$$Q_S = -5 + 5P$$

(a) Graph this function using prices of $1.20, $2.00, and $2.80 to locate three points along the curve.
(b) Then graph the marginal-cost curve from Question 2. Do the curves have the relationship to one another that you would expect.
(c) If there are 2000 such firms, how many units would be produced in the entire industry at each of the three prices given above?
(d) On a separate graph draw the market supply curve.

4. The algebraic equation for the market supply curve you graphed for Question 3 is as follows:

$$Q_S = -10,000 + 10,000P$$

Suppose that the market demand curve is given by the following equation:

$$Q_D = 14,000 - 2000P$$

(a) Graph both of these functions using the three prices $1.20, $2.00, and $2.80 as data points.
(b) At what price and quantity do the market demand and market supply curves intersect?
(c) Draw the demand curve for a representative firm based on this equilibrium along with the firm's marginal-cost function.
(d) What is the profit-maximizing output for the firm? From this result what can you say about the firm's economic profit? Explain.

5. A perfectly competitive firm has the following total cost schedule:

Q	TC	FC	VC	AVC	AC	MC
0	200					
2	238					
4	273					
6	306					
8	338					
10	370					
12	403					
14	437					
16	474					
18	515					
20	580					

(a) Based on this total cost, complete the above table.
(b) Graph the average-variable-cost, average-cost, and marginal-cost curves.
(c) On your graph identify the shutdown point and the break-even point for the firm.
(d) If the market price was $30, how many units would the firm produce? Would there be a positive, zero, or negative economic profit for the firm?
(e) What advice would you give the firm if price fell to $18. Explain.
(f) If price fell further to $15, what would you suggest to the firm? Would your advice be influenced by your long-run expectations?

6. Use the three pairs of graphs illustrated to show the oscillation of prices due to cobweb effects in the agricultural sector. Briefly explain each pair of graphs including why the time paths of the fluctuations may be convergent, divergent, or constant.

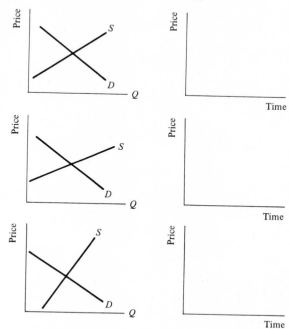

7. Suppose that the market for student labor is perfectly competitive, with many students available for part-time or full-time work, and with the college or university along with many local merchants providing many buyers of this student labor. The demand and supply curves are shown.

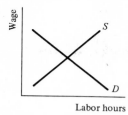

(a) Explain why the demand curve for labor (by the university, merchants, etc.) might have a negative slope.
(b) Explain why the supply curve for labor might have a positive slope.
(c) Suppose the government imposes an effective price floor (minimum wage). Show this price floor on the accompanying graph and explain the consequences to both employers and students. How would the wage (price) elasticity of demand for labor relate to your answer.

CHAPTER 10
MONOPOLY

If the four dominant types of market structure were placed along a continuum, monopoly would be at the opposite end from perfect competition. They represent the extreme cases between which we find monopolistic competition and oligopoly. An understanding of the workings of these extremes will help us in evaluating the intermediate cases, which make up the majority of all economic activity.

Whereas in perfect competition there were a great many sellers (producers), in monopoly there is but one seller (producer). Perfectly competitive firms were seen to be "price takers," but as we shall see, a monopolist is a "price setter." The differences that exist between the market structures are on the demand, or revenue, side. The nature of cost is the same for all market structures, being determined by technological factors and resource prices. Thus, the cost functions used in this chapter and those that follow will have the same general characteristics as those we have encountered previously. This is not to imply that there is no relationship between market structure and cost. Substantial economies of scale would be likely to lead to a monopoly situation rather than a more competitive structure.

CHARACTERISTICS OF A MONOPOLY

In Chapter 9, four characteristics were used to describe a perfectly competitive market: the number of producers or sellers (many), the type of product (homogeneous), the ease of exit and entry or mobility of resources (completely free), and the degree of knowledge about factors affecting the market (perfect or complete). We can use these same four characteristics to see how a monopoly differs.

First, as the name implies, for a monopoly there is a single seller, or producer, of the product. The monopolist is the industry. Thus the demand curve for the monopolist is the negatively sloped market demand curve rather than a horizontal line at some exogenously determined price as for a perfectly competitive firm. Telephone companies have local monopolies since in any given locality we either obtain telephone service from the single available supplier or do without. That single supplier can set price (within the confines of government regulation) and consumers adjust consumption to that price according to their own demand curve.

Next, the type of product for the monopolist can be considered unique. By definition, the monopolist is the only firm producing that particular good or service. For a pure monopoly, there must be no reasonable substitute product available. That is, the cross-price elasticity between the monopolist's product and all other products must be zero, or very nearly so. In the case of the telephone industry this is true. There are isolated examples of people using CB radios rather than having telephone service, but this is not a very effective substitute. The lack of close substitutes is an important feature of monopoly in distinguishing this market structure from monopolistic competition or oligopoly. Consider, for example, the beer industry. Only one firm can legally produce and sell Coors beer, so in a sense they have a monopoly over that narrowly defined product. However, there are so many reasonably close substitutes that we don't consider the Adolph Coors Company as a monopoly.

We said that in perfectly competitive industry firms have complete or perfect knowledge about all facets of the industry that may affect decisions within the firm. Since the monopolist is the industry, the same can be said of a firm that has a monopoly position.

With respect to resource mobility or the ease with which new firms can enter the industry, we can say that it is quite restricted. Sometimes it is restricted by government edict, sometimes by the vast capital investment needed to enter the industry, and sometimes by still other factors.

The factors that limit entry into a monopolistic industry are the very factors that give rise to the monopoly situation in the first place. There are several ways by which government policies create monopolies. By issuing patents the government creates a monopoly, at least temporarily. This was true in the early days of Alcoa's aluminum monopoly when that company controlled the rights to the most efficient production process. By requiring a license to operate, the government may also create a variety of monopoly situations. This is true in some forms of transportation such as licensing only one air carrier to a community or a single mass transit company for a city. In my community, the Teleprompter company has a government-sanctioned monopoly in the provision of cable television services. Governments can also contribute to the development of monopoly situations by imposing tariffs that restrict potential entry by foreign firms.

In many industries the huge capital requirements necessary to begin operations act as a barrier to entry and contribute to the existence of a monopoly. Suppose, for example, a group of citizens in Tulsa were dissatisfied with the telephone services provided by Southwestern Bell and wanted to enter the industry to provide a competitive alternative (we'll assume regulatory agencies would not object). To establish a network of telephones throughout the city, develop the linkages necessary for long-distance service, build the physical facilities and operating system, and string (or bury) additional telephone lines throughout the city would require such a vast investment that raising the necessary capital would be virtually impossible. A related problem is that once a monopoly is established, such as telephone service, new firms even with the necessary capital to start up would begin operations at such a low volume that they would almost certainly have to price themselves out of the market (unless they did have the financial backing to withstand fairly long-term operating losses).

A monopoly may also develop because one firm has control over a critical resource. Alcoa used control over bauxite reserves to protect the monopoly position in the production of aluminum that was originally developed through the protection provided by patent rights.

One of the most prevalent sources of monopoly is the existence of economies of scale throughout the relevant range of production. The first firm in the industry will always be able to underprice new entrants because average cost continuously declines. Since a monopoly develops in such a case as the result of natural economic forces, this situation is referred to as a *natural monopoly*.

Horizontal and/or vertical mergers also represent potential sources of monopoly power. However, mergers are now so closely watched by the Justice Department that it is unlikely that a monopoly could be developed in this manner in today's political-economic climate.

THE MONOPOLIST'S REVENUE FUNCTIONS

In our analysis of the behavior of monopolistic firms, we shall continue with our assumption that the operating objective is profit maximization in the absence of objectives dictated to the firm by an outside agency of government. We noted in the introduction to this chapter that the nature of the cost functions are the same among market structures. That is, the law of variable proportions continues to apply. The typical U-shaped unit-cost curves and related total-cost curve can then be combined with the monopolist's revenue functions to determine the price and output decisions that will maximize profit under various conditions.

Since the demand curve for the monopolist is identical with the industry demand curve, we know that it will have a negative slope, following from the "law of demand." The determination of the market demand curve was discussed fully in Chapter 4, and the related revenue concepts (total, average, and marginal revenue) were developed in detail in Chapter 5. Thus all we need do here is summarize those results and add a new relationship between price, marginal revenue, and price elasticity that will be useful to us in subsequent discussions.

Figure 10.1 should serve to refresh the understanding of the relationship between demand (D), total revenue (TR), average revenue (AR), price (P), marginal revenue (MR), and price elasticity (E_P). We see that D, AR, and P are all represented by the same negatively sloped line. They are just different ways of looking at a given relationship to the level of sales (Q). This relationship will always be illustrated by a linear function because it simplifies our diagrams and exposition without any significant loss of generality of the principles developed.

Total revenue begins at the origin (if sales are zero, no revenue is generated by the firm), increases at a decreasing rate, reaches a maximum, and then declines. Marginal revenue, which measures the slope of TR, begins at the same vertical intercept as demand and then declines (i.e., the rate of increase in TR declines) to zero at the level of sales where TR is at a peak and is negative beyond that point. For a linear demand curve, we see that MR always lies halfway between the vertical axis and the demand curve (this is unique to cases with linear demand). We also see in Figure 10.1 that demand is elastic ($|E_P| > 1$) above point A, inelastic ($|E_P| < 1$) below point A, and unitarily elastic ($|E_P| = 1$) at point A.

Demand is elastic when marginal revenue is positive, inelastic when marginal revenue is negative, and unitarily elastic when marginal revenue is zero. The relationship between marginal revenue and price elasticity of demand can be formalized as follows[1]:

$$MR = P - \frac{P}{E} \tag{10.1}$$

where $E = |E_P|$. In this form it is clear that when $E = 1$, $MR = 0$; when $E < 1$, $P/E > P$, so $MR < 0$; and when $E > 1$, $P/E < P$, so $MR > 0$. These relationships are, of course, consistent with Figure 10.1.

[1] This relationship can be proved with or without calculus, but the latter is cumbersome. Using calculus, we find:

$$TR = P \cdot Q$$

$$MR = P + Q\left(\frac{dP}{dQ}\right)$$

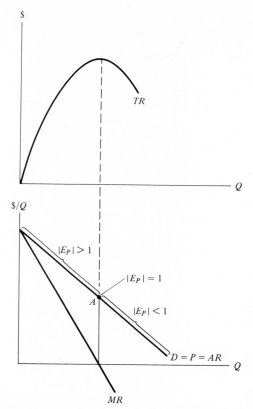

Figure 10.1 Price Elasticity and Revenue Functions The
relationship between total revenue (*TR*), demand (*D*), price (*P*),
average revenue (*AR*), marginal revenue (*MR*), and price elasticity
of demand (*E$_P$*) for a negatively sloped linear demand curve,
which is both the market demand and the monopolist's demand
curve.

$$E_P = \left(\frac{dQ}{dP}\right)\left(\frac{P}{Q}\right)$$

$$\frac{dP}{dQ} = \frac{P}{Q \cdot E_P}$$

$$MR = P + Q\left(\frac{P}{Q \cdot E_P}\right)$$

$$MR = P + \frac{P}{E_P}$$

Since $E_P < 0$, we will let $E = |E_P|$ and thus

$$MR = P - \frac{P}{E}$$

For various purposes, alternative algebraic forms of this relationship are often useful. By rearranging terms we can state the relation between marginal revenue, price, and elasticity as follows:

$$P = MR\left(\frac{E}{E-1}\right) \tag{10.2}$$

$$P = E(P - MR) \tag{10.3}$$

$$E = \frac{P}{P - MR} \tag{10.4}$$

For example, for a perfectly competitive firm with a horizontal demand curve, $E = \infty$. From either Equation 10.1 or 10.2 it should be clear that $P = MR$, a result we discovered in Chapter 9. We shall have occasion to refer to these equations in later discussions in this chapter and beyond.

SHORT-RUN PROFIT MAXIMIZATION

The general rule for profit maximization, as we saw in Chapter 9, is that marginal revenue should equal marginal cost. Let us see how this rule applies to a monopolist in the very short run (immediate or market period) and in the more general short run with some variable and some fixed inputs.

In the very short run the monopolist has a fixed quantity of output already produced and has no opportunity to change that amount. All costs of production have already been expended (i.e., they are all sunk cost); the marginal cost is therefore equal to zero. The firm will then maximize profit by selling the level of output at which marginal revenue is also zero. This is Q^* in Figure 10.2. Recall from Figure 10.1 that total revenue is maximized when marginal revenue is zero. Thus, in the market period, with all costs sunk, the profit-maximizing level of output corresponds with the revenue-maximizing level.

Price is determined from the demand curve at point A, directly above Q^*. The profit (and, in this case, revenue) maximizing price is P^*. If the existing stock of output is less than Q^*, such as Q_1, it should be sold at the corresponding price from the demand curve, P_1. However, if the stock of output available exceeds Q^*, the firm should dispose of the excess (above Q^*) rather than lower price below P^* to sell those additional units.

Now suppose that the firm is able to vary some inputs such that the typical U-shaped short-run cost curves represent the monopolist's cost structure. The profit-maximizing quantity (Q^*) is determined by the $MR = MC$ rule, and the associated price (P^*) is determined from the demand curve. Three possible cases are illustrated in Figure 10.3.

In Figure 10.3(a) price is greater than average cost at Q^*, so the

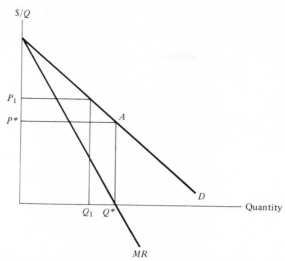

Figure 10.2 Monopoly Output and Price in the Market Period The profit-maximizing price and output for a monopolist in the market period are P^* and Q^*, respectively, if all costs are sunk cost ($MC = 0$) and if at least Q^* units are available. If just Q_1 units are in the existing stock, the profit-maximizing price is P_1.

monopolist obtains a positive economic profit. The dollar amount of profit is AB per unit, or the area of the rectangle $ABCP^*$ in total. Since entry is restricted, there is no reason that such a profit would not continue to exist.

The existence of monopoly does not necessarily imply that positive economic profits will result. In Figure 10.3(b), a case is illustrated for which $P = AC$, and profit is zero, at the profit-maximizing output Q^* (where $MR = MC$). A third possibility is depicted in Figure 10.3(c). If AC lies above demand at all levels of production, the monopolist will make a negative profit (a loss) even at the profit-maximizing level of output Q^*. The loss is AB dollars per unit, or the area $ABCP^*$ in total. The firm may continue to produce, however, if it is reasonable to expect cost reductions or an increase in demand, but only if the price P^* is at or above the average variable cost of producing Q^* units.

Note that in all three cases price is greater than marginal cost. This is a necessary result of profit-maximizing behavior when the demand curve has a negative slope since marginal revenue will always be below demand. Profit maximization implies $MR = MC$, and a downward sloping demand implies $P > MR$ for any Q. Thus, $P > MC$ for a profit-maximizing monopolist. It follows that there are too few resources allocated to the production of the product if the industry is monopolized (recall that resources are optimally allocated when $P = MC$). We shall save further

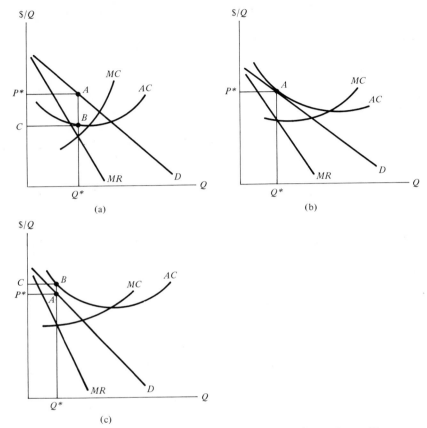

Figure 10.3 Monopoly Output and Price in the Short Run Three possible profit-maximizing situations for a monopolist in the short run. (a) The case in which positive economic profits exist. (b) In this case economic profit is zero. (c) In this case economic profit is negative.

evaluation of monopoly until after discussing profit maximization in the long run.

LONG-RUN PROFIT MAXIMIZATION

In the long run, with the ability to vary all factors of production including plant size, a monopolist will operate at the scale that minimizes the cost of producing the profit-maximizing level of output, Q^*. While this pattern of behavior is similar to the perfectly competitive firm, it will not necessarily lead to the same result (i.e., building the optimum size of plant and producing at the optimum rate of output for that plant).

Consider, for example, the situation illustrated in Figure 10.4. The monopolist produces the profit-maximizing output, Q^*, at the level where $MR = SRMC = LRMC$. However, the plant associated with the $SRAC$ curve is not used at its optimum rate ($Q^* < Q_o$, which is the optimum output for that plant size). The optimum size plant isn't even feasible since the demand curve intersects $LRAC$ in the negatively sloped portion. That means that the $SRAC$ curve for the optimum would be likely to lie above demand at every point resulting in an economic loss to the firm, rather than the long-run profit of $ABCP^*$ for the plant size illustrated.

The case we have drawn corresponds to the definition of a natural monopoly given earlier, since $LRAC$ declines throughout the relevant range of production. Thus a natural monopoly can be expected to operate with less than the optimum size of plant. This is not necessarily the case for every monopoly, however. It is possible that a monopolist would be led to build the optimum-size plant if demand were great enough that marginal revenue intersected $LRMC$ at point E in Figure 10.4. In this case, Q_M units would be produced. Production would be at the lowest possible average cost using the optimum-size plant at the optimum rate (price would still be greater than marginal cost, however). It is also possible that a monopolist would be led to build a plant larger than the optimum size if $MR = LRMC$ at a point such as F. This is illustrated by the electric utility company (Con Edison) at the extreme right along the $LRAC$ for electric power generation presented in Figure 8.10.

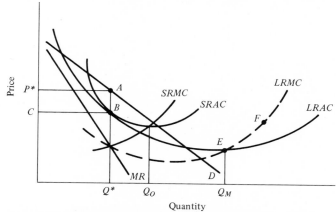

Figure 10.4 Monopoly Output and Price in the Long Run
Long-run profit maximization for a monopolist producing
with a plant of less than optimal size and at less than optimal rate
for the plant size represented by $SRAC$. The profit at output Q^*
is given by the rectangle $ABCP^*$. If demand were great enough
that $MR = LRMC$ at E, the optimal-size plant would be built and
used at an optimal rate.

MONOPOLY COMPARED WITH PERFECT COMPETITION

There are several ways in which the results obtained in perfectly competitive markets can be compared with those of a monopoly. It is often assumed that monopolies restrict output and charge a higher price relative to what would result if the industry were perfectly competitive. This may or may not be true. Two possibilities are illustrated in Figure 10.5.

In both parts of the diagram we have drawn a market demand curve (*D*). In Figure 10.5(a) the perfectly competitive market supply curve is drawn as the sum of the marginal-cost (supply) curves for each of the firms in the industry. Supply and demand intersect at *A*, determining the perfectly competitive price P_C and level of output Q_C.

Now suppose that a vast merger brought all these firms together into one monopolistic firm. Assuming that no economies or diseconomies of scale result, the marginal cost for this single firm is the horizontal sum of the marginal-cost curves for each plant (ΣMC) and the monopolist's profit-maximizing output would be Q_M, below the intersection of marginal revenue and marginal cost. The monopolist would price from the demand curve at P_M. Clearly, in this case the monopolist restricts output ($Q_M < Q_C$) and charges a higher price ($P_M > P_C$).

As illustrated in Figure 10.5(b), this need not be the case. The per-

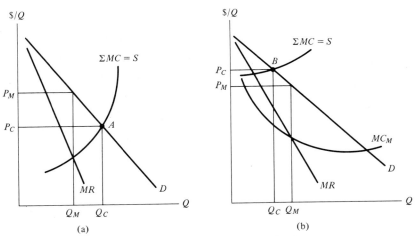

Figure 10.5 Comparison of Monopoly and Perfect Competition Comparison of the price and output for a perfectly competitive industry (P_C and Q_C) with those if the industry were a monopoly (P_M and Q_M). (a) In this case, where a monopolist takes over all the perfectly competitive firms and there are no economies of scale, the monopolist would produce less but charge a higher price. (b) In this case the monopolist is able to take advantage of economies of scale and actually produces a greater level of output and sells it at a lower price.

fectly competitive solution is the same as in part (a), where market supply intersects market demand (at point B) with price P_C and output Q_C. But now the monopolist is able to take advantage of scale economies that many small firms could not realize. The monopolist's LRMC declines over a significant range of production. The monopolist would produce Q_M units, where marginal revenue equals marginal cost (to maximize profit), and sell at the price P_M. Under this set of conditions, $P_M < P_C$ and $Q_M > Q_C$.

We may also wish to compare these market structures in terms of their productive efficiency and on the basis of how resources are allocated. For the case in Figure 10.5(a), perfect competition is the clear favorite on both counts. Although average-cost curves are not drawn (in order to keep the diagrams less cluttered), we know from our earlier analyses that at point A the perfectly competitive firms would be using the optimum size plants at the optimum rate of production. Production would be efficient in the sense that the product would be produced at the lowest possible unit cost. The monopolist, on the other hand, would produce less output and operate each plant at less than the optimum rate of output. Our criterion for an optimum allocation of resources is that $P = MC$. This is always true for the perfectly competitive profit maximizer, since $P = MR = MC$. But for the monopolist $P > MR = MC$, and so too few resources are allocated to that industry.

For the case illustrated in Figure 10.5(b), perfect competition would not be efficient in terms of production cost because the monopolist can take advantage of economies of scale. The minimum average cost would not be reached in Figure 10.5(b) but, as shown in Figure 10.4, it could possibly result that the monopolist would produce where LRAC is a minimum (if MR intersected LRMC at point E in that figure). Even then, however, $P < MC$, and too few resources would be allocated to the industry.

One final comparison we should call attention to is that *for the monopolist there is no such thing as a supply curve*, as we have defined the concept. In perfect competition the MC (above AVC) shows the quantities the firm would make available for sale at alternative prices (i.e., it is the supply curve). However, for a monopoly, that MC identifies the quantities that would be offered at various levels of marginal revenue. Any given level of marginal revenue could be consistent with many alternative prices, depending on the level and shape of the demand curve.

PRICE DISCRIMINATION: FIRST AND SECOND DEGREE

Price discrimination results when different buyers are charged different prices for a product which are not based on cost differences. If different prices result from variations in cost there is simply price differentiation among different classes of consumers.

Let us first consider what is often called "perfect price discrimination" or first-degree price discrimination. We know from Chapter 6 that as long as the demand curve for a product has a negative slope, there will be some consumer's surplus (an amount in excess of what is actually paid that the consumer(s) would have been willing to pay rather than do without the product). In first-degree price discrimination the seller is able to take the entire consumer's surplus.

We can look at this from the point of view of a single consumer or a group of consumers. In the latter case the seller must know exactly the nature of each consumer's demand function and sell each unit at the maximum price any consumer would pay. In Figure 10.6(a), if Q_0 units were sold in this manner, the revenue to the firm would be $OAEQ_0$, or the entire area under the demand curve. The consumer's surplus (AEP_1) would be entirely captured by the monopolist. Such perfect knowledge of every consumer's demand is unlikely, however.

For a single consumer there is a type of situation in which it is very possible that the entire consumer's surplus is taken by the seller. Assume that you have a beautiful antique oak dining table and are looking for a set of eight matched antique oak chairs to go with the table. Such a set is hard to find, but a likely place to obtain them is at an auction of household articles. Typically at such an auction the bidding is on a per-chair basis, but the terms of sale are "all or nothing." Suppose the eight chairs are represented by Q_0 in Figure 10.6(a), and your demand curve is the negatively sloped function D. At a price P_1 you would purchase eight such chairs, but would have a consumer's surplus of AEP_1. As the bidding progresses, particularly if a number of people are quite interested in the chairs, you might well bid up to the price P_2. Your total expenditure would be OP_2CQ_0 or, equivalently, $OAEQ_0$. That is, the seller (the auctioneer) may get you to pay the maximum amount you would be willing to pay rather than forgo buying the set of eight chairs. Of course, if there is little interest in the chairs by other bidders, you might get a "real bargain" at a price less than P_2, or even less than P_1 if the bidding starts low enough.

Second-degree price discrimination is illustrated in Figure 10.6(b). The consumer's surplus is again AEP_1. There are at least two pricing policies that firms may follow that will take part of that consumer's surplus. Consider first what is called "price skimming," in which a product is introduced at a high price (P_3) until the market is "saturated" at that price, then price is lowered (to P_2) until all that can be sold at that price is exhausted, and then price is lowered once more (to P_3). The number of stages depends on the product and company, but three are sufficient for illustration. In Figure 10.6(b), the shaded portion of the consumer's surplus is taken by the seller, while the triangles (1), (2), and (3) remain with consumers. Such a pricing policy is not terribly uncommon, particu-

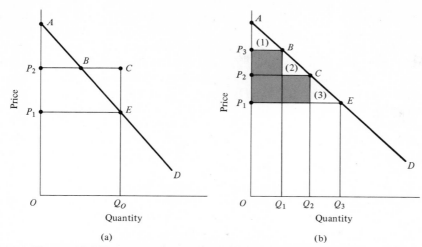

Figure 10.6 First- and Second-Degree Price Discrimination (a)
First-degree and (b) second-degree price discrimination. In the
first-degree case the entire consumer's surplus (AEP_1) is
transferred to the seller because Q units are sold at the price P_2
and the triangles ABP_2 and BCE are equal. In the second-degree
case a stepwise pricing policy transfers the shaded part of the
consumer's surplus to the seller, leaving the small triangles—(1),
(2), and (3)—to the consumer.

larly among large firms. In fact, in discussing this type of policy, *Business
Week* has called DuPont "a classic skimmer."

Another familiar form of second-degree price discrimination is the
"block pricing" strategy followed by many utilities (particularly electric
and natural gas). The first block of kilowatthours of electric power is sold
at a relatively high price (e.g., P_3) and successive blocks are sold at lower
prices (e.g., P_2, then P_1). The buyer's loss of consumer's surplus is again
the shaded portion of Figure 10.6(b) (and the buyer's loss is the seller's
gain). With more attention to energy shortages, there is considerable discussion of reversing this "block pricing" structure to discourage wasteful
use because the price of the last units consumed is relatively low.

PRICE DISCRIMINATION: THIRD DEGREE

Third-degree price discrimination is probably the most common form of
the three. It depends on the ability of the firm to segment the total market
into two or more submarkets that have different price elasticities of demand and to prevent resale of the product between submarkets. Some
examples of this form of price discrimination include: situations in which
the product is sold in both domestic and foreign markets; charging differ-

ent electricity rates for commercial versus residential users; varying the cost of long-distance calls by time of day; and charging a higher price for box seats than general admission seats for a professional baseball game.

To illustrate third-degree price discrimination, we will assume that the total market demand (D_M) for a product can be segmented into two separable submarkets $(D_1$ and $D_2)$ as shown in Figure 10.7. The market demand is the horizontal sum of the two submarket demand curves $(D_M = D_1 + D_2)$ and the marginal revenue for the market demand (MR_M) is the horizontal sum of marginal revenue for the submarkets $(MR_M = MR_1 + MR_2)$. Marginal cost is given as MC. These relationships are shown in Figure 10.7.

If the firm does not discriminate, the profit-maximizing output determination is familiar by now: Let $MR_M = MC$, produce $Q_T = 7000$ units, and price from the market demand curve $(P_N = \$4.25)$. Total revenue would be $29,750 (= \$4.25 \times 7000)$. Extending a line from $P_N = 4.25$ to D_1 and D_2, we find that 3250 units would be purchased in market 1 and 3750 units in market 2.

However, the firm can increase total revenue by allocating the 7000 units between the two markets such that $MR_1 = MR_2 = MC = 2$, and pricing according to the separate demand curves. In market 1, $MR_1 = 2$ at $Q_1 = 4000$. From D_1 we see that these 4000 units can be sold at a price of $4. This would generate revenue of $16,000 (= \$4 \times 4000)$. In market 2, $MR_2 = 2$ at $Q_2 = 3000$, which can be sold for $5 each. Revenue from market two would be $15,000 (= \$5 \times 3000)$. Total revenue to the firm would then be $31,000 (= \$16,000 + \$15,000)$, which is greater than if a nondiscriminatory pricing policy were followed.

The higher price will always be charged in the market with the less elastic demand. This can be shown using Equation 10.2; that is,

$$P = MR\left(\frac{E}{E-1}\right)$$

Since MR is equal for both submarkets, the smaller the value of E the larger the value of P (remember that the absolute value of E will be greater than one since the firm will always operate where marginal revenue is positive). For example, suppose $E_1 = 4$ and $E_2 = 3$ with $MR_1 = 2$. The two prices would be as follows:

$$P_1 = 2\left(\frac{4}{4-1}\right) = 2.67$$

$$P_2 = 2\left(\frac{3}{3-1}\right) = 3.00$$

In this hypothetical example, market 1 has the more elastic demand and appropriately the lower price.

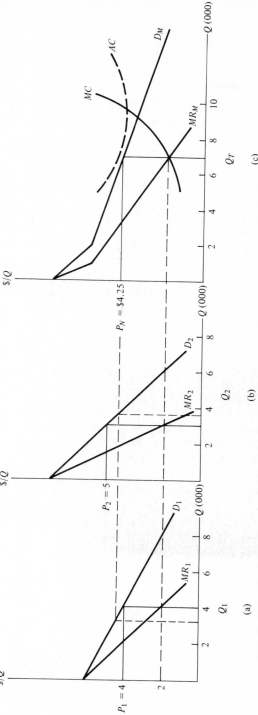

Figure 10.7 Third-Degree Price Discrimination   Third-degree price discrimination with two submarkets. The monopolist will produce where the marginal revenue associated with market demand (MR_M for D_M) is equal to marginal cost (i.e., $Q_T = 7000$ units). At Q_T, $MR_M = MC = 2$. The discriminating monopolist allocates the 7000 units between markets such that $MR_1 = MR_2 = MC = 2$. Thus $Q_1 = 4000$ and $Q_2 = 3000$. Prices are determined from the respective demand curves ($P_1 = 4$ and $P_2 = 5$). Total revenue would be $31,000. The nondiscriminating monopolist will still produce 7000 units but price from D_M at $4.25. Total revenue would then be $29,750, and profit would be reduced.

With specific reference to the situation depicted in Figure 10.7, we can solve for the price elasticities using Equation 10.4; that is,

$$E = \frac{P}{P - MR}$$

$$E_1 = \frac{4}{4 - 2} = 2$$

$$E_2 = \frac{5}{5 - 2} = 1.67$$

As expected, the lower price ($P_1 = 4$) is charged in the more elastic market ($E_1 > E_2$).

It is possible that the only way the monopolist can stay in business is to practice price discrimination. Consider, for example, what would happen if the average cost was the dashed curve in Figure 10.7(c). At every level of output, $AC > D$. The profit-maximizing level of output would cost $4.40 per unit, or $30,800 in total. The nondiscriminating monopolist would generate revenue of $29,750, as seen above, and thus the firm would incur a loss of $1,050. By discriminating in the pricing of the product, revenue of $31,000 could be obtained and the $1,050 loss would be turned to a $200 profit.

MONOPOLY REGULATION

Monopolies are usually regulated by one or more government agencies "in the public interest." Although it is not our purpose in this text to treat the topic of regulation exhaustively, we shall consider several alternative forms of regulation. The objective is usually to make the industry (monopolist) operate in such a manner that the results are closer to those that would evolve if the industry were competitive. Generally, this means reducing monopoly profits and/or improving the allocation of resources.

One approach is for the regulatory agency to set the price that the monopolist can charge and allow consumers to purchase the amount they wish at that price. This approach is illustrated in Figure 10.8. The demand and cost functions depicted are representative of what one might expect for an electric utility, for example. The profit-maximizing price and output, without regulation, would be P_1 and Q_1, respectively.

A common regulatory approach is to set price such that the utility earns just a normal rate of return (which is included in $LRAC$). That price would be P_A, at which consumers would be willing and able to purchase Q_A units. At this level, $P_A = LRAC$ and economic profit is zero. Consumers purchase more at a lower price than if the monopoly were unregulated ($P_A < P_1$ and $Q_A > Q_1$). While this is seen as being socially desirable, price is still greater than marginal cost and thus there are still too few resources allocated to the industry.

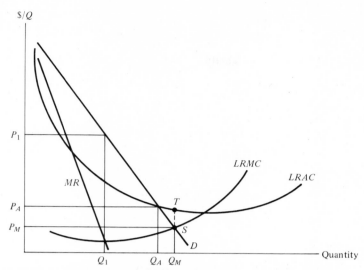

Figure 10.8 Monopoly Price Regulation   Price regulation of a natural monopoly. The unregulated profit-maximizing price is P_1, and the associated output is Q_1. A zero-profit price would be $P_A = LRAC$, at which the monopolist would produce Q_A units. Consumers would purchase more ($Q_A > Q_1$) and at a lower price ($P_A < P_1$). To achieve an optimal allocation of resources price should equal marginal cost, $P_M = MC$ and output would be Q_M. Such a price would, however, require a subsidy to keep the firm in business.

If the regulatory agency is more concerned with resource allocation, price will be set at P_M, such that Q_M units will be produced and purchased, and $P_M = MC$. However, at this price/quantity configuration there is a loss of TS dollars per unit. In order to keep the firm in business, a subsidy of at least Q_M times TS dollars would be necessary, which is not always popular.

We often hear people suggest that governments impose taxes of various kinds on monopolies. Let us evaluate the effects of three alternative taxes: a specific tax per unit, a lump-sum tax, and a percentage tax on profits. These can be analyzed with the help of Figure 10.9(a), (b), and (c), respectively.

A specific tax per unit of output will shift the average-cost and marginal-cost curves up by the amount of the tax (from AC_1 to AC_2, and from MC_1 to MC_2). The firm would react by reducing output from Q_1 to Q_2, following the profit-maximizing behavior of setting marginal revenue equal to marginal cost. Price would rise from P_1 to P_2, and average cost would increase from C_1 to C_2. Profit would indeed be reduced, but consumers would pay more (the increase in price would generally be less than the tax) and purchase less.

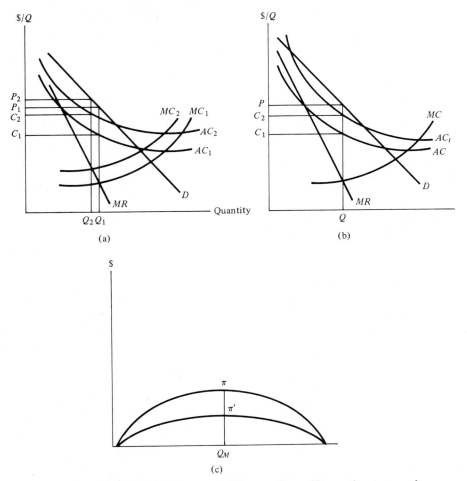

Figure 10.9 Effect of Taxes on Monopolies Alternative types of taxes affect a monopolist's price/output decisions. (a) A specific tax per unit would result in a higher price and reduced output. (b) A lump-sum tax would not change the level of output or price but would reduce profit. (c) A percentage tax on profit (accounting profit) would not affect output or price but would reduce the firm's profit.

In Figure 10.9(b) the lump-sum tax is seen to shift only the average-cost curve upward from AC to AC_t. The tax has the same effect as a fixed cost. Marginal cost is unchanged, so the monopolist's profit-maximizing price and quantity remain at P and Q. However, since average cost increases for that level of output from C_1 to C_2, profit is reduced. Consumers are unaffected by the tax, at least in terms of the price they pay for the product and the amount they consume.

The effect of a 50 percent profit tax is illustrated in Figure 10.9(c). Profit prior to the tax (π) increases up to the level of output Q_M and then declines. The output Q_M is determined by the profit-maximizing rule, $MR = MC$, as usual. After the tax, profit is one-half the previous amount at each level of output. After-tax profit is represented by the curve π'. We see that the maximum profit is still at Q_M, so the price and output decision of the firm is unchanged. Profits are, however, reduced.

It is clear that although these tax forms of regulation do reduce profit, they do not lower price, increase output, or improve on the allocation of resources. In fact, the specific tax per unit has an effect exactly the opposite of what would be desired.

SUMMARY

Monopoly represents a form of market structure in which there is a single seller of a product that has no close substitutes. Various forms of entry barriers protect the monopolist from potential competitors and permit economic profits to be maintained in the long run.

The demand curve for the monopolist is identical with the market demand curve since the firm is the industry. Thus, marginal revenue always lies below demand (which is the same line as price and average revenue). By equating marginal revenue and marginal cost to maximize profit, the monopolist is led to allocate too few resources to production (since $P > MR = MC$) of the product.

The existence of monopoly does not necessarily mean the firm will make a positive economic profit, although this is a likely result. A monopolist will usually not use the optimum size of plant or produce at the optimum rate for the plant that is used. In general, the results of monopolization of an industry that would otherwise be perfectly competitive reduces productive efficiency and allocative efficiency. In addition, there may be undesirable equity consequences since monopoly profits are likely to result.

It is possible for a monopolist to gain even greater advantage through price discrimination. With first-degree discrimination the monopolist can absorb the entire consumer's surplus, whereas with second-degree price discrimination only some part of the consumer's surplus is transferred to the seller. The latter is more common than the former. However, third-degree price discrimination is the most common. With this type of pricing policy, the firm must be able to segment the market into two or more separable submarkets that have different price elasticities of demand. The highest price will be charged in the market with the least elastic demand function.

Most monopolies are regulated by a government agency of some type. Price may be set to eliminate economic profit ($P = AC$) or to provide an optimal allocation of resources ($P = MC$). Taxes are an effective method of regulation only with respect to reducing profit. An understanding of the models we have developed for both perfect competition and monopoly provide a valuable set of tools to evaluate more common market structures as well as a wide variety of business decisions and public policy issues.

Selected Readings

Averch, Harvey, and Leland L. Johnson. "Behavior of the Firm Under Regulatory Constraint." *American Economic Review* 52 (December 1962), 1052–1069.

Fisher, Franklin M. "Diagnosing Monopoly." *Quarterly Review of Economics and Business* 19:2 (Summer 1979), 7–35.

Lerner, Abba P. "The Concept of Monopoly and the Measurement of Monopoly Power." *Review of Economic Studies* (June 1943), 157–175.

Taylor, L. D. "The Demand for Electricity: A Survey." *Bell Journal of Economics* 6:1 (Spring 1975), 74–110.

QUESTIONS

1. Write a short explanation of the following terms or concepts that were used in this chapter:
   (a) average-cost pricing
   (b) consumer's surplus
   (c) first-degree price discrimination
   (d) marginal-cost pricing
   (e) monopoly
   (f) natural monopoly
   (g) price setter
   (h) price skimming
   (i) profit maximization
   (j) second-degree price discrimination
   (k) third-degree price discrimination
2. Use the accompanying graph of demand, marginal revenue, average cost, and marginal cost to answer the questions that follow.

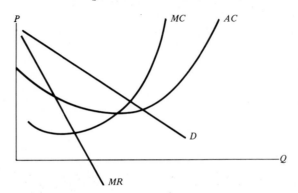

(a) At what quantity will profit be maximized? Indicate the corresponding price on the graph.

(b) What price would you determine if you were to regulate this monopolist such that a "fair rate of return" resulted (i.e., $P = AC$)? Indicate the corresponding price and quantity on the graph.

(c) At what pice and quantity would resources be optimally allocated? Indicate this price/quantity combination on the graph.

(d) Evaluate the consequences of your answers to (a) through (c).

(e) How would your answers to parts (a) through (d) be changed if the relevant functions were as depicted in the following graph instead.

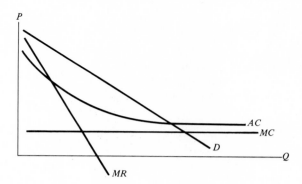

3. A monopolist has the following demand and average cost schedules:

Price	Quantity	Average Cost
80	10	10
70	20	5
60	30	9
50	40	16
40	50	25
30	60	36
20	70	45

Graph these functions and the corresponding marginal-revenue and marginal-cost functions. From your graph estimate the quantity that will maximize profit for the firm. At what price could this quantity be sold? In a separate graph draw the curves representing total revenue, total cost, and profit. What is the dollar value of profit at the profit-maximizing quantity found above?

4. Complete the graphs shown to illustrate the determination of price in two submarkets using third-degree price discrimination. Show the quantity that should be sold in each submarket as well as the price in each market. Does $Q_1 + Q_2 = Q_m$? Show the price that would be charged if the firm does not discriminate. How does this price compare to P_1 and P_2?

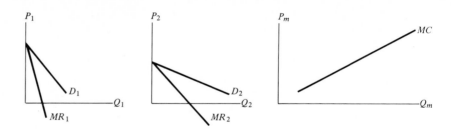

5. Explain the nature of second-degree price discrimination. Relate second-degree price discrimination to:
   (a) price skimming in general
   (b) pricing of long-distance phone calls
   (c) pricing of electric power to residential consumers
   (d) the fare structure of taxi rides
   (e) the pricing of Dacron and Qiana by DuPont; see "Pricing Strategy in an Inflation Economy," *Business Week* (April 6, 1974), 46.
6. Explain how third-degree price discrimination may be practiced in the following situations:
   (a) pricing of airline tickets
   (b) pricing of electric power
   (c) pricing of telephone service
   (d) pricing of theater tickets
   (e) setting tuition charges in higher education
   (f) setting the fare for mass transit
   In each of these cases, relate your answer to price elasticity of demand.
7. A monopolist has the following demand curve: $P = 200 - Q$. Construct a table showing the price (or average revenue), the total revenue, and the marginal revenue for quantities of 10, 20, 30, 40, 50, 60, 70, 80, 90, 100, 110, 120, 130, and 140 units (Q). Plot a graph of total revenue versus quantity immediately above a graph of demand and marginal revenue (such as the graph in Figure 10.1). Indicate the range over which demand is price elastic and the range of price inelasticity. At what price and quantity is demand unitarily elastic?
8. Why would a monopolist spend money on advertising? Consider the following industries and relate your answer to these industries.
   (a) telephone
   (b) natural gas
   (c) electric power
   (d) urban mass transit
   (e) Amtrak
   In the 1970s the concept of "demarketing" developed. How would this concept be related to advertising you have observed for any of the situations given above.
9. In the United States most monopolies exist under government regulation and/or with a license issued by a government agency. Under what circumstances would you advocate establishing or encouraging a monopoly for a

particular industry? What would you expect to be the consequences of establishing a monopoly in the following industries?

(a) steel
(b) automobiles
(c) soft drinks
(d) calculators
(e) food retailing

How do the demand, production, and cost concepts discussed in earlier chapters influence your answers?

CHAPTER 11
MONOPOLISTIC COMPETITION

Having now completed our discussion of the market structures that lie at the extremes of the continuum, we shall concentrate on the middle ground in this chapter and the next. Most business activity takes place in markets that are neither perfectly competitive nor completely monopolized. Thus the concepts we shall be exploring in Chapters 11 and 12 provide a framework that will help us understand the behavior of firms that form the core of business enterprise.

As the title implies, the market structure referred to as monopolistic competition has some characteristics resembling those of perfect competition and others that are more similar to a monopoly. As we have noted before, the differences that exist between the various market structures discussed in Chapters 9 through 12 are on the demand, or revenue, side. The cost side is the same for all since it is determined by technological factors and resource prices, which we will continue to assume are unaffected by the output market structure. Thus the cost functions used will have the same shapes as those used previously.

CHARACTERISTICS OF MONOPOLISTIC COMPETITION

The four characteristics we have been using to describe each market structure are: the number of firms in the industry, the relation between the products produced by each firm in the industry, the ease with which resources can flow into or out of the industry (resource mobility), and the degree of knowledge each firm has about factors affecting the market. We shall examine each of these in turn for monopolistic competition, comparing them with those for perfect competition and for monopoly.

There are many firms in a *monopolistically competitive industry,* but generally fewer than in industries that would be described as perfectly competitive. As we shall see, one result of having a large number of individual firms is that no one firm has very much discretion over price. Prices for the output of various firms tend to converge to a fairly small range but may not be the same for all firms, as was the case in perfect competition.

Next, in describing the type of product produced in a monopolistically competitive industry we come to what may be the most important distinguishing characteristic. Such industries are characterized by *product differentiation among firms.* Products within any industry, or product grouping, may be differentiated by actual physical variations, as well as by label, brand name, package, trademark, or other features that allow the consumer to tell the output of one firm from that of another.

Each firm has some monopoly power in that it has the sole right to produce and market its particular variety of the product. In Chapter 10 we mentioned the beer industry in this regard. The Adolph Coors Company has a monopoly in the production of Coors beer, but the company certainly does not have a monopoly in the production and sale of beer. There are a great many reasonably close substitutes, such that the cross-price elasticity between brands will generally be positive. Recall that in the case of pure monopoly there are no reasonable substitutes, and the cross-price elasticities between the monopolist's product and all other products are zero.

It is important to realize that product differentiation may or may not mean differentiation of the physical properties of the product. Campbell's tomato soup may be virtually identical to any other brand of tomato soup (including unbranded soup carrying only the generic label "tomato soup"), and yet some consumers have formed a strong preference for Campbell's—so much so that Campbell's has something over 80 percent of the soup market despite the existence of many very close substitutes.

The effect of brand image as a differentiating factor becomes all the more obvious when we consider the practice of "private branding" in which a major firm produces an identical (or nearly identical) product for sale under some other firm's private brand. In the replacement tire market more than one-third of the market is private branded (such as Atlas tires). Private branded shoes account for even a larger portion of that market, whereas in the gasoline market less than 20 percent is accounted for by private brands. In the early 1970s it was reported that nearly 70 percent of the Whirlpool Corporation's sales went for private brands sold by Sears (under the Kenmore name) and other major customers.[1]

Product differentiation and the existence of brands that allow consumers to distinguish the product of one firm from that of another creates the "monopoly" dimension of the market structure referred to as monopolistic competition. One very important consequence of this monopolistic influence is that the demand curve for individual firms has a negative slope similar to that of a pure monopolist rather than being horizontal as for a perfectly competitive firm. Each firm has some discretionary price control because consumers develop various degrees of brand loyalty such that a slight increase in price will not result in sales dropping to zero. Likewise, a slight decrease in price will not attract all consumers, since some will remain loyal to their preferred brand—at least for relatively small price differentials.

Although the demand curve facing a monopolistically competitive firm will have a negative slope, the similarity to a monopolist's demand curve should not be pushed much further. The existence of very close substitutes, as you should recall from Chapter 5, increases the price elasticity of demand. Thus, even though both have downward-sloping demand curves, sales for a monopolistic competitor will be much more sensitive to price changes than for a monopolist, ceteris paribus.

With respect to resource mobility into or out of the industry, monopolistic competition is much closer to perfect competition than to monopoly. *Entry to and exit from such industries is relatively easy.* Normally, there are very few, if any, restrictions imposed by governments. When restrictions do exist, they are usually easily dealt with, such as obtaining the required health permits to open a new restaurant. For most monopolistically competitive activities, the capital requirements to set up business are not large, at least relative to the cost of starting a new electric utility or other activity that would be classified as a monopoly. We shall see that this ease of entry and exit has important consequences in terms of the existence of long-run economic profits for firms in this type of market structure.

Firms in a monopolistically competitive industry *have reasonably complete knowledge about all facets of the industry that may affect decisions within the firm.* Each firm has a good feel for the prices that other firms pay for all the inputs to the production process. They all have essentially the same access to the existing technological base and, through trade associations, government publications, or private sources,

---

[1] For a more extended discussion, see Louis E. Boone and David L. Kurtz, *Contemporary Marketing*, 2d ed. (Hinsdale, Ill.: Dryden, 1977), pp. 226–227.

they all have the potential to obtain equal information concerning market demand for the industry. In addition, all firms have reasonable ability to know the prices charged by competing firms as well as the level of output or sales by those other firms.

Before going ahead with other aspects of this type of market structure, let us put these characteristics in the context of one example of a monopolistically competitive industry, the restaurant industry. If you pick up the Yellow Pages for any city, you will find a rather long list of entries under the heading "Restaurants." There are obviously a great many firms in the industry for most geographic areas. The firms have one clear characteristic in common: They are places where prepared meals can be purchased. But they may also be very different from one another. The meal may be eaten in at some, taken out at others, or in many cases both options are available. The menus are highly differentiated between firms: from pizza at the nearest Pizza Hut to beef Wellington at The Bakery in Chicago; from a sandwich at Big Al's to a fine Greek meal such as Souvlaki pork at the Akropol in Great Falls; from deep-fried fish and fries at Long John Silver's to a large, sweet lobster at Klein's in downtown Pittsburgh; and so forth in city after city. Look around your town and you'll see new restaurants opening with relative frequency; meanwhile, others change management, struggle along, and frequently go out of business. Inputs such as furnishings, food, beverages, labor, and so on are purchased from the same vendors, or labor market, by most firms in the industry, so each knows essentially what the others have to pay for various items. Trade associations, as well as other published data, provide information on the entire industry.

CLASSIFICATION OF PRODUCT GROUPS

Since each firm in monopolistic competition does have a monopoly over its own particular product, we must be careful to define the relevant activity in broad enough terms to encompass a workable product group composed of firms that produce products that are close substitutes for one another. If we used the classification "Greek restaurants" as a product group in a small city such as Great Falls, Montana, the market structure would become a monopoly (or duopoly[2] if one also includes a Greek/American restaurant). Since all restaurants compete for a particular part of the family budget and are very close substitutes for one another, it makes sense to consider restaurants as a meaningful product group for purposes of analysis. Other product groups would include cereals, clothing (or perhaps even shoes, slacks, sport clothes, etc.), soft drinks, beer, calculators, watches, magazines, candy, television sets, and so on.

[2] The term "duopoly" refers to a market structure with just two firms. This form of market will be discussed in Chapter 12.

A useful classification scheme for product groups is provided by the Standard Industrial Classifications (SIC codes) compiled by the federal government.[3] These begin with broad two-digit groups into which all types of businesses are classified as follows:

Division A: 01–09 Agriculture, Forestry, Fishing
Division B: 10–14 Mining
Division C: 15–19 Contract Construction
Division D: 20–39 Manufacturing
Division E: 40–49 Transportation and Other Public Utilities
Division F: 50–51 Wholesale Trade
Division G: 52–59 Retail Trade
Division H: 60–67 Finance, Insurance, and Real Estate
Division I: 70–89 Services
Division J: 90–93 Public Administration
Division K: 99   Others

Three- and four-digit classifications subdivide industries into smaller, more homogeneous product groups. For example, within the 50–59 grouping for Wholesale and Retail Trade, one finds group 57, "Furniture, Home Furnishings, and Equipment Stores." Within that section, group number 573 represents "Radio, Television, and Music Stores," and industry number 5732 identifies "Radio and Television Stores," while "Music Stores" are assigned SIC number 5733.

The information collected by the federal government on each product group includes the number of firms, sales volume, and number of employees broken down by state, county, Standard Consolidated Statistical Areas (SCSAs) and Standard Metropolitan Statistical Areas (SMSAs). Students in economics and business are almost certain to have occasion to refer to SIC codes in their schoolwork or later in a job situation, so it would be a good idea to spend a few moments in the library glancing through the *Standard Industrial Classification Manual*.

SHORT-RUN PRICING AND OUTPUT DECISIONS

There are two types of demand curves that can be constructed for a monopolistically competitive firm. Both are illustrated in Figure 11.1. The more steeply sloped demand curve (DD') represents the quantities a given firm would sell at various prices if other firms had the same price structure. Therefore this demand curve can be thought of as a "share-of-the-market" curve, along which the firm maintains a constant fraction of the total industry demand. But, as we shall see, this curve does not function as the operational demand curve for the firm.

[3] See *Standard Industrial Classification Manual* (Washington, D.C.: GPO, 1972) for a detailed description of the roughly 400 classifications used.

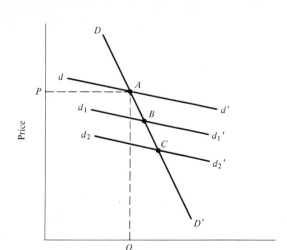

Figure 11.1 Demand Curves in Monopolistic Competition The two types of demand functions for a monopolistically competitive firm are the "big D" demand (DD'), which represents a given share of the market and the "little d" demand (dd') which is the operational demand as perceived by the firm. For any given "share-of-the-market" demand, there is a "little d" demand curve intersecting at each possible price. Examples are illustrated by the "little d" curves through points A, B, and C. At any price the perceived demand is more elastic than the market share demand.

Suppose that price was established at P with the corresponding sales at Q. The individual firm would perceive its demand curve as being the one labeled dd'. This "little d" demand curve is more elastic at P than the "big D" demand curve. The firm views dd' as the operational demand function since the products sold in the industry are generally very close substitutes for one another. Thus the firm assumes that a price increase might result in a substantial sales loss, whereas a price reduction could stimulate significant sales increases as customers are attracted away from competing firms.

It should be clear that determination of which demand curve is relevant depends on the reaction pattern of other firms in the industry. For a small price cut from P, sales could increase substantially if other firms do not cut price (movement along the "little d" demand curve), but would only increase slightly if the others also cut price (movement along the "big D" demand curve). Successive price cuts, sometimes called a *price war,* would lead to movement along DD', such as from A to B to C, and the establishment of lower and lower "little d" demand curves (d_1d_1' and d_2d_2' in Figure 11.1). We shall return to this issue later in the chapter when we discuss the long-run equilibrium for monopolistically competitive firms.

In the short run the "little d" demand curve is relevant for decision purposes because the number of other firms is usually large enough that the degree of recognized interdependence among firms is small. In Figure 11.2, the marginal revenue curve associated with the dd' demand curve is added, along with the typical short-run marginal-cost and average-cost curves. The firm finds the optimal rate of output (Q^*) at the point where marginal revenue equals marginal cost. Price is then determined from the demand curve directly above Q^*, whereas the average cost of producing that level of output is determined from the average-cost curve above Q^*. These are denoted on the vertical axis as P and C, respectively. For the situation illustrated in Figure 11.2, the firm obtains a positive economic profit since $P > C$. The amount of profit is represented by the shaded rectangle $PABC$, which equals quantity times the difference between price and average cost—that is, $Q^*(P - C)$.

Since firms in a monopolistically competitive industry are producing products that are very close substitutes for one another, we should expect the cost structure to be very similar for each firm. Differences may exist, however. For example, in the retail grocery industry, labor costs usually run about 10 percent of sales revenue. For some firms this cost will be slightly higher and for some it will be slightly lower, resulting in either higher or lower marginal and average costs. Such differences, along with different levels of the "little d" demand curve (due to customer preferences and loyalties), result in a differential between the prices charged by various firms. Thus in monopolistic competition a single market price

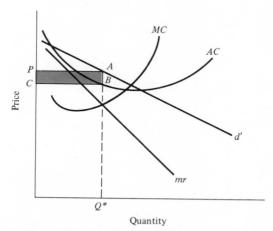

Figure 11.2 Monopolistically Competitive Firm with Positive Profit Determination of the profit-maximizing output (Q^*) for a monopolistically competitive firm that enjoys a positive economic profit because at Q^* price is greater than average cost. The amount of profit is represented by the area of the shaded rectangle $PABC$.

does not prevail, but rather prices are established within a fairly narrow band for all firms in the industry. The amount of price variation will vary in direct proportion to the degree of product differentiation and the consequent preferences and loyalties that consumers develop.

These factors (differences in demand and cost) also contribute to the observation that although some monopolistically competitive firms are making a positive economic profit, others in the same industry may have either zero or negative economic profit in the short run. The latter two situations are illustrated in Figure 11.3(a) and (b), respectively.

In Figure 11.3 we see that the optimum level of output (Q^*) is determined where marginal revenue equals marginal cost. In Figure 11.3(a) price equals average cost at Q^*, so the firm has zero economic profit. Figure 11.3(b) shows the case in which average cost is greater than price at Q^*, such that the best the firm can do in the short run is to minimize its loss (negative economic profit). The loss can be represented by the shaded rectangle $CABP$, which equals quantity times the amount by which average cost exceeds price—that is, $Q^*(P - C)$, where $C > P$.

LONG-RUN EQUILIBRIUM

Despite the fact that each firm does have a monopoly over the production of its particular product, *zero, or nearly zero, long-run economic profits*

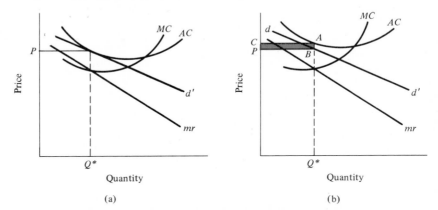

(a)   (b)

Figure 11.3 Zero and Negative Profit in Monopolistic Competition   In the short run a monopolistically competitive firm may have a positive, zero, or negative economic profit. The latter cases are illustrated in this figure. (a) In this case there is zero economic profit since at the profit-maximizing output (Q^*) price equals average cost. (b) In this case the best the firm can do in the short run is to minimize its loss by producing Q^* units (minimizing loss is the same as maximizing profit). At this output level, average cost exceeds price and the amount of loss (negative economic profit) is represented by the shaded rectangle $CABP$.

*will generally result for firms in monopolistically competitive indus-
tries.* The principal reasons for this are found in the characteristics we
have used to describe this type of market structure. There are many firms
that produce products, which, though differentiated, are very close substitutes for one another, and there is relatively easy entry into and exit
from the industry.

In some cases that would be considered monopolistically competitive except for ease of entry, positive economic profits may exist in the
long run. This is the situation which is frequently referred to as the
blocked-entry case. Such instances are most likely to occur due to legal
restrictions on entry rather than due to purely economic restrictions.

Consider, for example, the sale of alcoholic beverages at bars,
taverns, saloons, and the like. A political authority (state and/or local)
controls the issuance of the licenses necessary to enter the industry.
Existing firms will lobby heavily to prevent additional licenses from
being granted in order to protect their own profit potential (various social
and religious groups may aid them in this effort, but with a different
motive). Another example is in the taxi service industry, where individuals can enter with relatively little capital expenditure but are restricted
in most localities by the artificially limited availability of licenses by a
regulatory agency. The industry composed of thrift institutions (banks,
savings and loan associations, and credit unions) also provides a fairly
common case of blocked-entry monopolistic competition since branches
or new firms must obtain permission from a regulatory agency.

The long-run equilibrium in these cases can be illustrated using the
diagram in Figure 11.4. We see that the optimum rate of output is Q^* at
which $SRMC = LRMC = mr$. Price P is found from the demand curve
dd', and average cost is determined at level C from the $LRAC$ curve
($= SRAC$ at their tangency above Q^*). The profit represented by the
shaded rectangle $PABC$ will be maintained as long as entry is successfully blocked and as long as firms do not engage in a price-cutting war
(see the discussion below for the effect of such actions).

The *open-entry case* is far more common in monopolistically competitive industries. When resources are mobile rather than artificially restricted, profits will be "competed away" in the long run as new firms
enter, existing firms expand, and/or as firms engage in a price war. Let us
first examine how these actions affect the "big D" and "little d" demand
curves without simultaneously considering the relevant cost functions.
Doing so makes the exposition of the concepts and the accompanying
graphs easier to follow, and once these effects are understood we can add
in the cost curves using a separate graph to show the final zero-profit
long-run equilibrium.

First, let us consider the effect of new entrants on the "big D"—or
share-of-the-market—demand curve. Assume that in Figure 11.5(a) DD'

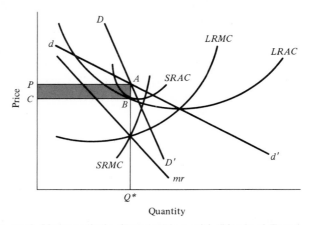

Figure 11.4 Monopolistic Competition with Blocked Entry With "blocked entry" a positive economic profit may exist in the long run under conditions that are otherwise monopolistically competitive. In such a case the firm equates $mr = SRMC = LRMC$ to determine the optimum rate of output, Q^*. Price P is then determined from the "little d" demand curve; average cost C is found from the tangency point where $SRAC = LRAC$. The amount of profit is represented by the shaded rectangle $PABC$.

represents the existing market share demand curve and that positive economic profits are resulting. New firms will enter such that each firm will have a new "big D" demand as the entire market is split among more individual firms. A shift from DD' to D_1D_1' would result and, assuming that the cost functions are stable, economic profit for each firm would be reduced. If, with DD', negative economic profits existed, we would expect firms to leave the industry. For remaining firms the new "big D" demand would be D_2D_2', and the economic loss would tend to be reduced since sales would be divided among fewer competitors.

Retail grocery sales may be considered a monopolistically competitive industry, with the coming and going of establishments a common occurrence in most communities. Groceries typically operate with a very thin "accounting profit margin" of 1 percent of sales, or even less in many cases. An accounting profit margin this low is certainly consistent with a zero economic profit. It is not uncommon to find many retail grocery outlets serving a market (something like one store for every 2000 persons). They offer differentiated products (full-scale supermarkets such as Safeway or A&P, "mom and pop" groceries, specialty food stores, and convenience stores such as 7-11), but ones that still are very close substitutes; entry is easy in that there are no or few legal restraints and low initial investment (something like $150,000 could get you started); and knowledge about the industry is readily available. Thus, the type of "big

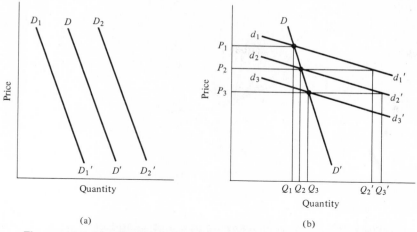

(a)   (b)

Figure 11.5 Monopolistic Competition with Open Entry In the
more usual case of "open entry," monopolistic competition
demand curve shifts will result if a nonzero profit exists. (a)
Starting with the "big D" demand function DD' if positive profits
exist, new entrants will shift the "share-of-the-market" demand to
D_1D_1'; whereas if negative profits exist at DD', firms will leave the
industry, shifting the "share-of-the-market" demand to D_2D_2'. (b)
Given a stable "big D" demand function, shifts of the "little d"
demand will further assure a zero-profit equilibrium. At price P_1 a
firm would anticipate increased sales to Q_2' if price is cut to P_2 but
would only realize sales of Q_2 due to competitors' reactions. From
P_2 the same process would take place to P_3, or some other price,
until zero economic profits result.

D" demand curve shifts illustrated in Figure 11.5(a) is common in this
industry.

We have seen that it is really the "little d" demand curve that is
important in determining the firm's output and pricing decisions. Once
the relevant "big D" demand function is determined, we can see how the
"little d" demand will slide up or down to establish a zero-profit long-run
equilibrium. Let us refer to Figure 11.5(b) and assume that the existing
price is P_1. Any one firm might expect to find it profitable to reduce price
to P_2 with an expected sales increase from Q_1 to Q_2' along d_1d_1'. However, this would mean that the increase in sales would come at the expense of the other firms in the industry. These other firms will likely also
cut price such that sales only increase to Q_2 along DD'.

This type of competition within monopolistic competition will continue to P_3 or some other level until a zero-profit equilibrium is reached,
as illustrated in Figure 11.6. We see that in the open entry case
the long-run equilibrium is such that $mr = SRMC = LRMC$, and
$P = SRAC = LRAC$. Thus economic profit is zero.

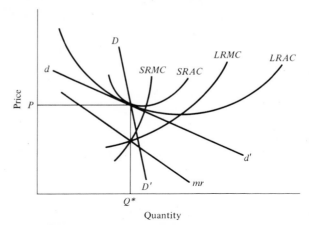

Figure 11.6 Monopolistically Competitive Long-Run Equilibrium After the demand curve shifts illustrated in Figure 11.5 are completed, a zero-profit long-run equilibrium will be obtained in the open-entry case, as shown here. The optimum level of output, Q^*, is determined by the intersection of mr, $SRMC$, and $LRMC$. Price is found from the "little d" demand curve, which is tangent to both the $SRAC$ and $LRAC$ curves about Q^*. Thus $P = SRAC = LRAC$, and economic profit is zero. There is no longer any incentive for firms to enter or exit the industry.

An example of this type of situation can be seen by reviewing the actions of A&P (and reactions by competitors) as they attempted to regain their position as the largest supermarket chain during the early 1970s. A&P introduced the WEO (Where Economy Originates) program of price cuts, hoping to increase sales significantly. However, retaliation in the form of comparable price cuts by other grocery stores led to substantially less increase in sales than expected and actual economic losses.[4] Price wars such as this, causing the "little d" demand to shift downward, may be becoming less common as firms become more sophisticated in predicting the likely response of competitors.

EXCESS CAPACITY

It has long been recognized that the optimum rate of output for firms in a monopolistically competitive industry will be less than the level at which either short-run or long-run average costs are at a minimum. There are two aspects to the excess capacity problem that result: First, the firm

[4] For discussions that further illustrate the monopolistically competitive nature of the grocery industry and focusing on A&P in particular, see "Can Jonathan Scott Save A&P?" *Business Week* (May 19, 1975), 128–136; and Peter W. Bernstein, "Jonathan Scott's Surprising Failure at A&P," *Fortune* (November 6, 1978), 35–44.

does not use the existing plant at the most efficient level; and, second, firms are led to build plants that are too small.

We can analyze both of these results with the aid of Figure 11.7, which shows the determination of the same zero-profit equilibrium as in Figure 11.6, except that we have now added the short-run average-cost and marginal-cost curves associated with the most efficient size of plant, $SRAC_E$ and $SRMC_E$, respectively (the "big D" demand curve has been omitted since it is not necessary for the analysis). The profit-maximizing rate of output for the firm is Q_1 units, which will be produced with the size plant represented by $SRAC_F$ and $SRMC_F$. If that size plant were operated most efficiently, Q_2 units would be produced. Thus, each firm tends to underutilize the plant it builds by the difference between Q_1 units and Q_2 units of output; this difference represents excess or unused capacity.

The most efficient size of plant is the one for which the short-run average cost and the long-run average cost are both minimized at the same rate of output. This is output Q_3 in Figure 11.7, with $SRAC_E$ and $SRMC_E$ representing the most technically efficient size production facility. Because the firm is faced with a negatively sloped demand function (dd'), the zero-profit tangency solution must be to the left of Q_3. Since Q_3 would be the socially optimal level of output if the market were perfectly

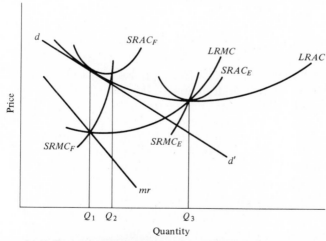

Figure 11.7 Excess Capacity in Monopolistic Competition In monopolistic competition with open entry, firms will build plants, such as represented by $SRAC_F$ and $SRMC_F$, that are smaller than the optimum (most efficient) size of plant represented by $SRAC_E$ and $SRMC_E$. Negative excess capacity measured by the difference between Q_3 and Q_1 results. Further, since each firm operates its facilities at less than the technically efficient level (Q_1 rather than Q_2) each has excess capacity.

competitive, the difference between Q_1 and Q_3 represents forgone production (negative excess capacity is sometimes used to define this difference).

It should be clear that the less steep the "little d" demand curve is the less severe the excess capacity problem becomes. This dd' demand function will be flatter the greater the degree of product substitutability (or, alternatively, the closer the products are to the perfectly competitive homogeneous case). Thus the greater the degree of product differentiation (product choice) we enjoy the more excess capacity we can expect, and it has been argued that prices will be correspondingly greater as well.

If entry is restricted, it is possible (although not particularly likely) that the marginal revenue curve (mr) could intersect at $SRMC_E = SRAC_E = LRMC = LRAC$ such that the firm would build the most efficient plant and utilize it at the most efficient level. Clearly, in such a case, dd' would be above average cost and positive economic profit would result (as long as entry remains blocked and price wars do not develop).

As long as entry is open, some excess capacity will exist. Since each firm builds a plant that is smaller than optimum, more firms may exist than would be desirable (more than if each built the optimum size plant and operated it most efficiently). Furthermore, since firms operate those plants at less than the most economical rate, each facility has some excess capacity.

NON-PRICE COMPETITION

We are all well aware that firms compete not only in terms of price but in other forms as well. In fact, it may well be that actual price competition is a minor aspect of the competitive struggle (rivalry) among firms in monopolistically competitive industries. Five forms of non-price competition are very prevalent: advertising, quality variations, design differences, locational effects, and provision of supplemental services. Some of these obviously become an integral part of the product differentiation dimension of this market structure.

Let us consider each of these forms of non-price competition in turn. Advertising is one of the most intriguing activities we observe in the economy. Its effects are powerful, or so we must believe since firms are willing to spend something in the order of *$50 billion* each year for advertising, and yet it is extraordinarily difficult (if not impossible) to measure the effectiveness of a particular promotional activity. Groceries, which we have used before as an example of monopolist competition, advertise extensively. If you pick up almost any local newspaper you'll find numerous examples.

What does the firm expect to gain from advertising? The intent is to shift their "big D" demand curve to the right. To the extent that this is successful, the firm must then compare, as best as possible, the marginal revenue due to the advertising with the marginal cost of the advertising, and continue with additional promotion only so long as the former exceeds the latter.

Another form of non-price competition involves variations in the quality of the product offered for sale by various firms. In the grocery industry such product quality variations appear to be most pronounced in the fresh meat, fresh vegetable, and baked goods departments. A few loaves of slightly stale bread or a head of wilted lettuce can turn a shopper in the direction of another store pretty quickly. In the hair cutting/styling industry, quality of service is also a form of non-price competition familiar to most people.

Differences in product design may provide a more profitable form of competition than attempting to offer a lower price. The tennis equipment industry provides an example we can use to illustrate. Tennis balls are generally pressurized to maintain a given amount of bounce. At least one manufacturer, however, maintains significant sales by producing a non-pressurized ball. Tennis racquet sales are also subject to non-price competition with different designs, including such examples as the Wilson T-2000, the Prince, the Head Advantage, and so forth.

The decision of where one locates the sale of a product is yet another way of competing on a non-price basis. Having a store near the entrance to a shopping mall is desirable for convenience goods such as groceries. Some firms compete by taking their line of products to the consumer's home for sale, Avon being a successful example of this form of non-price competition with other firms selling similar products at similar prices in a variety of department, drug, and discount stores. In the market for retail gasoline, sales location is a most important competitive factor.

The provision of supplemental services may also be used as non-price competition. Some groceries offer "free" carry-out services to get the groceries to the customer's car. A tire dealer may check and rotate tires after the first 5000 miles. Thrift institutions provide various types of services such as estate planning, family budget counseling, notary services, and help in selling real estate as forms of non-price competition.

All forms of non-price competition cost the firm something and should be evaluated using the general "equimarginal principle." As consumers, we should all be reminded that "there ain't no such thing as a free lunch" and that all the forms of non-price competition must be paid for some way (shifted forward as higher prices or backward as lower wages).

EVALUATION OF MONOPOLISTIC COMPETITION

There are a few analytical devices we can use to evaluate the social welfare effects of monopolistic competition; but, to a large extent, an evaluation must be subjective since certain value judgments are necessary. At the objective and analytical level we can say first that output will generally be less than socially optimal because price will be greater than marginal cost (due to the negatively sloped demand function). The difference, however, is likely to be small in many cases inasmuch as the demand curve may be very nearly flat if there are indeed many other firms and if products are very close substitutes for one another.

We can also say, with reasonable objectivity, that the price people pay is just sufficient for firms to attract and keep the necessary resources employed in that activity. Price will equal average cost in the long run and no economic profits will accrue (except in those cases of "blocked entry"). Further, it is generally accepted that because products are not produced at the minimum possible average cost, there is some excess capacity and overcrowding in monopolistically competitive industries.

Some people will argue that there is advertising waste as firms advertise (or give trading stamps) just to keep up with other firms that do the same. However, such an effect is probably relatively slight in monopolistic competition since firms tend to act in a fairly independent manner (recall that they use the "little d" demand curve for operational purposes). Furthermore, much of the advertising has other effects, such as reducing the cost to consumers of subscribing to newspapers and magazines, as well as supporting much radio and television entertainment, and it does provide *some* information about products.

Finally, we as a society attach considerable importance to the ability to avail ourselves with a wide variety of differentiated goods and services. Most of us would be unwilling to accept an economic environment in which there was only one grocery store at which to shop, or one style of tennis racquet to purchase, or one brand of beer to drink, and on and on.

SUMMARY

Monopolistic competition is a form of market structure that combines some of the elements of perfect competition with some characteristics of a monopoly. There are many sellers of the products that comprise the relevant product group, but rather than being homogeneous the output of one firm is differentiated from that of others in the industry. Although they are differentiated, the products within any group are close substitutes (they have a positive cross-price elasticity of demand).

Most monopolistically competitive activities require relatively little technical expertise that is not available in the public domain, and most require only modest financial investment. Thus entry into (and exit from) such industries is relatively easy.

The demand curve facing the firm has a negative slope but will generally be much more price elastic than for a monopolist because of the existence of many close substitutes. In the short run, firms may have either positive, negative, or zero economic profits. However, in the long run, profits will usually be competed away by the entry of new firms, expansion by existing firms, and/or via competitive price cutting. An exception is found in cases where entry is blocked by some factor (often political/legal) such as in attempting to open a new bar or tavern.

Non-price competition is characteristic of some monopolistically competitive industries. Such competition may take the form of advertising, quality differences, design variations, location factors, and the provision of supplemental services.

An evaluation of the social desirability of this form of market structure involves a subjective weighting of various facets. Output may be too low since price is greater than marginal cost, there is some excess capacity likely, and products are not produced at the lowest possible average cost. On the other hand, we benefit from having a wide variety of goods and services available and may well reach much higher levels in our preference (utility) structures than would be possible under perfect competition or monopoly.

Selected Readings

Chamberlin, Edward H. *The Theory of Monopolistic Competition.* Cambridge, Mass.: Harvard University Press, 1933.

Marvel, Howard P. "Competition and Price Levels in the Retail Gasoline Market." *Review of Economics and Statistics* 60:2 (May 1978), 252–258.

Nightingale, John. "On the Definition of 'Industry' and 'Market'." *Journal of Industrial Economics* 27 (September 1978), 31–39.

Robinson, Joan. *The Economics of Imperfect Competition.* New York: Macmillan, 1933.

QUESTIONS

1. Write a short explanation of the following terms or concepts that were used in this chapter:
   (a) "big D" demand curve
   (b) "blocked-entry" case
   (c) excess capacity
   (d) "little d" demand curve
   (e) monopolistic competition
   (f) non-price competition
   (g) "open-entry" case
   (h) product differentiation
   (i) SIC code

2. The accompanying two graphs illustrate two different short-run situations in a monopolistically competitive industry. Explain what types of adjustments you would expect in each case and illustrate the results in the figures.

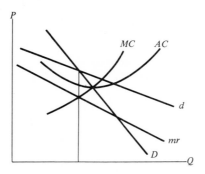 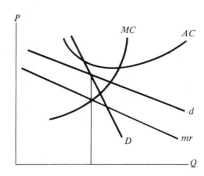

3. Write an essay explaining the characteristics of monopolistic competition. Pick some type of economic activity that you think corresponds closely to the economic model of monopolistic competition and explain how the characteristics discussed above relate to that activity.

4. Go to the yellow pages of the local telephone directory and make a list of local restaurants (if there are a great many, just take the first 30). Are there distinct "product groups" within this general listing? Organize the restaurants in your list into several groups such that within groups there is relative homogeneity and between groups there are greater differences. Describe the degree of substitutability within and between groups. Explain the types of product differentiation that exist both within and between groups. What would you expect to find if you were to estimate the price, income, and cross-price elasticities for the restaurants in your list? Would you describe this as a monopolistically competitive activity in your area? Explain why or why not.

5. Make a list of at least three forms of non-price competition that you have observed for each of the following:
   (a) grocery stores
   (b) clothing stores
   (c) appliance stores
   (d) higher education
   (e) bookstores
   Why do you think firms would engage in such activities?

6. How does advertising affect the demand for a monopolistically competitive *industry?* What about for individual *firms* in the industry? What influence would you expect advertising to have on the price, income, and cross-price elasticities of demand? Explain your answer.

7. Write an essay in which you evaluate the differences between monopolistic competition, perfect competition, and monopoly. Consider productive efficiency as well as efficiency in resource allocation. What are some other advantages you might attribute to monopolistic competition?

8. Evaluate the degree of product differentiation in the following product groups?
   (a) beer
   (b) cola drinks
   (c) coffee
   (d) running shoes
   (e) tennis balls
   (f) cereals
   (g) bicycles
   (h) digital watches
   (i) jeans
   (j) potato chips
   In each case identify both actual (physical) differentiation and perceived (psychological) forms of differentiation.
9. Make a comparison between the characteristics of monopolistic competition and your observations of grocery stores, shoe stores, and bars. Do you think there is any evidence of "excess capacity" in these activities? Explain your response.
10. Consider the offering of various sections of the principles of economics course at your school. In what ways is there product differentiation in the principles course? Can you identify other forms of product differentiation in higher education (in general, considering all schools)?

CHAPTER 12
OLIGOPOLY

Along the continuum of market structures from perfect competition to monopoly, we should place oligopoly nearest to monopoly. However, whereas the theory of monopoly behavior is fairly well defined and accepted, we shall see that there is no general model that provides a consistent explanation of the pricing/output decision for all oligopolists, much less one that yields consistently good predictions about their behavior.

In Chapters 9 and 10 we indicated that perfectly competitive firms are "price takers," whereas monopolists are "price setters." One of the interesting aspects of the study of oligopolies is that within an industry it is not uncommon for both behavior patterns to exist simultaneously, with one firm acting as the "price setter" and the others acting passively as "price takers." The latter firms act as if they were in a perfectly competitive industry and thus the framework developed in Chapter 9 will be useful to us in this chapter as well. Further, we will be able to apply many of the constructs developed in the chapters on monopoly and monopolistic competition in our analysis of oligopoly. As in the previous three chapters, we shall be using the cost relationships from Chapter 8, assuming that each oligopolistic firm purchases inputs in reasonably competitive markets (i.e., there are many firms that purchase the same inputs).

CHARACTERISTICS OF OLIGOPOLISTIC INDUSTRIES

To begin the discussion of oligopoly we shall once again refer to the characteristics used in Chapters 9 through 11 to describe each market structure and to distinguish between them: the number of firms in the industry; the relation between the products produced by each firm in the industry; the ease with which resources can flow into or out of an industry (resource mobility), and the degree of knowledge each firm has about factors affecting the market.

There are relatively few firms in an oligopolistic industry. By "relatively few," we mean that in comparison with the size of the total market the number of firms is small. The automobile industry provides a good example. For the United States automobile industry, sales are in excess of *$100 billion* annually. Of that total, three firms account for roughly 97 percent of the market. The total market is extremely large, and yet only a very few firms exist in the entire industry. Similar, though less extreme, cases include the chemical industry, which is dominated by firms like DuPont, Union Carbide, Dow Chemical, and Monsanto; the steel industry, with U.S. Steel, Bethlehem Steel, and LTV (Ling Tempco Vought) being the major producers; and the office equipment industry, in which IBM has well over three times the sales of the next largest firm, Xerox (other large firms in the industry include Honeywell, NCR, Burroughs, and Control Data).

The relatively small number of firms in each industry should lead us to think of an important behavioral characteristic that we might expect to be evident. Interestingly, it is one that went almost completely unregarded in the early development of the economic theory of oligopoly. That is, *oligopolistic firms should be expected to display considerable interdependence in their decision making.* It seems entirely reasonable to think that, in an industry that is dominated by a few firms, each one will evaluate the potential response of rival firms in making its own decisions regarding price and output.

In comparing the products produced by oligopolistic firms we must distinguish between two types of oligopoly. First, in the case of the *pure oligopoly* the output of one firm is very nearly identical with that of other firms; that is, products are essentially homogeneous. They are likely to carry the producing firm's name, brand, or trademark, but often in an inconspicuous manner. For example, building materials manufactured by Weyerhaeuser or Boise Cascade are generally made to meet certain construction specifications and, other than a fairly discreet branding, are virtually perfectly homogeneous. Steel girders for a bridge may have the U.S. Steel or Bethlehem name on them, but they are functionally equivalent.

The second type of oligopoly situation is referred to as a *differ-*

entiated oligopoly, in which case products have features that clearly differentiate the output of various firms from one to another. Such differences may be in actual physical characteristics or in such aspects as the package, time and place of delivery, services that accompany the sale of the product, warranty provisions, or such very subtle factors as company image. The automobile industry represents an example of a differentiated oligopoly. A Ford Fairmont is a very different product to consumers than a Cadillac Seville. Even cars that are nearly identical such as the Plymouth Horizon and Dodge Omni may have very strong consumer loyalties due to advertising or other factors that influence consumer behavior. Two dimensions of the television industry also provide examples of differentiated oligopoly. Zenith, RCA, Motorola, and GE television sets are all viewed as differentiated products by most consumers. The selection of "products" (shows) available to view is also produced within an oligopolistic framework, with ABC, CBS, and NBC being the dominant networks in the market although there are a good many other networks (such as special sports, news, and educational networks).

As long as products are not perfectly homogeneous, each producer has some degree of monopoly power, and thus in general we can expect oligopolistic firms to have negatively sloped demand functions. How responsive the quantity sold is to price changes depends to a large extent on the degree of product differentiation. There may be little room for price variation between firms in the building supply industry, whereas there is considerable difference between the price of products within the more highly differentiated product group "automobiles." As we shall see later in this chapter, some firms, particularly in the pure oligopoly case, are "price takers" and thus behave like perfectly competitive firms. For them a horizontal demand curve is relevant.

Entry into and exit from oligopolistic industries is usually considered to be very difficult. From the examples we have already given, it should be clear that the financial resources necessary to get started in oligopolistic industries can be very great. In addition, some problems that may confront potential entrants include: setting up a distribution system (automobile industry, for example); obtaining legal/regulatory permission (pharmaceuticals); and having to operate at initially higher average cost because of economies of scale (steel). More than one, or even all, of these factors may combine to limit entry (consider starting a new airline, for example). The same factors may make exit difficult, as well. Once a large financial commitment is made, particularly if facilities are highly specialized, resources may not flow out of an industry as quickly and easily as might be desired. Legal restrictions may also keep firms in an industry or market that they would otherwise abandon (e.g., the airline industry prior to partial deregulation).

The degree of knowledge about facets of the industry that may affect decisions within a firm has more variability in oligopoly than in other market structures. In pure oligopolies, knowledge about resource prices, transportation costs, existing technology, and other such factors is probably greater than for differentiated oligopolies. In either case, there are fewer proprietary secrets than most firms would like to admit. Employees frequently move from one firm to another in the same industry, suppliers gain access to information about the firms they service and may inadvertently (or purposely) pass it on to other firms, and a certain amount of outright industrial espionage is not unheard of in oligopolistic industries. Many firms place very close security around research and development activities, new product planning, and other activities they expect to provide them with a competitive edge and thus limit the flow of information within the industry. In some cases where there is no mandatory compliance, firms may even refuse to give information (such as inventory levels) to federal agencies, which use it solely to help in evaluating the state of the entire economy, since the *possible availability* of that information to rival firms is viewed as potentially damaging.

MODELS OF HISTORICAL SIGNIFICANCE

Much of the pioneering work in the development of oligopoly theory is of little practical value because of very restrictive (as well as naive and inconsistent) assumptions upon which the resulting theories were based. However, these theories are worth a brief review for two reasons. First, some familiarity with these models may help one understand the basis of some contemporary discussions in the economic profession and they are a part of the body of knowledge that one assumes an economist has. Second, and most important, a brief encounter with these theories develops a better appreciation for the problems encountered in modeling the behavior of oligopolistic firms. The discussion in this section is intended only to bring out the main features of five approaches to oligopoly theory.

We begin with the *Cournot model* (named after the French economist A. A. Cournot, who developed it). Cournot's model was developed for the extreme form of oligopoly: a *duopoly*, or two-firm oligopoly. He assumed that both firms were engaged in the business of selling mineral water from two springs located adjacent to one another, with one owned by each firm. Customers came to the spring with their own containers to get the water, and thus the only cost to the firms was the fixed cost of digging the wells. Therefore, marginal cost was zero for each firm. In Figure 12.1, marginal cost then coincides with the horizontal axis for each firm.

Assume that Firm A enters the market first. The demand curve for Firm A (D_{A_1}) is then the same as a monopolist's demand. The firm would

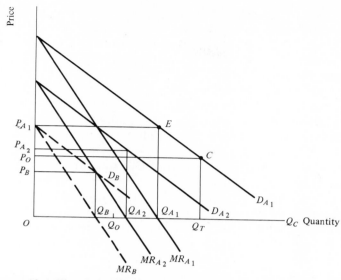

Figure 12.1 The Cournot Duopoly Model The Cournot duopoly solution assumes that there are zero marginal costs and that each firm expects the other firm's rate of output to remain fixed. Thus, Firm A enters first and assumes Firm B will maintain zero output. Firm A maximizes profit by producing Q_{A_1} units and setting price at P_{A_1}. Firm B assumes that A will always produce Q_{A_1} units and thus B's demand curve is D_B (market demand less Q_{A_1}). Firm B produces where $MR_B = MC$, or Q_B units, and sets price at P_B. Now Firm A assumes that B will continue to produce Q_B units and thus sees its demand as D_{A_2}. This leads Frim A to produce Q_{A_2} and set price at P_{A_2}. This process continues until each firm produces Q_0 units and sets price at P_0. Total industry output is $2Q_0 = Q_T$ with industry profit of $P_0 C Q_T O$ split equally between the firms.

maximize profit by setting $MR_{A_1} = MC = 0$ and producing Q_{A_1} units which would sell at price P_{A_1}. Now comes Cournot's critical assumption: Firm B will assume that Firm A will maintain the existing level of output regardless of Firm B's action, and Firm A makes the same assumption as well; for example, Firm A initially assumes that Firm B would sell zero units.

Thus firm B perceives its market as the total market less the Q_{A_1} units being sold by Firm A. Firm B's demand curve becomes the dashed line D_B. Firm B sets $MR_B = MC = 0$ and produces Q_B units to sell at the price P_B. Not recognizing the interdependence of the two firms, Firm A now assumes its demand curve to be D_{A_2} (which equals D_{A_1} less Q_B) and decreases production to Q_{A_2} and its price to P_{A_2}. And so the story goes, each firm continuing to assume that the other will maintain a constant level of production. Firm B would have a new demand curve to the right of D_B and would increase both output and price. Then Firm A's new demand would be to the left of D_{A_2} and its output and price would be reduced. This iterative process would continue until both firms were dividing equally a total output Q_T units (each producing $\frac{1}{2}Q_T = Q_o$) and both selling at the price P_o.

The competitive output would be Q_C (where market demand, D_{A_1}, intersects the horizontal axis) and the competitive price would be zero $(P = MC)$, resulting in zero profit. The monopoly output would be Q_{A_1} and the monopolist's price P_{A_1}. Monopoly profit would be the rectangle $P_{A_1}EQ_{A_1}O$. The duopoly solution lies between these extremes. Output will be Q_T (which equals two-thirds of Q_C) and price will be P_o, which equals two-thirds of P_{A_1}).

The *Edgeworth model* of oligopoly (duopoly) takes the same set of initial conditions as did the Cournot model (zero marginal cost and the same mineral water product), but makes two different assumptions: First, each firm has a maximum but equal rate of output; and, second, each firm assumes that the other will maintain a constant price (rather than a constant rate of output).

Figure 12.2 can be used to illustrate the consequences of this new set of assumptions. The two firms' maximum levels of output are A_X and B_X. The total market is split equally between firms such that D_A and D_B each represent one-half of the total market demand D_T. Firm A enters first and produces the profit-maximizing output A_1 (where its marginal revenue would equal zero) and sets price accordingly at P_1. Now Firm B realizes that by setting price just below P_1 at P_2 it can sell B_1 units in its market and as much as it wants (or can, due to production limits) in Firm A's market. In Figure 12.2, this would be B_X minus B_1 units that could be sold in Firm A's market. Firm A loses that amount of its sales and, assuming B will maintain price P_2, Firm A sets its price slightly lower, say at P_3. It can now sell A_2 units in its market (getting back sales previously lost to B) and A_X minus A_2 units in B's market.

This price cutting continues until the price P_4 is reached, at which point each firm sells its maximum output and each makes an equal economic profit of P_4A_X or P_4B_X. However, one firm will recognize that it could increase its profit by raising price to P_1 (A_1 or B_1 units could be sold because the other firm would, by assumption, keep price at P_4 and is already selling all it can produce). Now the other firm will raise price to just less than P_1, such as P_2, and the price cutting begins all over again. Unlike the Cournot solution, the Edgeworth solution does not lead to a stable equilibrium. The market will always be in a state of flux with price being cut down to the minimum level (P_4) then raised back to P_1, then down again, and on and on.

Both of these models suffer from the obvious failure of either firm to recognize that the other will in fact react to a particular quantity or price

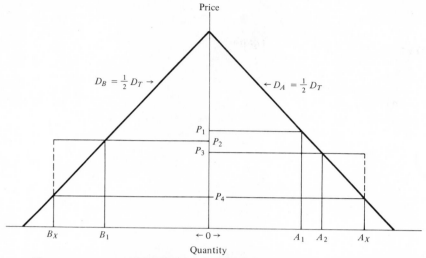

Figure 12.2 The Edgeworth Duopoly Model In the Edgeworth solution to the duopoly problem with zero marginal cost each firm assumes the other will maintain a constant price. If A enters first, it will produce A_1 units at price P_1 to maximize its profit. Firm B would assume A's price to be fixed at P_1 and would set price at P_2, selling B_1 units in its own market and B_X minus B_1 units in A's market. Firm A then cuts price to P_3 and such cuts continue until P_4 is reached, at which level each firm sells its maximum rate of output (A_X and B_X). At this point one firm realizes that its profit could be increased by setting price at P_1. The other firm increases profit by setting price just below P_1 (such as P_2). These price fluctuations continue indefinitely in the Edgeworth model.

strategy even though such reactions are observed repeatedly. In the 1930s, E. H. Chamberlin proposed a much improved model in which each duopolist recognized its interdependence in the marketplace. The model is similar to the Cournot model except for a more realistic assumption concerning the firm's awareness that both firms can do better by sharing the monopoly profit than by any other action.

The Chamberlin model is illustrated in Figure 12.3. We start, as with the Cournot model, with Firm A entering first. With demand curve D_A, marginal revenue MR_A, and $MC = 0$, the optimum output is Q_A units. The corresponding price is P_A. Firm B now enters, as in the Cournot model, under the assumption that their relevant demand is D_A minus Q_A units. This is the demand D_B. Setting its marginal revenue $MR_B = MC = 0$, we see that B would produce Q_B units at price at P_B.

But here is where the similarity to Cournot ends. Firm A recognizes that Firm B's decisions are based on what Firm A does and, recognizing this market interdependence, cuts output to $\frac{1}{2}Q_A$ (= Q_B) units. Firm B

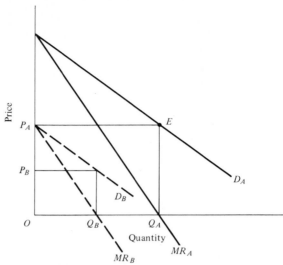

Figure 12.3 The Chamberlin Duopoly Model The Chamberlin duopoly model begins with the same assumptions as the Cournot model, but recognizes the market interdependence of firms. Firm A, with demand D_A, enters first and produces the profit-maximizing output Q_A and charges P_A per unit. This is the monopoly output and price. Firm B then enters, assuming their demand to be market demand (D_A) less Q_A units, or D_B. Thus, Firm B produces Q_B units and sells at price P_B. Here is where the Chamberlin model diverges from the Cournot model. Chamberlin assumes that Firm A recognizes the firms' interdependence and reduces output to Q_B ($= \frac{1}{2}Q_A$) while maintaining the price P_A. Firm B also recognizes the interdependence and raises price to P_A but keeps producing Q_B units. Thus total output is the monopoly output Q_A, and both firms charge the monopoly price P_A while sharing the monopoly profit (OP_AEQ_A).

now recognizes the interdependence as well and maintains output at Q_B units but raises price to P_A. So Firm A reduces output but maintains price, while Firm B maintains output but increases price. The result is that the two firms share the monopoly profit $OP_A EQ_A$ (which is greater than the shared profit of P_oCO_TO in Figure 12.1). Such market interdependence seems obvious to us today when we consider industries that are dominated by a very few firms.

THE "KINKED DEMAND CURVE" THEORY

Probably the most famous theory of oligopolistic pricing and output decisions was formulated by Paul Sweezy in the late 1930s. He developed the model in an attempt to explain the price rigidity that was presumed to exist in concentrated oligopolistic industries. We can present the principal elements of this model by drawing on the constructs of the "big D" and "little d" demand curves introduced in our discussion of monopolistic competition in Chapter 11.

Recall that the "big D" demand curve represents a particular share of the market for any single firm. If there are five firms in an industry, each of equal size, each would have a "big D" demand equal to one-fifth of the total market demand. Such a curve is given by DD' in Figure 12.4. The marginal-revenue curve associated with this "big D" demand is labeled MR-MR'. If all firms in the industry matched either price increases above P^* or decreases below P^*, this share of the market demand would be the effective operational demand curve for the firm.

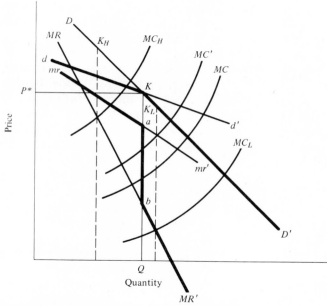

Figure 12.4 The Kinked Demand Curve Model The "kinked demand curve" model of oligopoly can be used to explain possible price rigidities. A kink in the demand curve exists at the prevailing price, P^*, with the "little d" demand function effective above P^*, whereas the "big D" demand is effective below P^*. The existence of the kink causes a discontinuity in the marginal-revenue function between a and b. As long as marginal cost passes through this region, there will be no incentive for price to change. Thus the cost of factors contributing to marginal cost, such as labor and materials, may change without bringing about a price change. Should marginal cost increase or decrease significantly, such as to MC_H or MC_L, new kinks would be established at K_H and K_L, respectively.

On the other hand, if a firm believed that it could make a price change without a corresponding change by other firms, its demand function would be more elastic at P^*. Such a function can be represented by the "little d" demand curve (dd') which represents the manner in which one firm's sales would change for various price changes *if* other firms kept price at P^*. The marginal-revenue function associated with dd' is $mr\text{-}mr'$.

In the ready-to-eat breakfast cereal market, the largest four firms account for more than 80 percent of total sales. Suppose that one of those firms decided to compete for sales by cutting price on all their brands rather than following their traditional non-price competition (advertising, introduction of new brands such as Crazy Cow, and other product differentiation strategies). Rather than to allow that firm to gain even greater market share, other firms would be likely to initiate retaliatory price reductions. Thus, below the prevailing price, P^*, the effective demand curve is KD' (the lower part of DD').

However, suppose General Mills, or one of the other leading cereal producers, decided to raise price. Since the products are very close substitutes among firms, others in the industry would stand to gain in market share and therefore would be less inclined to follow the price hike. Above P^* the effective demand is then the dK portion of dd'. We see then that the demand curve has a "kink" at the prevailing price under Sweezy's assumptions concerning firms' behavior patterns.

The marginal-revenue function that is associated with each part of this kinked demand curve is determined by the related demand function. To the left of K, $mr\text{-}mr'$ is the marginal curve, while to the right it is $MR\text{-}MR'$. Thus, for the entire kinked demand curve, the effective marginal revenue is $mr\text{-}a\text{-}b\text{-}MR'$. Note the vertical portion between a and b. As long as marginal cost intersects marginal revenue in that region, such as MC or MC', there is no incentive for the firm to change price.

The major shortcoming of this theory is that it fails to explain how P^* is originally established, and thus it has received considerable critical comment. One explanation does, however, seem tractable. Suppose that we first consider only the "big D" demand function and the associated marginal-revenue curve, and that $MC = MR$ at the point b. Each firm would then establish price at P^*. Marginal cost could then increase through the interval $a\text{-}b$ without a price change following Sweezy's argument, as summarized above. A decline in marginal cost from $MC = MR$ at b to MC_L would move P^* down along DD'. The new kink would be at K_L, with the corresponding price at the same height along the price axis. A new "little d" demand would cut through K_L.

If MC increased beyond point a, the following scenario seems likely. The factors that would cause cost to increase for one firm would also be likely to affect others in the industry as well, and we can assume that the firms are sophisticated enough to recognize their interdependence. Thus, all firms would base decisions on the market share demand and marginal-revenue curves (DD' and MR-MR'). A new kink would be formed at K_H and price would be correspondingly higher. In addition, barring further significant cost changes, price would again be fairly stable since a new "little d" demand curve would pass through K_H and the Sweezy behavior pattern would continue.

CARTELS

When there are relatively few firms in an industry, the opportunity for firms to organize to increase profits, prevent entry, or otherwise enhance their own interests is more likely than when there are many firms in the industry. A cartel is such an organization among firms and is generally illegal in the United States but prevalent elsewhere. Two forms of cartels will be discussed: the centralized cartel and the market-sharing cartel.

The centralized cartel is not unlike the Chamberlin duopoly solution discussed earlier. All firms in the industry agree to yield decision-making power to a centralized committee, which in turn attempts to maximize industry profits by operating as if the industry were a multiplant monopoly. Figure 12.5 illustrates the manner in which a perfect centralized cartel works for the simplest case of a two-firm (duopoly) industry.

If all firms are cooperating in the efforts of the cartel, the central committee could construct the industry marginal-cost curve by adding (horizontally) the marginal cost of all the participants. Thus, in Figure 12.5, $MC_1 + MC_2 = \Sigma MC = MC_I$, which is the industry marginal-cost curve. The industry, or market, demand is D_I, and the associated marginal-revenue curve is MR_I. Industry profits will be maximized by producing the level of output (Q^*) at which $MC_I = MR_I$, and price should be set at P.

To ensure that industry profits are maximized, production of the Q_I^* units must be allocated among firms following the equimarginal principle: That is, each firm should produce the level of output at which its marginal cost equals industry marginal cost and marginal revenue. For the two-firm case illustrated in Figure 12.5, $MC_1 = MC_2 = MC_I = MR_I$. Firm 1 would produce Q_1^* units and Firm 2 would produce Q_2^* units. Note that $Q_1^* + Q_2^* = Q_I^*$. The amount of profit earned by the cartel is the difference between total cartel revenue (PQ_I^*) and the total cost incurred by members of the cartel. This profit is then allocated among members by the centralized cartel committee. Alternative allocation schemes could include sharing profits on the basis of each firm's share of total production, according to firm size in terms of employment or assets or on an "as-earned" basis (i.e., each firm's total revenue minus its own total cost).

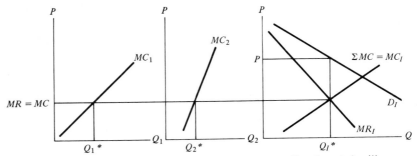

Figure 12.5 Cartel Behavior A perfect centralized cartel will establish a pricing strategy such that the industry obtains the same profit that would evolve if the industry was a monopoly. By summing the marginal-cost curves (horizontally) for all firms in the cartel, we obtain the industry marginal cost MC_I. Equating MC_I with MR_I, the profit-maximizing rate of output, Q_I^*, is determined. Price P is then found from the market, or industry, demand curve D_I. Production is allocated among firms following the equimarginal principle. In the two-firm case illustrated here, this means that $MC_1 = MC_2 = MC_I = MR_I$, and Firm 1 produces Q_1^* units while Firm 2 produces Q_2^* units ($Q_1^* + Q_2^* = Q_I^*$). The monopoly profits earned by the cartel may be distributed on an "as-earned" basis among firms, by sales volume, by asset size, or by other rules determined by the centralized cartel committee.

Such arrangements may appear very desirable since total profits for the industry are indeed maximized. However, a number of problems are likely to develop. Under the equimarginal principle some firms may not be allocated any production, or may be allocated a small amount leaving them with high average costs and zero (or negative) profit. These firms may then break away from the cartel, setting a price slightly below the cartel price, thus weakening the entire cartel. Some firms in the cartel, particularly the larger ones, may attempt to put pressure on the central committee for preferential treatment in profit allocation. In addition, there is always incentive for firms to "cheat" on the cartel by offering lower prices (secretly), which if undetected by the cartel could greatly increase that firm's profit.

A less formal type of cartel arrangement is often referred to as a *market-sharing cartel*. The primary difference is that many decisions are left to the discretion of individual firms rather than in the hands of a central committee. Industry output may be allocated by collectively setting some minimum price and allowing each firm to compete for sales through whatever forms of nonprice competition are appropriate to the industry (product differentiation, advertising, etc.). Examples might include the services of optometrists, attorneys, and accountants (particularly in states that prohibit price advertising).

Associations may also allocate sales by a quota system. The system could be based on production capacity, past sales, employment, geographic location, or any other basis agreed upon by the firms involved. Tacit collusion in allocating sales in such ways is probably not uncommon, even though illegal, in the United States economy.

PRICE LEADERSHIP

Although cartels and outright collusion among firms in an industry may lead to an equalization of prices within an industry, less formal arrangements may lead to similar results with respect to price. These are *price leadership* arrangements, of which three types are most worthy of discussion here: barometric-firm price leadership; price leadership by the low-cost firm in the industry; and dominant-firm price leadership. In each industry one firm (not always the same one in each time period) sets price, and the other firms take that price as given. Thus the price takers behave as though they were perfectly competitive firms (except under these conditions an outside firm, rather than market demand and supply, determines the price).

In the case of *barometric price leadership* one firm becomes the price setter because over time it has been successful in its pricing strategy. Other firms are willing to follow that firm's lead rather than perform price analysis themselves because it saves time and expense and, in addition, reduces friction and uncertainty in the marketplace. A barometric price leader is not necessarily one of the largest firms in the industry, and it may not have the lowest cost in the industry. But the firm must have a proven record of successful operations to develop a following of other firms that respect its policies enough to continue to match the price signals emitted by the leader.

Price leadership by a low-cost firm results when one firm has a comparative cost advantage and thus has a profit-maximizing price that is less than the profit-maximizing price of other firms. This situation is illustrated in Figure 12.6. Once more a duopoly case is diagramed for ease in exposition. Assume that the firms produce products that are close enough as substitutes that the market demand (D_M) is split equally between firms. Each firm's demand is then D_f, with marginal revenue MR. The lower-cost firm's marginal-cost and average-cost curves are subscripted with an L, whereas those for the higher-cost firm are subscripted with an H.

The low-cost firm will maximize profit by producing Q_L units, where $MR = MC_L$. Pricing from D_f, the price would be P_L. The high-cost firm would prefer to have the price be P_H, at which they would produce Q_H (such that $MR = MC_H$). However, once the lower price P_L is established, the high-cost firm has no choice but to sell at the lower price and would

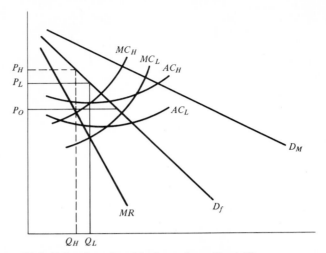

Figure 12.6 Price Leadership by a Low-Cost Firm
Determination of price by a low-cost firm price leader. In
this two-firm case, total demand is split equally between firms
such that each has demand D_f and marginal revenue MR.
Equating marginal revenue and marginal cost, the low-cost firm
(represented by AC_L and MC_L) would set price at P_L. The
higher-cost firm (AC_H and MC_H) would maximize profit with a
price of P_H but must accept the lower price in order to remain in
the industry. If the low-cost firm wished, it could set price at P_o
which would price the other firm out of the industry since
$P_o < AC_H$ at all levels. Fear of antitrust prosecution may deter such
a pricing strategy.

produce Q_L units. This assumes that the firms have a cartel-type agreement to split sales along D_f. If this were not true, the "dominant-firm"
model discussed below would be appropriate. Of course, the low-cost
firm could price the higher-cost firm out of the market by setting price at
P_o or at any other level that is below the latter's average cost at all levels
of output. However, fear of antitrust prosecution will generally prevent
such an action.

Many oligopolistic industries are characterized by having one firm
that is quite large and dominates the industry. Such a firm may function
as the price leader for the entire industry (the automobile industry with
General Motors as the price leader represents an example). In
dominant-firm price leadership the price leader sets the industry price
and then allows the other smaller firms to sell what they wish at that
price. Thus the smaller firms behave as though they were perfect competitors.

This situation is illustrated in Figure 12.7, in which D_M represents the market demand for the product. The amount that would be supplied by the followers at each price is determined by summing (horizontally) their marginal-cost functions just as we found the supply for a perfectly competitive industry in Chapter 9 (see page 200). This is shown by the line labeled $\Sigma MC_f = S_f$ in Figure 12.7.

The demand for the price leader, D_L, is found by subtracting the quantity supplied by the following firms at each price (S_f) from the corresponding market demand, D_M. From D_L we can find the leader's marginal revenue, which is labeled MR_L. The price leader equates marginal revenue with marginal cost $(MR_L = MC_L)$ to maximize profit. They produce Q_L units and price from their demand curve (D_L) at price P^*. This becomes price for the followers as well as marginal revenue (MR_f) since the followers act as price takers. The quantity supplied by the followers in total is determined by $MR_f = S_f = \Sigma MC_f$. Each of the following firms produces the rate of output at which MR equals its own marginal cost. Total industry output is Q_T $(= Q_f + Q_L)$.

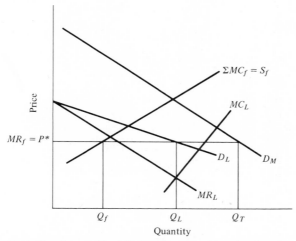

Figure 12.7 Dominant Firm Price Leadership In dominant-firm price leadership, the dominant firm allows the followers to produce and sell what they wish at the price the leader (dominant firm) sets. Thus, the followers behave as though they were perfectly competitive firms. The quantity the followers supply at each price is given by $\Sigma MC_f = S_f$. The demand for the leader, D_L, is thus D_M minus S_f. By equating the leader's marginal revenue, MR_L, with its marginal cost, MC_L, the leader's profit-maximizing output, Q_L, is found and price, P^*, is determined from D_L. The followers, acting as price takers, accept that price and equate it with their MC functions. For the entire group of followers, Q_f units would therefore be produced. Total industry output Q_T equals Q_f plus Q_L.

LIMIT PRICING

The possibility of limit pricing arose in our discussion of price leadership by the low-cost firm when we indicated that at the price P_0 the higher-cost firm could effectively be excluded from the market (see Figure 12.6). When an existing firm is making a positive economic profit it may elect to price below the profit-maximizing price in order to reduce or eliminate the likelihood that new firms will attempt to enter the market.

In Figure 12.8 the existing firm's demand and marginal-revenue functions are labeled D and MR, respectively. The existing firm operates at a plant scale represented by the short-run cost functions $SRAC_E$ and $SRMC_E$. Thus the profit-maximizing rate of output is Q^*, and the associated price is P^*. The industry long-run average-cost curve is $LRAC$.

If new firms could be expected to enter at the scale represented by $SRAC_N$, they could do so and earn a profit at price P^*. However, existing firms may realize that the present value of long-run profits may be greater if they prevent entry, even if at the cost of some short-run profit. Thus the existing firm may set price at P_o. The firm would still earn a positive economic profit but would prevent entry since P_o is less than $SRAC_N$ at all levels of output.

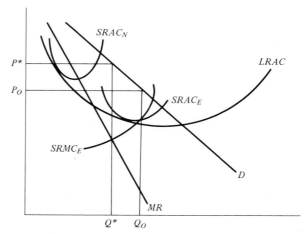

Figure 12.8 Limit Pricing Limit pricing may be used to protect long-run profits of an existing firm. The existing firm, represented by $SRMC_E$ and $SRAC_E$, would maximize profit by producing Q^* units and setting price at P^*. However, a new firm operating at the scale represented by $SRAC_N$ would find it profitable to enter at that price. Doing so would erode the existing firm's market. To prevent that from happening, price could be set at a level, such as P_o, that would still provide a positive economic profit to the existing firm but make it impossible for a new firm to enter at the scale represented by $SRAC_N$ without incurring an economic loss. Thus P_o would limit entry into the industry.

A firm considering entry into an industry such as this must realize that even if the existing price were high enough to permit them to earn a profit, entry may not be desirable. If existing firms maintain their current levels of output in the face of additional competition, price can be expected to fall. As the demand curve in Figure 12.8 shifts to the left due to entry, the current rate of output for that firm, Q^*, could be sold only at a lower price. If entry causes price to fall below the level represented by the minimum point on $SRAC_N$, a new entrant would incur an economic loss.

OTHER FEATURES OF OLIGOPOLY

There are two additional aspects of oligopolistic industries that deserve mention—non-price competition and research and development. In many oligopolistic industries there is intense rivalry (or competition for sales) among firms. Much of this rivalry takes place within a framework of relative price stability as firms avoid potential price wars that could be detrimental to all involved.

The most conspicuous form of non-price competition is in the form of sales promotion, particularly advertising. We see advertisements from such concentrated industries as computers and ready-to-eat breakfast cereals. Advertising helps the firms involved decrease the elasticity of demand for their brand(s) as well as serving to increase total market demand for the product.

There is considerable debate about the relative merits of advertising, which we will not review in detail here. However, two points should be mentioned. First, it is frequently argued by some that advertising increases the cost of goods since the cost of advertising must be paid in some way, while others argue that advertising decreases prices by permitting firms to produce at lower per-unit cost due to the greater rate of output. This is an empirical question that must be answered on a case-by-case basis. The result depends on the relationship between the added cost of advertising and the corresponding decrease in production cost (which in turn depends on how much of an increase in demand is stimulated by the advertising). Advertising may also act as a barrier to entry—as in the ready-to-eat cereal industry, where advertising expenditures may run as high as 10 percent of every sales dollar.

We should also recognize that there are benefits to society that result from advertising that are independent (or potentially so) from consumers of the product. We are able to purchase magazines and newspapers at a lower price than would be true if it were not for advertising revenue collected by these media. We are also able to view television shows and hear radio broadcasts at near-zero marginal expenditures since they are supported by advertising. This advertising is frequently paid for by firms that we would consider oligopolistic: Ford, IBM, General Mills, American Home Products (Anacin), Texaco, United Airlines, General Electric, AMF, Goodyear, etc.).

Nonprice competition also includes product differentiation, which most people count as a positive feature since it allows consumers considerable freedom of selection among many products, each of which could satisfy a particular need. We can pick from hundreds of thousands of potential automobiles (considering all the brands and options available) to satisfy our personal transportation needs. Other forms of nonprice competition are represented by guarantees, locational factors, supplemental services, and so forth.

Another important aspect of oligopolistic industrial structures is the relatively high level of research and development supported by firms such as those mentioned above. Small firms near the perfectly competitive end of the market structure spectrum usually operate at a very low profit margin and thus do not have the funds to support research and development. The retail sale of groceries is an example. Even large chains like A&P and Safeway typically have a margin of less than 1 percent (even in accounting terms, which overstate profits relative to economic analysis). The food processing industry, which is more concentrated than food retailing, only spends about 0.5 percent of sales on research and development; the average in aerospace is roughly 2.8 percent; in electronics, 2.6 percent; and in the leisure-time industry, nearly 5 percent of sales (firms like Kodak, Polaroid, AMF, Brunswick, and Milton Bradley).

SUMMARY AND EVALUATION OF OLIGOPOLY

We have seen that oligopoly is the term economists use to describe the industrial structure in which there are relatively few firms (or a few very large firms with many smaller fringe firms). Products may be differentiated, such as in the automotive industry, or homogeneous, as in the case of such pure oligopolies as the basic steel industry. Entry is usually difficult, largely because of high capital costs required to enter such industries.

It would be hard to establish an exact percent of all economic activity that occurs in this type of market structure since there is no clear point of separation between monopolistic competition and oligopoly. However, it is clear that many goods and services are produced and/or sold in an oligopolistic framework. It may then be surprising that there is no single generally applicable model of oligopoly. The reason for this is that all models of firm behavior depend critically on the assumptions upon which they rest, and in oligopolistic settings there does not appear to be a uniform set of assumptions that would be generally applicable.

Early work in oligopoly theory dealt primarily with the simplest case of duopoly and was lacking in applicability because of very restrictive and naive assumptions. Each model made some contribution by providing insight into some aspect(s) of oligopolistic behavior. For example, the "kinked demand curve" theory, despite its shortcomings, helps explain why prices may be rigid in some oligopolistic industries.

The fact that there are relatively few firms in the industry leads to the possibility that they will follow collusive behavior to increase combined industry profits. By forming cartels, an oligopolistic industry may be able to function as a monopoly. However, natural economic forces tend to cause cartels to break down as individual firms "cheat" on the cartel agreement. The fewness of firms, particularly in industries characterized by one dominant firm, also leads to the possibility of price leadership arrangements developing, either explicitly or tacitly.

It is difficult to evaluate the precise welfare effects of oligopoly. Other things equal, output would be less (more) and price higher (lower) than if the industry were perfectly competitive (monopolized). However, many (if not most) oligopolistic industries could not exist in perfectly competitive form due to economies of scale in production. These scale economies may not be sufficient, on the other hand, for the industry to develop as a natural monopoly.

An oligopolistic firm will generally operate with a positive economic profit (though not necessarily) and with price greater than marginal cost. Thus we can conclude that too few resources are allocated to such industries. Further, it would only be by chance that an oligopolistic firm would operate efficiently in terms of producing the rate of output at which $LRAC$ is a minimum (there is no evidence that they would even build plants of optimum size, much less operate them at the most efficient rate).

Oligopolistic firms are frequently the focus of considerable criticism in terms of wasteful promotional activities and overproliferation of superficially differentiated products. Since there are also potential benefits associated with promotion and product differentiation, it is difficult (or even impossible) to reach general agreement with respect to these features of oligopolies.

Selected Readings

Asch, Peter, and J. J. Seneca. "Is Collusion Profitable?" *Review of Economics and Statistics* 58:1 (February 1976), 1–12.

Bain, Joe S. "Economies of Scale, Concentration and the Condition of Entry in Twenty Manufacturing Industries." *American Economic Review* 44:1 (March 1954), 15–39.

Demsetz, Harold. "Accounting for Advertising as a Barrier to Entry." *Journal of Business* 52:3 (July 1979), 345–360.

Modigliani, Franco. "New Developments on the Oligopoly Front." *Journal of Political Economy* 66 (June 1958), 215–232.

QUESTIONS

1. Write a short explanation of the following terms or concepts that were used in this chapter:
   (a) cartel
   (b) Chamberlin model
   (c) Cournot model
   (d) differentiated oligopoly
   (e) duopoly
   (f) Edgeworth model
   (g) interdependent decision making
   (h) "kinked demand curve" theory
   (i) limit pricing
   (j) oligopoly
   (k) price leadership

2. Explain the characteristics which distinguish an oligopolistic market from the others covered in earlier chapters. Relate these characteristics to the following:
   (a) automobiles
   (b) steel
   (c) computers
   (d) aluminum
   (e) television programming
   (f) brewing
   Which of these would be more closely related to a "pure oligopoly" and which would be more correctly associated with a "differentiated oligopoly"? Explain why.

3. Use the graph shown as the basis for a complete explanation of the Cournot duopoly situation for Firms A and B. Explain the graphic solution carefully after adding the necessary demand and marginal revenue functions. In your explanation, be certain to state the assumptions of the Cournot model completely.

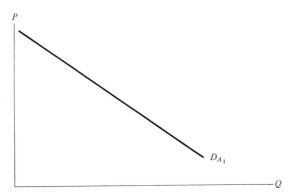

4. Use the accompanying graph as the basis for a complete explanation of the Edgeworth solution to the duopoly case. Explain the graphic solution carefully, including the assumptions upon which the Edgeworth solution is based.

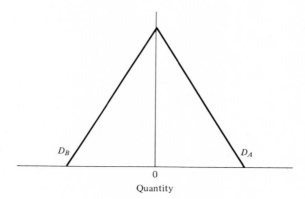

5. Use the graph shown as the basis for a complete explanation of the Chamberlin duopoly model. Explain the graphic solution carefully including the additional demand and revenue functions. State the assumptions in the Chamberlin model and compare this solution to the Cournot solution.

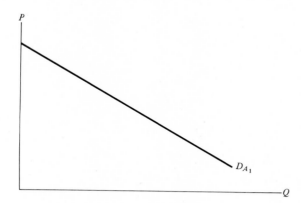

6. Paul Sweezy is credited with developing the "kinked demand curve" theory of oligopolistic behavior. What was the principal characteristic of oligopolistic behavior that Sweezy was trying to explain? Use the graph below as the basis for explaining his thesis (add marginal-revenue and cost curves as appropriate to your discussion). If the marginal cost were to shift out of the "discontinuity" in the marginal-revenue curve, what adjustments would you expect?

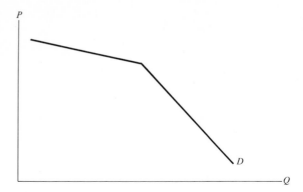

7. Suppose that the accompanying graphs represent the marginal-cost curves for three separate firms in an oligopolistic market (MC_1, MC_2, and MC_3) and the industry demand and marginal-revenue curves. Determine the price that should be set and the total amount that should be produced if the three firms join together to form a cartel with the intent of maximizing industry profits. Show the quantity that each of the three firms should produce.

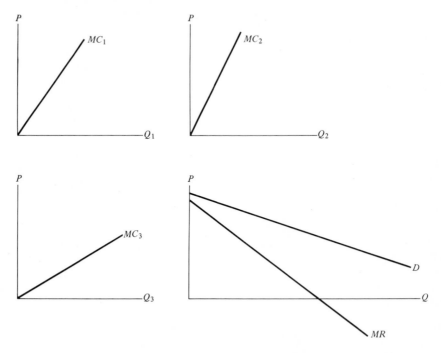

8. Explain how price leadership by the low-cost firm in a duopoly situation works when the two firms split the market equally. Under what circum-

stances would the higher cost firm be willing to sell at a price that is less than the profit maximizing price for them?

9. In the graphs shown, the marginal-cost curves for two price takers are given in the left and center panels, whereas the industry demand curve is drawn in the right-hand panel. The dominant firm price leader's marginal-cost curve (MC_L) is also given in the right-hand graph. From these functions derive the follower's supply curve, the leader's demand and marginal-revenue curves, the quantity and price that will maximize the leader's profit, and the quantity each of the two followers would produce.

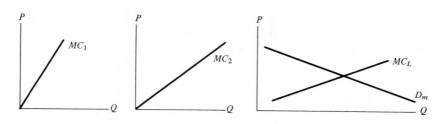

10. Explain the concept of limit pricing using a graph such as the one in Figure 12.8 as the basis for your discussion. Suggest several situations in which you believe limit pricing may be practiced.

11. Evaluate the consequences of having such industries as those in the following list organized as oligopolies:
    (a) automobile industry
    (b) pharmaceutical industry
    (c) computer industry
    (d) steel industry
    In addition to pricing and resource allocation, you should also consider the role of research and development, advertising, possible collusion, and price leadership.

12. There are many indices that can be used to evaluate the degree of monopoly power in any market. Three of these are:

$$\text{Bain index} = \frac{P - AC}{P}$$

$$\text{Lerner index} = \frac{P - MC}{P}$$

$$\text{Rothschild index} = \frac{\text{slope of the firm's demand } (D_f)}{\text{slope of the industry demand } (D_m)}$$

Determine the value of each of these indices based on the graphs shown below, considering just AC_0 for now. What differences would result in your evaluation of monopoly power using these indices if AC_1, were the average-cost curve rather than AC_0.

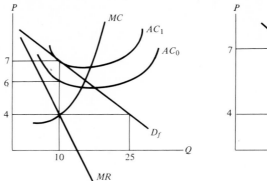 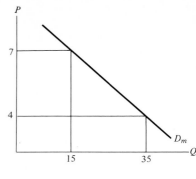

13. Some people have argued that advertising can act as a barrier to entry in some cases. Consider several oligopolistic industries and evaluate the extent of their advertising as well as the types of advertising they use. Do you think that such advertising can act to reduce entry? Relate your answer to consumer preferences, product differentiation, and price elasticity of demand.

CHAPTER 13
FACTOR MARKETS

FACTOR DEMAND: COMPETITIVE OUTPUT MARKETS
FACTOR DEMAND: MONOPOLISTIC INFLUENCE IN THE OUTPUT MARKET
FACTOR SUPPLY
MONOPSONISTIC INFLUENCE IN THE FACTOR MARKET
DETERMINATION OF FACTOR PRICES
ECONOMIC RENT
INCOME DISTRIBUTION
SUMMARY
SELECTED READINGS
QUESTIONS

Thus far the thrust of our discussion has focused on the demand, production, cost, and price of goods and services in the economy. We have only mentioned inputs to the production process explicitly in Chapters 7 and 8, and assumed that the input prices were given. We now turn our attention to the market forces that interact to determine these factor (input) prices.

The pricing of factors of production is not entirely dissimilar to the pricing of output. Essentially, both are determined by supply and demand. The demand originates in the producing sector, but in turn it is determined by the demand for the relevant output. Thus we say that the demand for factors of production is a derived demand; that is, it is derived from the demand for goods and services. We shall assume that the supply of factors comes from individuals in the society—that is, factors are privately owned and made available according to the will of the owners.

Through most of the analysis in this chapter we shall use the labor factor of production as the focal point of the discussion. Rather than thinking of producers as actually buying laborers, it is better to think in terms of them purchasing the productive services of labor for a given period of time. For many factors there is not an exchange of ownership involved in transactions, but rather it is the right of use which is exchanged. We can, of course, think of situations in which there is a transfer of ownership, such as in the sale of productive land.

In the first four sections of this chapter we shall consider the demand and supply of factors under alternative assumptions concerning market structure in both input and output markets. In the fifth section we shall then put together various scenarios of these market structures to evaluate the determination of factor prices. The remainder of the chapter will be devoted to other related matters, such as the personal and functional distribution of income in the economy.

FACTOR DEMAND: COMPETITIVE OUTPUT MARKETS

Let us begin by assuming that each buyer of a particular factor uses only a small portion of the total amount of the factor used in the entire economy (i.e., the input market is competitive). Thus no one producer (buyer of the factor) would have any control over the price of the factor. The producer would take factor prices as given and determine the amount of each factor to employ accordingly. With more than one variable factor we have seen (in Chapter 7) that the firm will employ factors such that the marginal product per dollar spent on each factor is equal for all inputs.

What we want to do now is determine the demand for a particular factor by each firm and for the entire set of firms using that factor. In doing so we shall further assume that the firms employing the factor sell their output in perfectly competitive markets such that the output price is given to each firm (each firm is a price taker). This assumption and the one above will be relaxed in subsequent sections.

Let us state an important relationship at the outset: *A firm will hire additional units of an input only so long as the additional revenue gained from the sale of the resulting output is at least equal to the additional cost of the last unit of the input employed.* For the purpose of this section we have assumed that the input is purchased in a competitive market such that the input price is constant and thus the additional expense of hiring one more unit of the input is simply equal to its price. The determination of the additional revenue received by the firm is not quite as straightforward, however. Under the conditions stated, this revenue is called the *value of the marginal product (VMP)* of the input.

Table 13.1 is useful in explaining how *VMP* is determined. The first two columns represent a simple production function with labor L as the only variable input used in the production of the product Q. As indicated by the third column, production is characterized by diminishing marginal productivity (which we know from Chapter 7 is reasonable). The fourth column contains the constant price at which output is sold (P_Q). We see that the additional output attributable to the second unit of labor is 18 units. Since these 18 units can be sold at the constant price of $2 each, the value of the marginal product of the second unit of labor is $36. *VMP* for

Table 13.1 DETERMINATION OF THE VALUE OF THE MARGINAL PRODUCT OF A VARIABLE INPUT (LABOR)*

L	Q	MP	P_Q	VMP
0	0	—	$2	—
1	20	20	2	$40
2	38	18	2	36
3	54	16	2	32
4	68	14	2	28
5	80	12	2	24
6	90	10	2	20
7	98	8	2	16
8	104	6	2	12
9	108	4	2	8

* L = amount of labor used; Q = output produced at each level of labor; $MP = \Delta Q/\Delta L$; P_Q = the price at which the output is sold; $VMP = (P_Q) \cdot (MP)$ = the dollar value of the output produced by successive units of labor input.

each unit of labor can be determined in the same manner, and are all given in the last column of Table 13.1.

If the market price per unit of labor (wage rate) was $30, the firm would find it profitable to hire the first 3 units of labor, but no more. For the first three, $VMP > \$30$; but beyond $L = 3$, $VMP < \$30$. If the price of labor were to drop to $22 per unit, the firm would find it profitable to expand production to $Q = 80$, using 5 units of labor. We see, then, that more units of labor will be hired at a lower wage rate than at a higher one. We can generalize at this point to say that a firm's demand for a single variable factor will be negatively sloped as a function of the factor price under conditions of perfect competition in the input and output markets (we shall see later that factor demand will be negatively sloped even under other assumptions concerning market structure).

Let P_f be the price of any single variable factor and VMP_f be that factor's value of marginal product. From the discussion above, we know that the firm will continue to hire the factor as long as $VMP_f > P_f$ and would not choose to hire a unit of the factor if $P_f > VMP_f$. Thus, the firm will always employ the factor at a rate such that $P_f = VMP_f$ (given the conditions assumed at present). Thus, VMP_f represents the firm's demand (d_f) for the single variable factor, as shown in Figure 13.1.

Now suppose that the firm can vary more than one input at a time. As we saw in Chapter 7 (see page 132), a change in the price of any one

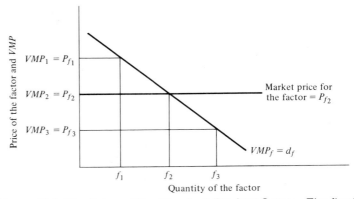

Figure 13.1 The Value of the Marginal Product Curve The firm's demand (d_f) for a single variable factor, given competitive input and output markets, is the value of the marginal product (VMP_f) curve. If the factor price were P_{f_1} the firm would use just f_1 units since beyond f_1, $VMP_f < P_{f_1}$. As the factor price falls, the firm will employ more of the variable factor, such as f_2 units at P_{f_2} and f_3 units at P_{f_3}. If the market price for the factor is P_{f_2}, the profit-maximizing firm would employ f_2 units. Beyond f_2 units, $VMP_f < P_{f_2}$, at less than f_2 units, $VMP_f > P_{f_2}$, and therefore it is always profitable for the firm to move towards f_2 in the use of this variable factor as long as the factor price is P_{f_2}.

factor may cause a change in the amount of other factors used as well. For example, if we assume that the firm wishes to maximize Q for a given cost and if the price per unit of labor decreases, the firm will reach a new equilibrium, as illustrated in Figure 13.2. The original level of output is Q_1 and the new (higher) level is Q_2, with the amount of labor and capital employed increasing from L_1 to L_3 and K_1 to K_2, respectively. Movement from A to B represents a substitution effect (keeping output constant but substituting labor for capital since the former has become less expensive). The movement from B to C is an output effect (analogous to the income effect discussed in Chapter 6, page 101). This portion of the total change is attributable to the decreased production cost stemming from the reduced price per unit of labor.

As illustrated in Figure 13.2, a decline in the price of one factor may cause an increase in the use of other factors as well as an increase in usage of the factor whose price has fallen. These other inputs may be complementary or substitutes, but the effect of using more of other inputs will be to shift the VMP curve to the right for the factor whose price declined. Thus, as one factor price declines when several factors are variable, the firm's demand curve for that factor (d_f) is made up of points from a shifting VMP_f curve. This is shown in Figure 13.3. The original factor price is P_{f_1}, and the rate of factor usage is found from VMP_f to be f_1.

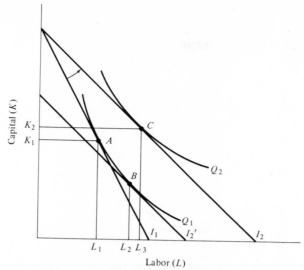

Figure 13.2 Effect of the Wage Rate on Labor Utilization A decline in the price of labor, represented by movement from isocost I_1 to isocost I_2, causes the firm's equilibrium to shift from A to C with output increasing from Q_1 to Q_2. The total increase in labor hired is from L_1 to L_3, and the increase in capital used is from K_1 to K_2. The increase in labor usage can be divided into a substitution effect that is determined by drawing I_2' parallel to I_2 but tangent to the original isoquant, Q_1. Movement from A to B is a pure substitution of labor for capital, since labor is now less expensive, while keeping output constant. Movement from B to C, an output effect, is attributable to the lower cost of production due to the lower cost per unit of labor.

As the factor price declines to P_{f_2}, the factor's value of marginal product shifts rightward to VMP_f', such that the amount of the factor employed increases to f_3 rather than f_2.

From this discussion it should be clear that several influences are at work in determining a firm's demand for a particular factor of production. First, the level of usage of other factors affects the demand for a particular factor since the marginal product of one factor depends on the amount of other factors it has to work with. Second, the state of technology will influence marginal productivity and thus the demand for each factor. Finally, note that the demand for final products is an important determinant of the demand for a factor via the $VMP = (P_Q)(MP)$ relationship illustrated in Table 13.1. As product demand increases, we can generally expect P_Q to increase, and thus VMP will increase (i.e., d_f will increase).

Individual consumer demand curves can be summed horizontally to arrive at the market demand curve for a product. Similarly, we can sum

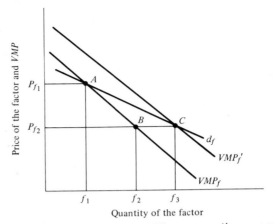

Figure 13.3 Shifting VMP Curve When more than one factor is variable, a decline in the price of one, such as from P_{f_1} to P_{f_2}, will cause more of other factors to be used as well (see Figure 13.2). This in turn shifts the VMP_f curve to the right to VMP_f'. Instead of the increase in factor use being from A to B (or f_1 to f_2) along VMP_f, factor usage increases from A to C (or f_1 to f_3). Thus the firm's demand for the factor (d_f) is no longer just VMP_f but a series of points along a shifting VMP_f function.

firms' demand curves for a factor to determine the market demand for that factor. However, in the summation process an adjustment must be made for what is called a *market effect.*

The market effect arises as follows. When the factor price falls, all firms will be led to increase employment of the factor, as described by Figure 13.3, which in turn increases product output. Because the output market is assumed here to be perfectly competitive, product price will fall. This fall in product price is reflected in a lower VMP_f and thus a lower demand for the factor. This is illustrated in Figure 13.4.

Suppose that we begin with factor price P_{f_1} and a single firm's demand d_f. A decline in factor price to P_{f_2} would at first stimulate the firm to increase usage from f_1 to f_3. However, as all firms do the same, product price will fall such that factor demand becomes d_f'. Along d_f' only f_2 units of the factor will be demanded. In aggregating for all employers of the factor it is points such as f_1 and f_2 that must be summed at the respective factor prices.

If there were n firms of equal size in the market for the factor, the market demand (D_F) would be F_1 ($= nf_1$) at price P_{f_1} and F_2 ($= nf_2$) at price P_{f_2}. Such a market demand is shown in the right-hand panel of Figure 13.4. The market demand for a factor is therefore the horizontal summation of individual firms' demands for the factor after adjusting the latter for market effects.

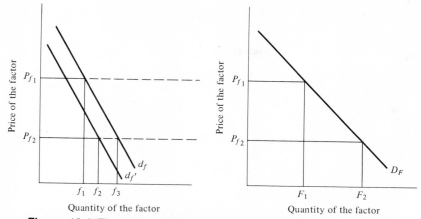

Figure 13.4 The Market Demand for Factors: Competitive Output Market The market demand for a factor (D_F) with perfectly competitive input and output markets is the horizontal sum of every firm's factor demand at each price, after adjusting for "market effects." The market effects result because of the following chain of events: the factor price declines; firms use more of the factor; more output is produced; output price falls; each firm's VMP_f shifts left (their factor demand curves shift such as from d_f to d_f').

FACTOR DEMAND: MONOPOLISTIC INFLUENCE IN THE OUTPUT MARKET

The essential analytical methods underlying factor demand and supply are the same for conditions with monopolistic influences in the output market as they are for the competitive case discussed in the preceding section. Some modifications in determining the demand conditions are necessary, but in the end it is the interaction of factor demand and supply that will determine resource prices and employment.

In this section we shall consider the effect that monopolistic influences in the output market have on factor demand. Since price is no longer constant for all levels of sales, value of marginal product does not represent the monetary return to the firm that results from hiring an additional unit of a variable factor of production. When the firm hires an additional unit of labor, the additional output is still measured by the marginal product. However, since price must be reduced to sell the increased output, that output adds less to total revenue than price times marginal product.

The term *marginal revenue product (MRP)* is used to describe the additional revenue a firm will obtain from selling the increased output due to employing an added unit of a variable factor when there are monopolistic influences in the output market. Marginal revenue product is calculated as follows:

$$MRP = MP \cdot MR$$

where MP and MR represent marginal product and marginal revenue, respectively (when the output market is competitive, $MRP = VMP$ since $P = MR$). The determination of MRP is illustrated in Table 13.2.

We know that when monopolistic influences exist in the output market, the demand and marginal-revenue functions will have a negative slope (see Chapters 10, 11, and 12, dealing with monopoly, monopolistic competition, and oligopoly, respectively). Further, from our discussion of production (Chapter 7) we know that in the relevant range marginal product is also negatively sloped. It follows that the marginal-revenue product function will have a negative slope as well. This is evident in the data given in the rightmost column of Table 13.2. Suppose that the wage rate per unit of labor, say one day's labor (including cash and fringe benefits), was $85. For the firm represented in Table 13.2, the firm would find it profitable to hire the sixth unit of labor but not the seventh unit. The general principle is that if the wage is less than MRP that unit of labor should be employed, but if the wage exceeds MRP that unit of labor should not be employed. Thus, if labor units are entirely divisible, labor should be hired at the level for which the wage rate equals MRP.

This relationship is generalized in Figure 13.5. The MRP function is not only negatively sloped but may even become negative as illustrated.

Table 13.2 DETERMINATION OF MARGINAL REVENUE PRODUCT FOR A VARIABLE FACTOR (LABOR)*

L	Q	MP	MR	MRP
0	0	—	—	—
1	20	20	80	1600
2	38	18	62	1116
3	54	16	46	736
4	68	14	32	448
5	80	12	20	240
6	90	10	10	100
7	98	8	2	16
8	104	6	-4	-24
9	108	4	-8	-32

* L = amount of labor used; Q = output produced at each level of labor; $MP = \Delta Q/\Delta L$; $MR = \Delta TR/\Delta Q$ (derived from the demand curve, $P = 60 - 0.5\,Q$); $MRP = MP \cdot MR$ = the dollar value of the output produced by successive units of labor input.

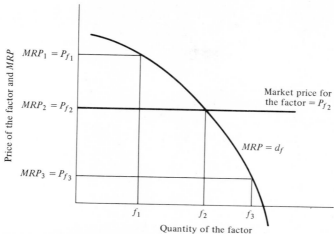

Figure 13.5 The Marginal-Revenue Product Curve The firm's demand (d_f) for a single variable factor, given monopolistic influences in the output market, is the marginal-revenue product (MRP) curve. If the factor price were P_{f_1}, the firm would employ f_1 units since beyond f_1 the additional cost of a unit of the factor is greater than the additional revenue that would result to the firm; that is, beyond f_1, $P_{f_1} > MRP$. As the market price of the factor declines, firms will employ more units of the factor. It is always most profitable for the firm to hire a factor such that the factor price is equal to MRP. If the market price is established at P_{f_2}, the profit-maximizing firm would then employ f_2 units of the factor.

When f_1 units of the single variable factor of production are employed, the MRP would equal MRP_1. If the wage rate was P_{f_2}, it would clearly be profitable to hire the f_1th unit of variable factor, since $MRP_1 > P_{f_2}$. However, with the same wage rate, it would not be profitable to hire f_3 units of the variable factor since $MRP_3 < P_{f_2}$. Thus the optimum employment of this variable factor would be f_2 units, at which level $MRP_2 = P_{f_2}$.

The MRP curve then shows the quantities of a single variable factor that the firm would hire at various factor prices: f_1 units at P_{f_1}, f_2 units at P_{f_2}, f_3 units at P_{f_3}, and so forth for other possible factor prices. For this reason, when there is only one variable factor, the MRP curve represents the firm's demand curve for that factor of production (d_f).

When more than one factor is variable, changes in the price of any one factor may affect the amount of other factors employed as well (see Figure 13.2). This in turn has the effect of shifting the MRP function for the factor whose price has changed. For a price decline more of all inputs are likely to be used such that the MRP function shifts to the right. This is illustrated in Figure 13.6.

When the factor price declines from P_{f_1} to P_{f_2}, the marginal-revenue

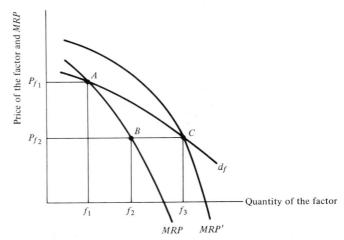

Figure 13.6 Shifting MRP Curve When more than one factor is variable, a decline in the price of one, such as from P_{f_1} to P_{f_2}, will cause more of the other factors to be used as well (see Figure 13.2). This in turn shifts the *MRP* curve to the right to *MRP'*. Instead of the increase in factor use being from A to B (or f_1 to f_2) along *MRP*, factor usage increases from A to C (or f_1 to f_3). Thus the firm's demand for the factor (d_f) is no longer just *MRP* but a series of points along a shifting *MRP* function.

product curve shifts from MRP to MRP'. At P_{f_1} we would expect f_1 units of the factor to be employed. As the factor price falls to P_{f_2} we see that, due to the shift of the marginal-revenue product function, the quantity of the factor employed increases to f_3 rather than f_2. The lines connecting points such as A and C combine to form the demand curve for a factor (d_f) when more than one factor may be varied.

The market demand for the factor will be the horizontal sum of the demands of the various firms employing the factor *if* all those firms are pure monopolists. This is because there are no external effects when all firms are monopolists. A decrease in price by any of the monopolists—and the related increase in sales, along with consequent increases in production—does not have any effect beyond those internalized in the marginal-revenue functions of the individual monopolists. On the other hand, if the output markets are not completely monopolized (but rather are monopolistically competitive or oligopolistic) expansion of output by any one firm will cause the "big D" demand to shift to the left. This in turn means that each firm's MRP function shifts to the left. In these cases the summation of individual factor demand curves follows the procedure described in Figure 13.4 (except that MRP curves replace VMP curves). In any case, the market demand (D_F) for the factor will be a negatively sloped function, as shown in Figure 13.7.

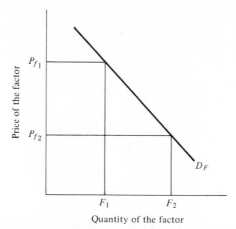

Figure 13.7 The Market Demand for Factors: Imperfectly Competitive Market Output The market demand for a factor (D_F) with monopolistic influences in the output market is the horizontal sum of every firm's factor demand at each price, after adjusting for "market effects" when necessary (when the output market is not a perfect monopoly).

It should now be clear that more units of a variable factor of production will be demanded at a lower factor price than at a higher factor price. This has been shown to be true regardless of the nature of the output market structure or the number of variable factors being considered. The only differences encountered are in the determination of each firm's factor demand (d_F) and/or the method of adding the factor demands for all firms involved (whether or not an external effect occurs).

FACTOR SUPPLY

In Chapter 9 we saw that the supply of commodities produced in perfectly competitive markets is a positively sloped function: The higher the price the greater the quantity firms would be willing and able to supply. The same relationship generally holds for factors of production as well. Owners of the factors can be expected to make a greater quantity of them available at higher factor prices than at lower prices.

For labor inputs we can apply the methodology of indifference curve analysis to determine the quantity of labor supplied at various prices (wage rates). In Figure 13.8 the horizontal axis represents the total number of hours available for work and leisure, with leisure time increasing from left to right. The vertical line at 16 hours represents the maximum possible amount of leisure time each day (assuming that 8 hours are necessary for maintenance—that is, eating and sleeping). The vertical

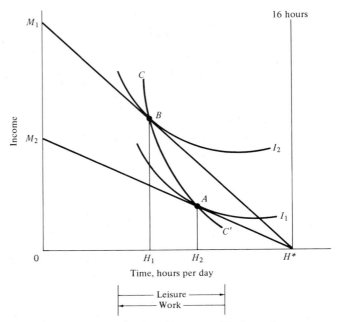

Figure 13.8 Individual Choice Between Work and Leisure Determination of the number of hours worked at different wage rates using indifference curve analysis. The budget constraint M_1H^* represents a higher wage rate than M_2H^* (i.e., $M_1/H^* > M_2/H^*$). At the lower wage the individual's equilibrium is at A, with $H^* - H_2$ hours worked. With the higher wage, $H^* - H_1$ hours would be worked. The indifference curves I_1 and I_2 represent the income versus leisure trade-off according to the individual's preference structure.

axis measures the income earned by allocating labor hours to work rather than leisure. If H^* (= 16 hours) of time is allocated to leisure activities, earned income would be zero.

The line M_1H^* is a budget constraint that represents the alternative levels of income that can be generated from all possible combinations of work and leisure at a particular wage rate. The wage rate is represented by the slope of the budget constraint. If one worked the entire 16 hours, the income earned would be M_1 and thus the wage rate per hour would be $M_1/16$, or M_1/H^*. At a lower wage rate, less income would be earned for the same number of hours of work. Thus the budget constraint M_2H^* represents a lower wage rate than M_1H^*. The wage rate associated with M_2H^* is M_2/H^*.

The curves labeled I_1 and I_2 represent two indifference curves for the individual's trade-off between leisure time and work (income), with I_2

preferred to I_1. As the wage rate increases from M_2/H^* to M_1/H^*, we see that the individual's utility maximizing combination of leisure and work moves from A to B. The effect of this changing equilibrium on the number of hours worked depends on the nature of the preference structure represented by I_1 and I_2. In the example illustrated in Figure 13.8 the number of hours worked increases from $H^* - H_2$ to $H^* - H_1$ for the wage rate increase given.

If we were to trace out equilibrium points for many different wage rates, a curve such as CC' would be formed. This curve would show the number of hours worked and income earned at various wage rates. Since this curve slopes upward to the left (for the case illustrated), the individual depicted must work more hours at a higher wage than at a lower one. Thus that person's labor supply curve would be positively sloped if hours worked were plotted versus the wage rate.

This is done in Figure 13.9, where the horizontal axis represents the number of hours worked and the vertical axis measures the wage rate. The points labeled A' and B' could be determined from points A and B, respectively, in Figure 13.8. This positive relationship between the wage rate and number of hours a person would be willing to work (and forgo leisure) is the labor supply curve (S_L).

While this relationship is most likely to be positive for the majority of the world's labor resources, it may well not be appropriate in some cases. It is conceivable that the wage rate could reach a high enough level that

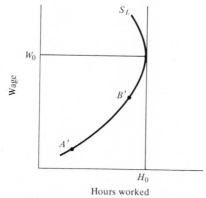

Figure 13.9 Individual Labor Supply Curve In general, the labor supply curve will be positively sloped with points on the curve, such as A' and B', corresponding to A and B in Figure 13.5. There may be a wage rate so high (W_0) that the quantity of labor supplied might reach a maximum (H_0) and actually decline at even higher wage rates. This would give rise to a "backward bending" supply curve for labor.

the labor supply function might bend backward. For example, it could be that up to wage W_0 the number of labor hours worked would increase with rising wage rates, but above that wage fewer hours would be worked. Thus a worker might at first be induced to work longer than a normal 40-hour work week if the wage rate increased. However, as the wage rate increases, and money income increases, one might find that additional hours of work, and the associated income, is not worth the sacrifice of leisure time (i.e., time to enjoy the fruits of one's work effort). We might then find that a critical wage (W_0) could be reached that would maximize the number of hours a person would work (H_0), and that at a higher wage the individual would actually prefer to work fewer hours. The observation that many firms are finding it difficult to entice overtime work (especially on weekends) from their employees even at high over-time rates provides some support for the notion that the labor supply function could become "backward bending" at some point.

The market supply curve for labor is found as the horizontal sum of all individual labor supply curves. This is illustrated in Figure 13.10 for a simple case of just two laborers providing the entire market supply. At the lower wage (W_1) Laborers 1 and 2 (S_{L_1} and S_{L_2}) work H_1 and H_2 hours, respectively. Thus, the total labor supply at W_1 is H_{T_1} (= $H_1 + H_2$). At the higher wage, W_2, Laborer 1 supplies H_2 hours while Laborer 2 supplies H_3 hours. Summing $H_2 + H_3$, we find the total hours of labor supplied at W_2 to be H_{T_2} hours. The market supply curve for labor is shown in the right-hand panel of Figure 13.10 by the curve S_{LM}.

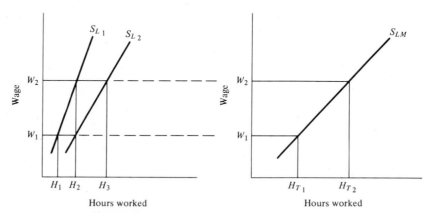

Figure 13.10 Market Labor Supply Curve   The market supply of labor (S_{LM}) is found as the horizontal sum of all individual labor supply curves. In the case illustrated here there are two laborers supplying the entire market such that $S_{LM} = S_{L_1} + S_{L_2}$ at each possible wage. At wage W_1, $H_{T_1} = H_1 + H_2$; and at wage W_2, $H_{T_2} = H_2 + H_3$.

MONOPSONISTIC INFLUENCE IN THE FACTOR MARKET

A *monopsony* is defined as a market situation in which there is only *one buyer* of the commodity or service being exchanged. This is obviously an extreme case, such as the federal government being the only buyer of Minuteman missiles. However, there may be many more situations in which there are relatively few buyers, each of which has sufficient market power to influence the market price significantly. In these cases we say that there are monopsonistic influences (note the similarity to monopolistic influences on the seller's side in monopolistic competition and oligopoly). Some of the most important examples of monopsonistic market influences occur in the market for resources. There are many cases of geographic areas in which there is but one (or perhaps only a few) employer(s) of labor resources. Communities that are dominated by a military base (Great Falls, Montana), a university (Gainesville, Florida), state government (Harrisburg, Pennsylvania), or a corrections institution (Carson City, Colorado) represent examples.

The degree of monopsonistic power in the input markets can vary from pure monopsony to oligopsony or monopsonistic competition. The basic analytical principles involved are essentially the same in these cases, so we will focus our attention on the pure monopsony case. We have already seen that the supply of factors will generally be positively sloped as a function of the factor price (see the preceding section). In the two earlier sections we assumed that there were many buyers of the input factors such that no one buyer had any effect on factor prices. As a result of this assumption, each firm behaved as a price taker in factor markets, and thus the factor supply curve facing each firm was a horizontal line at the existing factor price.

However, a monopsonist faces a positively sloped factor supply function since the monopsonist is the sole buyer of the factor. This has important consequences to the firm's behavior, just as the downward sloping demand curve of a monopolist influences behavior in the output market. As the monopsonist increases output and thus employs additional units of the inputs, the price that must be paid for those factors goes up. The positively sloped supply curve of the factor represents the average cost per unit of the resource (just as the demand curve represents the average revenue, or price, of output). We then use the terms *factor price* and *average resource cost* (ARC) as synonymous. Since the average resource cost increases as more units are employed, it follows that the marginal resource cost (MRC) will be greater than ARC. Marginal resource cost is the additional expense to the monopsonist of employing one more unit of the resource. This is illustrated in Table 13.3.

These same relationships can be shown graphically as in Figure 13.11. The lower positively sloped function is labeled with both an S_f and

Table 13.3 DETERMINATION OF MARGINAL RESOURCE COST FOR A MONOPSONIST

UNITS OF THE RESOURCE EMPLOYED (f)	PRICE PER UNIT OF THE RESOURCE (ARC)	TOTAL COST OF THE RESOURCE ($TRC = f \cdot ARC$)	MARGINAL RESOURCE COST ($MRC = \Delta TRC / \Delta f$)
1	$3.00	$ 3.00	$ 3.00
2	4.00	8.00	5.00
3	5.00	15.00	7.00
4	6.00	24.00	9.00
5	7.00	35.00	11.00
6	8.00	48.00	13.00
7	9.00	63.00	15.00

with *ARC*, the former indicating that this curve represents the market supply of the factor and the latter indicating that the same line represents the average resource cost of the factor to the monopsonist. The more steeply sloped, and higher, line is the marginal resource cost—that is, the addition to the total cost of the resource resulting from employing one additional unit of the factor.

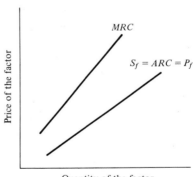

Figure 13.11 Monopsony With monopsony in the input market the supply curve for the factor (S_f) is the supply curve facing the single buyer of the factor (the monopsonist). This curve also represents the relationship between factor price P_f and the quantity of the factor supplied and is therefore also the average resource cost *ARC* of the factor. As the single buyer increases the quantity of the factor employed, a higher factor price must be offered such that the total cost of the resource increases by more than just the price of the last unit hired. This additional cost, the marginal resource cost, is shown by the *MRC* curve. Since *ARC* has a positive slope, *MRC* will lie above *ARC* and be more steeply sloped. *MRC* is the important function for decision making by the monopsonist.

Marginal revenue is the important decision-making function from the seller's perspective. It should not be surprising then that marginal resource cost is the relevant decision variable for the buyer. If there are many buyers such that the buyer's side of the market is perfectly competitive, $MRC = P_f$ and thus is a horizontal line at P_f, as illustrated in Figures 13.1 and 13.5.

Now suppose that the monopsonist employs more than one variable resource. The firm's profit-maximizing behavior may be generalized from our discussion of the selection of the optimum combination of inputs presented in Chapter 7 and the relationships illustrated in Figure 13.2. The principles developed in these earlier discussions assumed that there were a sufficient number of buyers that factor prices were taken as given. Using two variable factors A and B with prices P_A and P_B, respectively, the optimality condition would be expressed as

$$\frac{MP_A}{P_A} = \frac{MP_B}{P_B}$$

where MP_A and MP_B represent the marginal products of the factors. That is, the marginal product per dollar spent on each resource should be equal to maximize output for a given cost or to minimize the cost of producing a given level of output.

Under monopsonistic situations in which the factor prices are not constant to the firm, factor prices must be replaced by the marginal resource cost. The optimality condition is then

$$\frac{MP_A}{MRC_A} = \frac{MP_B}{MRC_B}$$

That is, resources should be employed such that the marginal product per marginal resource cost is equal for all resources.

DETERMINATION OF FACTOR PRICES

At the beginning of this chapter we noted that demand and supply forces are the important ingredients in determining the price for various resources or factors. Having developed these forces in the four preceding sections we can now show how they combine to determine a factor price under alternative sets of conditions using labor as the factor. We will illustrate three cases: (1) competitive labor supply and demand; (2) monopsony in the hiring of labor; and (3) the case of bilateral monopoly in which there is a single buyer of labor inputs combined with a labor organization which acts effectively as the sole supplier of labor services.

The diagram in Figure 13.12 illustrates the first and simplest of these cases. The labor supply curve S_L is shown to be a positively sloped function with more units of labor willing and able to be employed at a

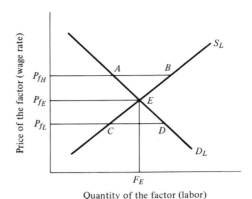

Figure 13.12 Market Price Determination for Factors
Determination of an equilibrium price for a factor is the
most straightforward when there are no monopolistic or
monopsonistic influences in the marketplace. The market supply
curve for labor, S_L, is the horizontal sum of individual labor supply
curves, whereas the market demand curve, D_L, is the horizontal
sum of every firm's labor demand (taking "market effects" into
account). The equilibrium factor price, P_{f_E}, and quantity of the
factor employed, F_E, is determined by the intersection of S_L and
D_L. At a factor price below the equilibrium, firms would want to
hire more inputs than would be available at that price. For
example, at the price P_{f_L} a shortfall of CD units would result. At
prices above the equilibrium price unemployed resources would
exist since more would be supplied than firms would be willing
and able to hire. At P_{f_H}, for example, resource (labor)
unemployment would be AB.

higher wage (factor price, P_f) than at a lower wage. This curve S_L represents the horizontal summation of the individual labor supply functions
as determined using indifference analysis in Figure 13.8. For ease of
exposition, only the positively sloped portion of the market labor supply
function is shown.

The market demand for labor is represented by the curve labeled D_L
and, as mentioned earlier, is a "derived demand" since it is so greatly
dependent on the demand for the output generated in the production
process. In the two earlier sections on factor demand we distinguished
between the derivation of each firm's factor demand (d_f) according to the
type of market in which the output is sold (competitive or monopolistically influenced). However, as illustrated in Figures 13.4 and 13.7, the
market demand (D_L) for a factor (labor) is negatively sloped in either
case. Thus, for our present purpose, the nature of the output market is not
important.

At point E in Figure 13.12 the quantity of labor demanded exactly
equals the quantity of labor supplied at the wage rate P_{f_E} (the equilibrium

wage rate). Thus, the labor market is in equilibrium at that wage and F_E units of labor would be employed. If the wage rate were less than the equilibrium level, such as at P_{f_L}, fewer workers would be willing to work than firms would wish to hire. A shortfall of CD units of labor would result. On the other hand, if wages were artificially held above the equilibrium level, for example at P_{f_H}, unemployment would result. The labor force would want to provide more units at that rate than would be consistent for firms to hire (given the VMP or MRP curves underlying D_L). The amount of unemployment would be AB units of labor.[1]

Now let us suppose that the demand for labor is derived from a single firm. In this case, that firm's demand for labor is the market demand (i.e., $D_L = d_L$). But, as we discussed in the preceding section, a single buyer of a factor will view the supply curve as an average resource cost (ARC) function. Since this is positively sloped, the marginal resource cost (MRC) will lie above and be more steeply sloped. These relationships are illustrated in Figure 13.13.

The profit-maximizing firm will equate marginal resource cost (MRC) with the additional revenue resulting from the decision of how many units of labor to employ. Recall that $d_L = VMP$ or MRP depending on the output market, but in either case d_L represents the additional revenue to the firm from employing each additional unit of labor. Thus the equilibrium for the firm will be at E, where $d_L = MRC_L$, rather than where $D_L = S_L$. The monopsonist will hire L_E units of labor and recognizes from the labor supply curve that this many units can be employed at a wage P_{L_E}. Note that this wage is less than the competitive wage ($P_{L_E} < P_{L_C}$) and that the number of units of labor employed is less than if the situation were competitive ($L_E < L_C$).

What would happen, however, if the monopsonist was not able to completely exert this control over the wage and level of employment because of union (or other collective) monopoly power on the other side of the marketplace? This type of situation is called a *bilateral monopoly*. The union would act as the sole "seller" of labor services and thus would have monopoly power. An interesting case of monopsonist versus monopolist develops. Monopoly control of inputs is not insignificant or scarce. The American Medical Association has almost complete monopoly control in providing physicians' services in the economy. In many cities various unions have nearly as much monopoly power in controlling the labor available for such things as plumbing, electrical work, and even public school teachers.

The unions are not always naive about economic affairs (although not often objective, either). They recognize that the firm's demand for labor is negatively sloped and, thus, when additional units of labor are em-

---

[1] This is a type of price floor as discussed in Chapter 2 and illustrated in Figure 2.4.

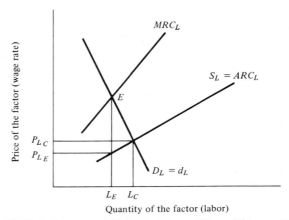

Figure 13.13 Influence of Monopsony on Wage Rates If there is just one firm employing a resource (labor) there is a monopsonistic market, and the firm's labor demand d_L is also the market demand D_L. The monopsonist views the labor supply curve S_L as the average resource cost of labor ARC_L and realizes that the marginal resource cost of labor MRC_L lies above ARC_L and is more steeply sloped. The monopsonist will follow profit-maximizing behavior by employing L_E units (the level where $MRC_L = D_L$). The monopsonist will also realize that L_E units of labor can be hired for the price P_{L_E}, as given by the labor supply curve. This result can be compared to the competitive situation in which the factor price would be P_{L_C} and L_C units would be employed.

ployed, the marginal wage revenue (MWR) lies below the demand for labor function (D_L). These curves are illustrated in Figure 13.14 along with the monopsonist's average resource cost ($ARC_L = S_L$) and marginal resource cost (MRC_L) curves.

The union will attempt to arrive at a wage P_{f_U} by equating the marginal wage with the labor supply function S_L. However, the monopsonist will want to follow the strategy presented in Figure 13.13, equating MRC_L with D_L. This would result in the price P_{f_M} in Figure 13.14. We see that the monopolistic union will always be led to a higher price than the monopsonistic buyer of labor services ($P_{f_U} > P_{f_M}$). Economic theory cannot predict the exact wage that would be established in such cases, but can determine that it will be somewhere between these extremes. The relative bargaining strength and skill of the monopsonist and the monopolist (union) will determine whether the result will be closer to P_{f_M} or P_{f_U}. Note that the union's demand will be greater than the competitive equilibrium wage, associated with point E, while the monopsonist's offer will be less than the competitive wage. Both the monopoly power of the union and the monopsonistic power of the firm tend to reduce the level of employment below the competitive level (L_E).

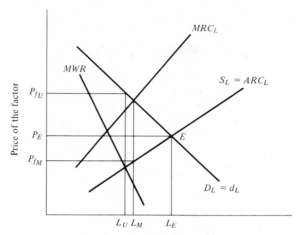

Quantity of the factor (labor)

Figure 13.14 Bilateral Monopoly in the Labor Market A wage conflict results when a monopolistic seller of labor (a union) faces a single employer (a monopsonist). The monopsonist would want a wage/employment configuration determined as in Figure 13.13, with a wage of P_{f_M} and L_M units employed. The union, on the other hand, would attempt to equate the marginal wage revenue function (MWR) with the labor supply function (S_L) and set the wage at P_{f_U} from the labor demand curve D_L. Economic theory can only delineate these bounds. The actual wage will fall between them and be influenced by factors such as the bargaining strength of the monopolist (union) and the monopsonist (producer). We can see that the perfectly competitive wage falls between the extremes at P_E.

ECONOMIC RENT

In discussing the pricing of factors of production, we have been able to avoid making a distinction between the long and the short run because our analysis has been couched entirely in terms of marginal productivity, which is applicable to variable factors of production. Since all factors are variable in the long run, the concepts presented thus far are all appropriate in the long run.

However, in the short run some factors are fixed. The return to fixed factors is traditionally referred to as an *economic rent*. Strictly speaking, this is true only if the factors are absolutely fixed in supply regardless of the adjustment period. The term *quasi-rent* is used for those fixed factors that may be varied over a longer period.

Figure 13.15 can be used to illustrate how the amount of economic rent is determined. The average variable cost (AVC), average-cost (AC), and marginal-cost (MC) curves are drawn and defined in the same man-

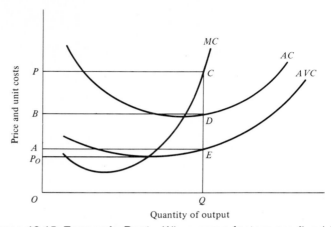

Figure 13.15 Economic Rent When some factors are fixed in supply, their return is referred to as an economic rent. Assuming perfect competition with the price at *P,* the firm depicted in this diagram would produce *Q* units. Total revenue would be equal to the area *OPCQ,* of which the area *OAEQ* would pay for the variable costs involved in producing *Q* units. The remaining revenue *APCE* is then the return attributable to the fixed factors and is thus the economic rent. A portion of the economic rent, in this example, is pure economic profit to the firm (the area *BPCD*) since only *ABDE* would be necessary to compensate the fixed factors.

ner as in Chapter 8, Figure 8.3 (and elsewhere). We will assume that the output market is perfectly competitive and that the market price of the product is *P.* At that price the profit-maximizing firm would produce *Q* units (i.e., where $P = MR = MC$).

The total revenue to the firm $(P \cdot Q)$ would be represented by the rectangle *OPCQ.* The amount *OAEQ* of that revenue would be just enough to attract (hire) the variable factors needed to produce *Q* units (i.e., *OAEQ* represents the return to the variable factors). The remainder of the total revenue represents the return to the fixed factors, or the economic rent. In the case depicted in Figure 13.15, this amounts to *APCE* dollars. *ABDE* of this is the return to the fixed factors in an opportunity cost sense. However, recall that the *AC* curve represents the entire cost to attract all resources. Thus, *OBDQ* would be sufficient revenue for this firm to produce *Q* units and pay all of the factors their respective opportunity costs. This implies that the firm could operate if price were at some level lower than *P,* and still make an economic profit (as long as price was greater than the minimum of *AC*). That portion of economic rent above the opportunity cost of fixed factors is pure economic profit (i.e., the area *BPCD*).

In Figure 13.15 economic rent is positive, but this is not necessarily the case. Rent would be zero if price were P_o in which case all variable costs would be paid but none of the fixed cost could be recovered. At prices above P_o but less than the minimum AC, economic rent is positive but the return to fixed factors is not equal to their opportunity costs elsewhere in the economy so the firm makes an economic loss.

INCOME DISTRIBUTION

Before ending our discussion of factor markets and the return to factors of production, let us look at some data for the United States' economy to see just how factor returns are distributed. There are several ways of looking at the distribution of factor returns. First, we will look at returns by the broad categories used by the U.S. Bureau of Economic Analysis. In the first quarter of 1980, total national income was $2031.4 billion. Of that, the percentage breakdown by function was as follows:

Compensation of employees and proprietor's income	82.9%
Rental income of persons	1.3%
Corporate profits	8.5%
Net interest	7.3%
Total	100.0%

Note that this is not a perfect approximation to the economic meaning of wages, rent, profit, and interest as returns to labor, land, entrepreneurship, and capital. Nonetheless, this distribution of the national income sheds some light on how the total income of the economy is divided among various functional areas. How much various individuals receive is, of course, determined by their relative work effort, inheritances, and so on.

It is also interesting to see how the national income is distributed by industry. This is shown below in percentage terms for five-year intervals, beginning in 1950:

Industry	1950	1955	1960	1965	1970	1975
Agriculture, forestry, and fisheries	7.5	4.8	4.2	3.6	3.0	3.4
Mining and construction	7.1	6.8	6.4	6.3	6.4	6.4
Manufacturing	31.4	32.4	33.3	30.1	26.8	25.0
Transportation	5.5	4.8	4.3	4.1	3.8	3.6
Communications and Utilities	3.0	3.6	4.1	4.1	4.0	4.1

Wholesale and retail trade	16.9	15.8	15.5	15.0	15.2	15.7
Finance, insurance, and real estate	9.4	10.6	11.6	11.3	11.5	11.5
Services	8.9	9.3	10.7	11.3	12.8	13.5
Government	9.7	11.4	12.6	13.3	15.8	16.0
Other	0.5	0.8	0.6	0.8	0.6	0.8

The most interesting features of these data are with respect to some general trends in the relative importance of various industries in generating national income. The first four categories have all shown relative declines while the service (especially including finance, etc.) and government sectors show an increasing importance in our economy (in terms of the share of national income generated in those industries).

Let us now look at income distribution in terms of how equally (or unequally) it is divided among families. There is some evidence that over time there has been a slight trend toward greater income equality (note that this is not necessarily desirable or equitable). For illustrative purposes we shall use 1975 data. In that year total family income in the United States was distributed as follows:

Percent of Families	*Percent of Income*
Lowest 20	5.4
Next 20	11.8
Next 20	17.6
Next 20	24.1
Next 15	25.5
Top 5	15.6

The last quintile (top 20 percent) is broken into two groups to emphasize the relatively high concentration of income among the highest segment of the population. The top 5 percent of all United States families received 15.6 percent of the total money income for all families in 1975. Combining the last two subgroups to the top 20 percent, we see that those one-fifth of all families received 41.1 percent of all income.

These relationships can be illustrated graphically by using a Lorenz curve, as shown in Figure 13.16. The 45° line *AB* represents the line of perfect equality. Along that line the first 20 percent of all families would receive 20 percent of all income, the first 50 percent of all families would get 50 percent of the total income, and so forth. The 45° line would be the Lorenz curve for such perfect equality.

Clearly, the income distribution data shown above do not represent an equal distribution among families. By graphing the cumulative percent of income received versus the cumulative percent of families, we can get a visual image of the degree of inequality (remember this is not synonymous with inequitable) in income distribution. The more such a Lorenz curve bows away from the perfect equality Lorenz curve (*AB*) the greater the degree of inequality. To do this our first task is to calculate the cumulative percents from the data given above, as follows:

	Cumulative Percent of Families	*Cumulative Percent of Income*
A	0	0.0
D	20	5.4
E	40	17.2
F	60	34.8
G	80	58.9
H	95	84.4
B	100	100.0

The letters to the left correspond to points so denoted in Figure 13.16. We see that the line connecting these points bows away from the 45°

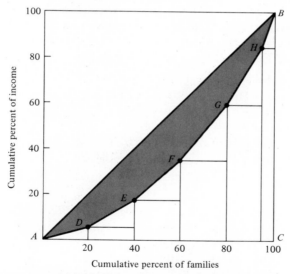

Figure 13.16 Lorenz Curve of Income Distribution A Lorenz curve illustrating the amount of inequality in income distribution. The Lorenz curve is the line *ADEFGHB* for family income distribution in the United States for 1975. The closer the Lorenz curve comes to the 45° line (*AB*), the more equal the distribution, whereas a more bowed Lorenz curve represents greater inequality. A Gini coefficient can be calculated as the ratio of the shaded area to the area under the 45° line to provide a quantitative measure of inequality. Such a quantitative measure makes various comparisons more meaningful.

"perfect equality Lorenz curve" (*AB*). The area between these two curves (*AB* and *ADEFGHB*) is usually called the *area of concentration,* and of course can be measured as the area of the polygon *ABHGFED* (the shaded area in Figure 13.16).

The ratio of the area of concentration to the entire area under the line *AB* (the area of triangle *ABC*) is called the Gini coefficient, which provides a quantitative measure of the degree of equality (or inequality). The closer the Gini coefficient is to one the more concentrated the income, whereas the closer it is to zero the more equal the income distribution.

Let us calculate the Gini coefficient for the data on family income distribution given above. First, the area of the triangle *ABC* is relatively easy to find since it is simply equal to one-half times its height times its width. Thus, the area of the triangle *ABC* is equal to 5000 (= 0.5(100)(100) = 0.5(10000) = 5000). Since Lorenz curves are always plotted on axes with height and width of 100 percent, the triangle *ABC* always has an area of 5000.

The area of concentration can be calculated as follows: (1) Find the sum of the areas of the triangles and rectangles under the Lorenz curve (these are shown in Figure 13.16); and (2) subtract this sum from the total area under the line *AB* (i.e., from 5000). For the income data given above and plotted on Figure 13.16 this is done below:

$$
\begin{aligned}
\text{Area under } AD &= 0.5(20 \times 5.4) &&= 54 \\
+ \text{ Area under } DE &= 0.5(20 \times 11.8) + 5.4(20) &&= 226 \\
+ \text{ Area under } EF &= 0.5(20 \times 17.6) + 17.2(20) &&= 520 \\
+ \text{ Area under } FG &= 0.5(20 \times 24.1) + 34.8(20) &&= 937 \\
+ \text{ Area under } GH &= 0.5(15 \times 25.5) + 58.9(15) &&= 1074.75 \\
+ \text{ Area under } HB &= 0.5(5 \times 15.6) + 84.4(5) &&= \underline{461} \\
= \text{ Total area under the Lorenz curve} && & 3272.75
\end{aligned}
$$

The area of concentration is then: 5000 − 3272.75 = 1727.25. To determine the Gini coefficient, we simply divide the area of concentration (1727.25) by the area of the entire triangle *ABC* (5000). Thus, for family income distribution in the United States for 1975 the Gini coefficient measure of concentration is 1727.25/5000 = 0.345.

SUMMARY

The demand for factors of production (or resources) is called a derived demand since it is derived from the demand for the goods and services those inputs are used to produce. The supply of factors comes from the individuals in the society who own those resources. We have used labor as the major example, but in our society most other resources are privately owned, as well, rather than being owned by governments. Some examples would include crop land, office buildings, mineral deposits, and so forth.

When output markets are perfectly competitive each firm's demand for a single variable factor is the value of the marginal product (VMP) function (which equals output price times the factor's marginal product). If more than one factor is variable an adjustment for shifts in VMP must be made. The market demand for a factor is determined by adding all of the individual firm's factor demand functions. If all firms employ more of a factor, output increases and market price may decline. If so, this will influence the VMP function and a further adjustment becomes necessary. This is called a "market or external effect."

If the output market is not competitive, the determination of a firm's factor demand involves using the concept of the marginal-revenue product (MRP) rather than VMP. The difference is simple ($VMP = P_Q \cdot MP$, while $MRP = MR_Q \cdot MP$) and is necessary since under nonperfectly competitive output markets one additional unit of sales results in added revenue that is less than price ($MR < P$). Otherwise, the determination of the firm's factor demand and the market factor demand follows the same method as for perfectly competitive output markets.

The supply of labor can be determined using an indifference curve analysis, the basics of which were introduced during our earlier discussion of consumer behavior. In general, more units of labor (and other factors) will be made available at higher factor prices than at lower ones. However, the possibility exists that the supply curve for labor may bend backward when the wage rate reaches some critical high level. The increasing difficulty of getting people to work overtime, especially weekends, provides some support in this regard.

Some factor markets may be dominated by a single employer, in which case monopsonistic power over employment and factor prices will result. The tendency will always be for the monopsonist to employ fewer resources and at a lower factor price than if the market were perfectly competitive. If, in addition, a strong union controls the available supply of labor, the market is characterized as a bilateral monopoly (a single seller, the union, selling to a single buyer, the monopsonist). In this case, the economic theory allows us to establish the bounds within which a wage settlement is likely, but the exact level depends on the relative bargaining strength of the two sides.

Selected Readings

Feldman, Roger, and Richard M. Scheffler. "The Supply of Medical School Applicants and the Rate of Return to Training." *Quarterly Review of Economics and Business* 18:1 (Spring 1978), 91–98.

Reder, M. W. "An Analysis of a Small Closely Observed Labor Market: Starting Salaries for University of Chicago MBAs." *Journal of Business* 51:2 (1978), 263–297.

Rees, Albert. "The Effects of Unions on Resource Allocation." *Journal of Law and Economics* (October 1963), 69–78.

Rottenberg, Simon. "The Baseball Player's Labor Market." *Journal of Political Economy* (June 1956), 242–258.

QUESTIONS

1. Write a short explanation of the following terms or concepts that were used in this chapter:

   (a) average resource cost
   (b) backward-bending labor supply
   (c) bilateral monopoly
   (f) derived demand
   (e) economic rent
   (f) factor demand
   (g) factor supply
   (h) factors of production
   (i) Gini coefficient
   (j) income vs. leisure indifference curve
   (k) Lorenz curve
   (l) marginal resource cost
   (m) marginal-revenue product
   (n) marginal wage revenue
   (o) "market effect"
   (p) monopsony
   (q) quasi-rent
   (r) value of the marginal product

2. Use the accompanying graph as the basis for an explanation of the effect of minimum wage legislation on employment. The rate of unemployment for youth, women, and nonwhites is generally above the overall unemployment rate. For example, for 16- to 19-year-olds, the unemployment rate is typically about 2.5 times the overall rate. Why do you think this is so? What relevance does marginal productivity theory have to your answer? Do you believe that minimum wage laws help or hurt young people who are in the labor market?

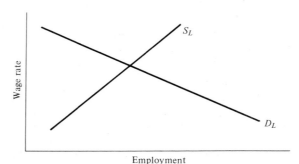

3. We are well aware that the income distribution in the United States is unequal, and few would argue that the national income should be equally distributed among households. However, many tax and welfare policies are designed to lessen the inequality. Suppose that we had the following information on income distribution:

| | Percent of Income | |
Families	Period 1	Period 2
Lowest 20%	4.0	5.5
Next 20%	12.0	12.5
Middle 20%	17.5	18.0
Next 20%	23.5	23.5
Highest 20%	43.0	40.5
Highest 5%	18.0	15.0

Use a Lorenz curve to illustrate the change in income distribution between periods 1 and 2. Would you say that policies during this interval were having the desired effect of moderating the inequality of the income distribution among households?

4. At present, what is your individual employment objective after completing college (or after graduate studies)? How do the concepts discussed in this chapter relate to that field of employment? What are your expectations concerning demand-and-supply forces in the labor market you plan to enter?

5. A firm employs two broadly classified factors of production A and B. The marginal productivities of the two factors at current rates of usage are $MP_A = 150$ and $MP_B = 100$. The unit cost for the factors are 25 and 20 dollars for A and B, respectively. Is this firm currently employing factors efficiently? Explain why or why not. If not, what type of adjustment should be made? Explain why such an adjustment would improve the firm's profit.

6. Draw a mapping of two isoquant curves representing output from the use of labor and capital inputs. Then draw an isocost curve tangent to the higher of the isoquants. Explain why this point of tangency is considered the optimum combination of inputs. Now suppose that unions are able to bargain for an increased wage such that the isocost curve rotates until it is just tangent to the lower isoquant. What will happen to the amount of labor hired and the quantity of output produced (assuming total expenditure on factors to be constant). Now suppose that the firm maintains the same level of output after the increased wage rate. Would they continue to hire as many units of labor as prior to the wage hike? Illustrate your answer on the graph.

7. Why is the demand for labor composed of points along a shifting VMP curve, or MRP curve, rather than points along a single such curve? Under what circumstances is the VMP appropriate for determining the demand for a factor and when is the MRP curve appropriate?

8. Develop an indifference curve diagram to explain how the wage rate can be expected to influence the number of hours a person decides to work. In such an analysis why is leisure rather than work typically measured from left to right along the horizontal axis?

9. The salary earned by professional athletes has been rising dramatically. The *average* salary of major league baseball players, for example, is close to $100,000 per year. Use the concepts developed in this chapter to explain these high salaries. Why are owners willing to pay so much?

10. Most colleges and universities are faced with severe budgetary problems. Assume that your school has a fixed budget and that the faculty votes to become unionized (or is already unionized). If the union bargains for higher

faculty benefits, what effect is this likely to have on your institution? (Consider such things as the number of faculty employed, class size, use of nonfaculty educational inputs such as TV instruction or the use of graduate students as teachers, expansion of computer and library facilities, and the ability to support intercollegiate or intramural athletics.)

11. It wasn't too long ago that a strike by professional athletes would have been unthinkable, but today with strong players' organizations such strikes are very real possibilities. Use the concept of a bilateral monopoly to explain the professional sports industry. How closely does the bilateral monopoly model fit this situation?

CHAPTER 14
GENERAL EQUILIBRIUM AND WELFARE ECONOMICS

EFFICIENCY IN CONSUMER EXCHANGE
EFFICIENCY IN PRODUCTION
GENERAL EQUILIBRIUM AND OPTIMAL WELFARE
PERFECTLY COMPETITIVE PRICES AND GENERAL EQUILIBRIUM
THE INPUT/OUTPUT FRAMEWORK
SELECTED READINGS
QUESTIONS

Thus far the majority of our discussion has focused on partial equilibrium analysis; and so it is with most of microeconomics. For example, we may look at the immediate impact of a change in the price of gasoline on the quantity of gas demanded, ceteris paribus. Everything but the object of our immediate attention is assumed to be "held constant." This method of analysis has proved to be very useful in evaluating economic phenomena in the public and private sectors and in making decisions about economic matters. In many situations very little is lost in doing so. A change in dairy markets has very slight impact on the aluminum industry, the emergence of Big Sky Airlines had little effect on the market for pocket calculators, and so on.

However, as indicated by the circular flow diagram of the economy presented in Figure 1.1, in some way everything in the economy is related to everything else. Thus it becomes of interest to trace the effects of a change in one part of the economy on other sectors. This is especially true when we consider some of the dominant sectors of the economy such as housing, the auto industry, or steel. The ramifications of having a major automotive manufacturer go out of business are much more far reaching than can be usefully evaluated in a partial equilibrium framework that might focus just on the automotive industry per se. A general equilibrium approach, such as input-output analysis, provides greater insight into such events.

Much of the basis for an overview of general equilibrium has already been introduced in parts of Chapters 6 and 7, as well as in our discussion of perfect competition. In this chapter we draw together elements of the theory of consumer equilibrium with production equilibrium to see how efficiency in both can lead to an optimal level of output of various goods and to an optimal welfare for society.

EFFICIENCY IN CONSUMER EXCHANGE

We will begin by reviewing the problem of consumer exchange as introduced in Chapter 6. We simplify the analysis, without any loss of generality, by assuming that the economy is composed of just two consumers (Ann and Bob) and just two goods (Coke and pizza). Both consumers have a preference structure for Coke and pizza, which can be described by a mapping of indifference curves that exhibit the expected properties (negative slope, convex to the origin, and so on; see Chapter 3).

In Figure 14.1 (which is a slightly modified version of Figure 6.4) Ann's preference structure is represented by the indifference curves superscripted with an A; I_1^A through I_6^A, with the subscripts indicating a rank ordering of level of satisfaction (I_6^A being the most preferred of the curves illustrated for Ann). Bob's preferences are depicted by a similar indifference mapping. His indifference curves are superscripted with a B and are ordered in the same manner as Ann, using subscripts (I_6^B is preferred to I_5^B and so on, with I_1^B representing the lowest satisfaction of the indifference curves shown for Bob). Note that, as in Figure 6.4, Ann's origin is at the lower left corner of the diagram (O_A), and Bob's origin is at the upper right corner (O_B). Thus, Ann has more Coke as we move from left to right and more pizza as we move from bottom to top, whereas for Bob the opposite is true.

The distance $O_A W$, along the bottom of the diagram, represents the total quantity of Coke available for consumption (note that this equals $O_B W'$, along the top of the figure). The total amount of pizza available is measured by the distance $O_A W'$, along the left, or by $O_B W$ at the right edge of the illustration. Suppose that these quantities of the goods are arbitrarily distributed between Ann and Bob such that Ann has $O_A C_1$ units of Coke and $O_A P_1$ units of pizza, while Bob has the remainder of each ($O_B C_1'$ of Coke and $O_B P_1'$ of pizza). This allocation is represented by the point F in Figure 14.1. Ann has been given a relatively large amount of pizza and relatively little Coke. Bob, on the other hand, has a greater share of the Coke but a small portion of the available pizza.

At this allocation (point F) Ann and Bob's levels of satisfaction are given by their indifference curves through that point, I_3^A for Ann and I_2^B for

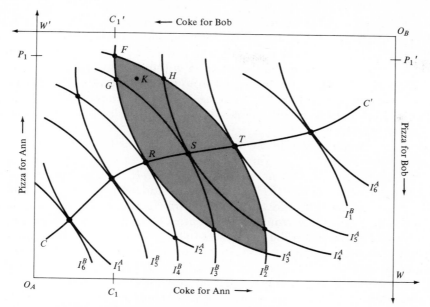

Figure 14.1 Efficiency in Consumer Exchange Efficient exchange in consumption will take place such that the marginal rate of substitution is equal for all consumers. This will lead to a Pareto optimal distribution of commodities along the contract curve CC'.

Bob. Ann's marginal rate of substitution of Coke for pizza ($MRS^A_{C:P}$) is relatively high at F. Recall that the marginal rate of substitution is the negative of the value of the slope of an indifference curve at any point, and that it is also equal to the ratio of the marginal utility of the good on the horizontal to the marginal utility of the good on the vertical. Thus, for Ann: $MRS^A_{C:P} = MU^A_C/MU^A_P$. Her high $MRS^A_{C:P}$ at point F indicates that it would take relatively little additional Coke to compensate her for giving up one unit of pizza while remaining at the same level of satisfaction (along I^A_3).

For Bob the opposite is true. His marginal rate of substitution of Coke for pizza ($MRS^B_{C:P}$) is relatively low at F. That is, it would take a substantial amount of Coke to compensate him for the loss of one unit of pizza, keeping him at a constant level of satisfaction (along I^B_2). Thus we find that at F, Bob would be fairly willing to trade some of his Coke for one more unit of pizza, whereas Ann would not require very much Coke in exchange for a unit of pizza. Under these circumstances we should expect that Ann and Bob would be led to a voluntary exchange in which the two goods would be redistributed with more Coke going to Ann and more pizza to Bob than at the original allocation (point F).

The important condition that makes such exchange likely is that $MRS^A_{C:P} > MRS^B_{C:P}$; that is, Ann's indifference curve is more steeply sloped at F than is Bob's. Therefore F is not a Pareto optimal point since either consumer could be made better off without making the other worse off through an exchange. Movement from F to H would leave Bob at the same level of satisfaction but increase Ann's satisfaction to I^A_4, while a change from F to G would keep Ann's satisfaction constant and would increase Bob's from I^B_2 to I^B_3.

Some exchange would always be beneficial until $MRS^A_{C:P} = MRS^B_{C:P}$; that is, until the two consumers' indifference curves have the same slope (are tangent to one another). Starting from F, such points would fall upon the line segment RST. At R, Bob would reap all the benefits of exchange, but Ann would be no worse off than at F. If exchange took place from F to T, Ann would get the entire benefit while Bob's satisfaction would be unchanged. Exactly where they would end up along RST is indeterminate, but an intermediate point such as S is likely unless one of the consumers is a far superior bargainer than the other.

All of the points in the set that comprise the line segment RST are Pareto optimal because once one of those points is obtained, no further exchange is possible without decreasing the well-being of at least one of the individuals. Each possible initial distribution of goods would lead to a different set of Pareto optimal points. If all such points are connected, they form what we have called a contract curve (CC'). Thus the line CC' represents all possible points of efficient exchange in consumption since along that line, the marginal rate of substitution of Coke for pizza is equal for all consumers (Ann and Bob in our simplified example).

EFFICIENCY IN PRODUCTION

Let us now suppose that these two products, Coke and pizza, are produced using just two factors of production, labor and capital. Once more simplifying to a two-dimensional case significantly reduces the complexity of the problem without any meaningful loss of generality. We assume that labor and capital can combine to produce these products in a manner such that various levels of production can be represented by isoquants having the standard properties introduced on page 123 (e.g., they are negatively sloped, convex to the origin, and dense).

The Edgeworth box diagram in Figure 14.2, which is a slightly modified version of Figure 7.13, can be used to determine how a given amount of labor and capital may be combined optimally for the production of Coke and pizza. Isoquants for the production of pizza are labeled with superscript P's (referring to pizza) and numerical subscripts indicating the rank order of each output level. Thus, Q^P_1 is the lowest isoquant

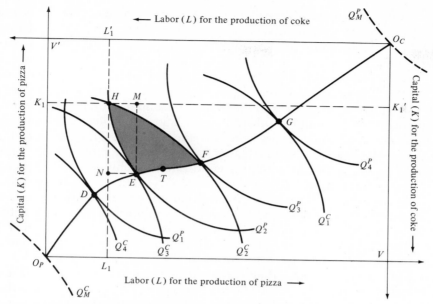

Figure 14.2 Efficiency in the Production of Two Goods
Efficiency in production is obtained when factors are
combined such that the $MRTS_{L:K}$ is equal in the production of all
goods. These combinations fall along the contract curve $O_P O_C$.

shown for pizza. The origin for the production of pizza is at the lower left
corner of the diagram (O_P). As one moves to the right from O_P, more labor
is used in making pizza while moving upward from O_P indicates increasing use of capital in producing pizza.

The isoquant mapping for Coke production has its origin at the upper
right corner of the Edgeworth box. Superscript C's indentify Coke
isoquants and again subscripts rank levels of production (for example, Q_4^C
represents greater production of Coke than Q_3^C).

We assume that the total quantity of factors of production (labor and
capital) are fixed. The amount of labor available is $O_P V (= O_C V')$ and the
quantity of capital available is $O_P V' (= O_C V)$. If the entire amount of
both factors was used to produce pizza, no Coke would be made and Q_M^P
of pizza could be produced (the subscript M indicates that this is the
maximum amount of pizza the society could produce given the factors
available and the existing infrastructure of technology). This is represented by the point O_C at the upper right corner of Figure 14.2. On the
other hand, if the entire amount of both labor and capital was allocated to
the production of Coke, we would be at O_P, the lower left corner of the
diagram, and would produce the maximum possible quantity of Coke
(Q_M^C) but no pizza.

Suppose that we arbitrarily assign O_PL_1 units of labor and O_PK_1 units of capital to the production of pizza and the remainder of the factors (O_CL_1' of labor and O_CK_1' of capital) to the production of Coke. This allocation, represented by point H in Figure 14.2, would allow for the production of Q_2^C units of Coke and Q_2^P units of pizza. Note that at H the slope of Q_2^P is greater than the slope of Q_2^C. We have seen in Chapter 7 that the absolute value of the slope of such an isoquant curve measures the marginal rate of technical substitution of labor for capital in the production of the commodity represented by the isoquant. Thus the marginal rate of technical substitution of labor for capital in the production of pizza ($MRTS_{L:K}^P$) is greater than the marginal rate of technical substitution of labor for capital in producing Coke ($MRTS_{L:K}^C$). Therefore, we could increase output of at least one of the commodities by reallocating the factors such that more labor and less capital were used in pizza production (less labor and more capital being used to make Coke).

For example, suppose that we increased the use of labor in pizza production by HM ($= NE$). In doing so, we could free up HN ($= ME$) units of capital, without reducing the output of pizza (staying on Q_2^P). The additional units of labor would have to come from the production of Coke, but the newly freed capital could be substituted for that labor in Coke production. This would allow for production of Q_3^C units of Coke rather than the original Q_2^C units, without diminishing pizza production, at point E in Figure 14.2. At E no further exchange of factors could increase production of one good without decreasing the other and so E is a Pareto optimal point of production.

At this Pareto optimal allocation of resources, the slope of Q_3^C is equal to the slope of Q_2^P; that is the two isocost curves are tangent. Given the initial allocation of factors at H, reallocations would lead to increased production of at least one commodity, without decreasing the other, until a Pareto optimal point is reached. The set of such optimal points for this starting point compose the line segment ETF. If we identified all possible tangencies of isoquants for pizza and Coke, they would trace out the contract curve O_PO_C containing the entire set of Pareto optimal allocations of the factors between products.

From this contract curve, which shows the alternative efficient levels of production of the two commodities, we can derive the production possibilities curve for pizza and coke. This is illustrated in Figure 14.3. Each point along this production possibilities curve represents a possible combination of production of pizza (measured on the vertical axis) and Coke (measured along the horizontal axis). These points are derived from the contract curve in Figure 14.2, with the various quantities determined by the pizza and Coke isoquants.

Let us consider four specific points to clarify the relationship between the contract curve and the production possibilities curve. First, the

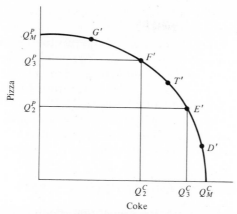

Figure 14.3 The Production Possibilities Curve The production possibilities curve is derived directly from the Pareto optimal points that form the contract curve (see Figure 14.2). Each point along the production possibilities curve is thus efficient in the use of factors of production.

vertical intercept of the production possibilities curve identifies the maximum quantity of pizza that could be produced if all of the economy's productive factors were allocated to pizza and none to Coke. This is the extreme upper right corner of Figure 14.2, at which zero Coke is produced and pizza production is at the level we have identified as Q_M^P; i.e., the maximum possible output of pizza. Thus, the vertical intercept of the production possibilities curve in Figure 14.3 is Q_M^P units of pizza. Similarly, the horizontal intercept of the production possibilities curve (Q_M^C) represents the maximum potential output of coke when no pizza is produced. This point corresponds to the extreme lower left corner of the Edgeworth box diagram of Figure 14.2.

Clearly it is unlikely that any society would choose to allocate all factors of production to just one form of output. In our present example it is probable that both some pizza and some Coke would be produced. The point F' on the production possibilities curve represents the production of Q_3^P units of pizza and Q_2^C units of Coke. By looking back to Figure 14.2 one can see that this point corresponds to point F along the contract curve (where isoquants Q_3^P and Q_2^C are just tangent). Should fewer factors be used to produce pizza (and more for Coke) we would move toward the lower left along the contract curve, to points like T, E, or D. These combinations of output are represented by T', E', and D', respectively, on the production possibilities curve of Figure 14.3. As one moves from F' to T' to E' to D' (or F to T to E to D, in Figure 14.2) less pizza and more Coke are produced. For example, we have seen that, at F' (or F), Q_3^P units of pizza and Q_2^C units of Coke can be produced. Reallocating factors such that production results at E' (or E) the output of pizza is reduced to Q_2^P, while Coke production increases to Q_3^C.

The absolute value of the slope of the production possibilities curve represents the rate at which it is possible to switch from the production of one good to another, while maintaining efficiency in production (i.e., remaining on the contract curve). This is referred to as the marginal rate of product transformation of Coke for pizza ($MRPT_{C:P}$). We see, in Figure 14.3, that as one moves from left to right the $MRPT_{C:P}$ increases. That is as more and more Coke is produced it is technically necessary to give up greater and greater amounts of pizza for each additional unit of Coke.

GENERAL EQUILIBRIUM AND OPTIMAL WELFARE

We have identified criteria for consumer efficiency in exchange and for efficiency in the production of goods and services, but we have yet to deal with the question of which bundle of commodities along the production possibilities curve would best serve the society. We know that all the points along the curve are optimal from the perspective of production because the marginal rates of technical substitution of labor for capital are equal for all goods (in our simplified example, $MRTS_{L:K}^P = MRTS_{L:K}^C$). Thus all these bundles are optimal; however, one may be "better" than others.

In Figure 14.4 two identical production possibilities curves are drawn on separate axes. In Figure 14.4(a) we assume that the production of Coke is given at C_1 units and the production of pizza is at P_1 units. How this combination of outputs was determined does not matter. It is purely arbitrary. But, given that bundle of commodities we can construct an Edgeworth box for our two consumers, Ann and Bob, with origins represented by O_A and O_B respectively. This Edgeworth box is then essentially the same as the one used in Figure 14.1 in explaining exchange between consumers. We shall assume that the C_1 and P_1 units of the products are allocated to Ann and Bob on some random basis and that they are free to make any exchange they wish. We know from our discussion above that they will be led to some Pareto optimal point along the contract curve. Suppose the point they reach is the one labeled E. At that point the consumers are in equilibrium because their indifference curves are tangent (i.e., $MRS_{C:P}^A = MRS_{C:P}^B$).

The absolute value of the slope of the line SS' (through E) measures the marginal rate of substitution of Coke for pizza for both consumers since it is drawn tangent to the indifferent curves I_3^A and I_1^B at E. This tells us the rate at which both of the consumers are willing to give up pizza for an additional unit of Coke.

Now let us compare this rate to the rate at which it is technically necessary to give up pizza for Coke at the present rate of output of the two

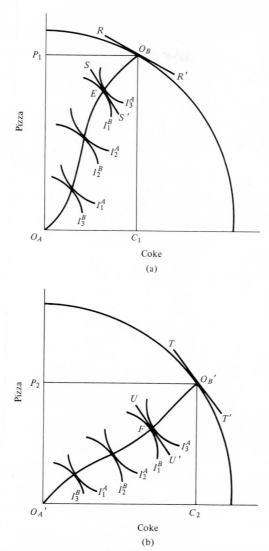

Figure 14.4 The Optimum Product Mix Although all points on
the production possibilities curve are efficient, one may be
preferable to others. (a) An Edgeworth box for consumer
exchange is drawn for the output combination C_1, P_1. If the
consumer equilibrium is at E, a reallocation of production can
improve welfare because the $MRPT_{C:P} < MRS_{C:P}$. Production of
more coke and less pizza would be desirable. (b) Movement to a
point such as $O_B{}'$, at which the $MRPT_{C:P} = MRS_{C:P}$, would improve
consumer welfare.

products at O_B (P_1 of pizza and C_1 of Coke). At the end of the previous section we defined this as the marginal rate of product transformation of Coke for pizza ($MRPT_{C:P}$) and said it could be measured as the absolute value of the slope of the production possibilities curve. At O_B the slope of the production possibilities curve is the slope at the tangent to the curve RR'.

Comparing RR' with SS' we see that the latter is more steeply sloped. We can then conclude for the present levels of production and distribution of goods, that the following is true:

$$MRS^A_{C:P} = MRS^B_{C:P} > MRPT_{C:P}$$

That is, consumers are willing to give up more pizza for an additional unit of Coke than is technically necessary, given the conditions that presently exist. Therefore, a reallocation of factors favoring the production of more Coke and less pizza would be desirable.

Such a reallocation is illustrated in Figure 14.4(b), with P_2 units of pizza and C_2 units of Coke being produced ($P_2 < P_1$ and $C_2 < C_1$). Movement to this point on the production possibilities curve (O_B') provides a different bundle of commodities to be distributed between Ann and Bob. Therefore a new Edgeworth box is established with Ann's origin at O_A' and Bob's at O_B'. After some initial distribution we would once again expect exchange to result until the consumers reach a point on the contract curve such as at F. At this distribution the marginal rate of substitution of Coke for pizza is the same for both consumers and is measured as the absolute value of the slope of the line UU'.

At the rate of production given by P_2 and C_2 the marginal rate of product transformation of Coke for pizza is measured by the absolute value of the slope of the line TT' (the tangent to the production possibilities curve at O_B'). At this new allocation of factors of production (producing P_2 and C_2 rather than P_1 and C_1), the slope of TT' equals the slope of UU'. Thus

$$MRS^A_{C:P} = MRS^B_{C:P} = MRPT_{C:P}$$

Further, since all points on the production possibilities curve come from a contract curve showing efficient combinations of factors, we know that $MRTS^P_{L:K} = MRTS^C_{L:K}$. This is then a general equilibrium solution to the problems of allocating factors of production among goods and of distributing the outputs among consumers.

We should note that the solution shown in Figure 14.4 is not necessarily unique. It is possible that there are one or more points along the contract curve O_AO_B at which the slope of the indifference curves would equal the slope of the production possibilities curve at O_B. However, given an initial distribution that would lead to an equilibrium at E, some reallocation of factors (such as in the lower panel of Figure 14.4) would be desirable. Once that reallocation is completed and we are at O_B', there may be points other than F at which marginal rates of substitution and product transformation are equal. The point obtained depends on how goods are initially distributed.

PERFECTLY COMPETITIVE PRICES AND GENERAL EQUILIBRIUM

Let us now take a brief look at how the price mechanism, with perfectly competitive markets, may lead to the results determined above. We know from Chapter 9 that perfectly competitive markets provide all consumers with the same set of product prices for whatever quantities are demanded. Further, from Chapter 3 we know that consumers will adjust their personal consumption pattern such that: $MRS_{C:P} = P_C/P_P$. Here we will continue with the two good cases using Coke and pizza as examples. The price of Coke is P_C and the price of pizza is P_P. Suppose this equality did not hold and that: $MRS_{C:P} > P_C/P_P$ for at least some consumers. These consumers would attempt to sell pizza and use the proceeds to buy Coke. Doing so would have several effects: With more people trying to sell pizza, the price of pizza would drop and as they seek to buy Coke, the price of Coke would rise. These two effects would combine to increase P_C/P_P. Further, recall that the marginal rate of substitution diminishes (indifference curves are convex to the origin) and thus as more Coke and less pizza is consumed the $MRS_{C:P}$ will decline. Eventually $MRS_{C:P}$ will then equal P_C/P_P. Since all consumers face the same set of prices the $MRS_{C:P}$ will be equal for all consumers. That is, a point on the contract will be obtained.

The question of whether this $MRS_{C:P}$ will equal the $MRPT_{C:P}$ remains to be answered. We have seen that the $MRPT_{C:P}$ is measured by the absolute value of the slope of the production possibilities curve. This slope is $\Delta P/\Delta C$ (the change in pizza output divided by the change in Coke production). As one moves along a production possibilities curve (such as from F' to E' in Figure 14.3), the money not spent on producing pizza will equal the additional money spent on factors to produce Coke. If MC_P is the marginal cost per unit of pizza and MC_C is the marginal cost per unit of coke, then $(\Delta P)(MC_P) = (\Delta C)(MC_C)$. It follows that

$$\frac{\Delta P}{\Delta C} = \frac{MC_C}{MC_P} = MRPT_{C:P}$$

We also know that (in perfect competition) firms will produce where price equals marginal cost, and so we can expect that $MC_P = P_P$ and $MC_C = P_C$. Thus

$$MRPT_{C:P} = \frac{MC_C}{MC_P} = \frac{P_C}{P_P}$$

and we have seen above that

$$MRS_{C:P} = \frac{P_C}{P_P}$$

Therefore, it follows directly that the marginal rate of substitution for all consumers will equal the marginal rate of product transformation under conditions of perfect competition. That is,

$$MRS_{C:P} = \frac{P_C}{P_P} = MRPT_{C:P}$$

It can be shown that monopolistic or monopsonistic influences in markets will prevent the attainment of these conditions through the price mechanism. For example, assume that Coke is sold in an imperfectly competitive market, whereas pizza is sold in a perfectly competitive one. Consumers will still follow behavior such that, $MRS_{C:P} = P_C/P_P$. In pizza production, firms will still produce where $MC_P = P_P$. But Coke producers will produce where $MC_C = MR_C$, and since the Coke market is imperfectly competitive, $MR_C < P_C$ (MR_C is the marginal revenue from selling Coke). The $MRPT_{C:P}$ remains equal to MC_C/MC_P. Therefore we find that

$$MRPT_{C:P} = \frac{MC_C}{MC_P} = \frac{MR_C}{P_P} < \frac{P_C}{P_P} = MRS_{C:P}$$

The output of Coke will therefore be too low and the production of pizza will be too high to be optimal.

THE INPUT/OUTPUT FRAMEWORK

Input/output provides an empirical way of looking at general equilibrium in the economy. We know that when there is change in one sector of the economy, many other sectors may be influenced, changes in those sectors stimulate more changes in still other sectors, and on and on goes the process. For example, increased consumer demand for cars would stimulate the automotive industry directly. As the auto industry expands, the steel, rubber, aluminum, and many other sectors of the economy will experience growth. As these sectors expand, the clothing, recreation, furniture, agricultural, and housing sectors will be affected. There will even be feedbacks that further stimulate the auto industry (e.g., as steel production increases, steelworkers may purchase more cars). Clearly, tracing all of these effects through the economy is a very complex matter.

However, roughly four decades ago Wassily Leontief developed an empirical method of analyzing such complex interactions using what is called an input/output table. Basically, an input/output table is a matrix with each row showing how the output or sales of a particular sector of the economy is distributed among all sectors of the economy, including final demand. In the same manner, each column indicates all of the inputs used by each sector of the economy. All values are in dollars. To illustrate the concept in a simple manner we will consider an economy composed of just three sectors: agriculture, housing, and manufacturing. An input/output table for this economy might look like the one presented in Table 14.1.

The output of any sector of the economy can either be purchased by the same sector, by other producing sectors, or consumed as a final good by individuals, government, or business. When the output of a supplying sector is consumed as a final good (i.e., not an input for further processing), the transaction is listed under final demand in the input/output table. The input/output table *includes all transactions in the economy*, including both interindustry and intraindustry activity, whereas the national income and product accounts deal only with transactions of final goods and services in order to avoid double counting. So with input/output analysis we must be aware that double counting does occur, but this is necessary to obtain the ability to discern the markets (sectors) where the output from each sector is sold and to see the interactions in the economy.

The "value added" row of the input/output table shows the resource cost for labor and capital incurred and the profit earned by the sector listed in the column heading. As can be seen in Table 14.1, the row total for each sector equals the column total for the respective sector. The reason for this equality is that the rows and columns of an input/output table are accounting identities; that is, the sum of the revenues for an industry equals the sum of the costs incurred plus the profits earned.

Although quite a few input/output tables have been developed for the United States economy, at various levels of aggregation, probably the most widely used are those produced by the U.S. Department of Commerce. They provide tables broken down to as fine a level as those containing four-digit SIC data. Three types of tables are developed: the transactions table, the direct requirements table, and the total requirements table.

Table 14.1 INPUT/OUTPUT TRANSACTIONS TABLE

SELLING INDUSTRIES	PURCHASING INDUSTRIES			FINAL DEMAND	TOTAL DEMAND
	AGRI-CULTURE (1)	HOUS-ING (2)	MANU-FACTURING (3)		
Agriculture (1)	10	50	20	100	180
Housing (2)	5	10	60	30	105
Manufacturing (3)	70	5	0	45	120
Value Added	95	40	40		
Total	180	105	120		

The transactions table is what we typically refer to as an input/output table such as the one illustrated by Table 14.1. Each row in this table indicates how the output of a given industry is distributed among all industries and final users in the economy. In our example the agricultural sector produces $180 of total output, of which $80 are intermediate goods sold to other industries (including some to the agricultural sector) for use in producing products or services, while the remaining $100 of output are sold for final consumption.

Each column of this table shows the purchases and the value added for each sector. The agricultural sector purchases $10 of its own output, $5 from housing, and $70 from manufacturing. There is then $95 of value added for the agricultural sector.

If we refer to a given row of this table as the ith row and to each column as the jth column, then we can identify sales from industry i to industry j as X_{ij}. In our example, X_{12} would represent the $50 of sales from agriculture to housing, X_{31} would represent the $70 of sales from manufacturing to agriculture, and so forth. We use the designation X_j to represent the total sales for any of the sectors heading each of the j columns. In this example $X_1 = 180$, $X_2 = 105$, and $X_3 = 120$.

The direct requirements table, which is derived from the input/output (or transactions) table, presents in each column the dollar amount of input each industry listed down the left side of the table must supply for the industry named in the column heading to produce one dollar's worth of output. The direct requirements matrix is composed of elements (a_{ij}) which may be defined as follows:

$$a_{ij} = \frac{X_{ij}}{X_j}$$

These a_{ij} values are referred to as the technical coefficients because they are determined by the existing production technology. The direct requirements table is shown as Table 14.2.

Let us look at the calculation of two of the technical coefficients to illustrate explicitly how these values are determined. We will first calculate a_{12}, the value of output from agriculture (Industry 1) that the housing

Table 14.2 DIRECT REQUIREMENTS TABLE FOR INPUT/OUTPUT ANALYSIS

SELLING INDUSTRIES	PURCHASING INDUSTRIES		
	AGRICULTURE (1)	HOUSING (2)	MANUFACTURING (3)
Agriculture (1)	0.056	0.476	0.167
Housing (2)	0.028	0.095	0.500
Manufacturing (3)	0.389	0.048	0

sector (Industry 2) uses per dollar's worth of output in the housing sector:

$$a_{12} = \frac{X_{12}}{X_2} = \frac{50}{105} = 0.476$$

To determine the value of output from manufacturing used per dollar of agricultural output we must calculate a_{31}.

$$a_{31} = \frac{X_{31}}{X_1} = \frac{70}{180} = 0.389$$

The remaining technical coefficients are calculated in the same way. Note that in Table 14.2, $a_{33} = 0$. This is because in our simplified example $X_{33} = 0$.

The shortcoming of the direct requirements table is that, as its name suggests, only direct requirements are shown. In Table 14.2 we see that in order for Industry 3 to produce $1.00 of output, $0.50 of input from Industry 2 would be required, along with $0.167 of output from Industry 1. But, for Industry 2 to produce that $0.50 of output they would in turn require inputs from Industries 1 and 3, as well as from their own industry; and on it goes in this manner, ad infinitum. The direct requirements table does not take into account these "second-round" effects.

However, a third table, the total requirements table, can be constructed that takes all these interactions into account. This table is often called the Leontief inverse matrix and is generated from the direct requirements table using matrix algebra. If we let A represent the matrix of all of the technological coefficients a_{ij}, the total requirements matrix R is found as:

$$R = (I - A)^{-1}$$

where I is an identity matrix. That is, we subtract A from the identity matrix and solve for the inverse of the resulting matrix.

The columns of the total requirements matrix show the amount of total input, direct and indirect, which each industry listed along the left side of the table must supply for the industry identified by the column heading to produce one dollar of output for final demand. The total requirements table is given here as Table 14.3. Thus we see that for each

Table 14.3 TOTAL REQUIREMENTS TABLE FOR INPUT/OUTPUT ANALYSIS

SELLING INDUSTRIES	PURCHASING INDUSTRIES		
	AGRICULTURE (1)	HOUSING (2)	MANUFACTURING (3)
Agriculture (1)	1.321	0.726	0.584
Housing (2)	0.335	1.319	0.716
Manufacturing (3)	0.530	0.345	1.262

one dollar of final output, the agricultural industry (Industry 1) must purchase $0.530 of output from the manufacturing sector (Industry 3).

Given this information about interrelationships within the economy, we can use input/output analysis to evaluate how a change in final demand for any one sector will influence all other sectors. Doing so involves some use of matrix algebra but we can summarize the results without dealing with the mechanics. It can be shown that if the total requirements matrix is multiplied by the final demand vector, the product equals total demand. So for our initial final demand (see Table 14.1) we have:

$$
\begin{array}{ccc}
 & Final & Total \\
Total\ Requirements & \times\ Demand\ =\ Demand \\
Matrix & Vector & Vector
\end{array}
$$

$$
\begin{pmatrix}
1.321 & 0.726 & 0.584 \\
0.335 & 1.319 & 0.716 \\
0.530 & 0.345 & 1.262
\end{pmatrix}
\times
\begin{pmatrix}
100 \\
30 \\
45
\end{pmatrix}
=
\begin{matrix}
180 \\
105 \\
120
\end{matrix}
$$

Although this result is trivial since it simply gets us back to where we started, consider the ramifications of the process. We can now find the total demand vector, including all rounds of interactions, for any specified set of final demands, and given that new total demand for each industry, we can calculate the new transactions matrix (that is, for example, how much Industry 2 will have to purchase from Industries 1 and 3 as well as how much of their own output they will use, given the new final demand vector).

Suppose by way of example that final demand increases by 15 for the manufacturing sector (Industry 3). The new level of total demand for all three sectors would be found as:

$$
\begin{array}{ccc}
 & Final & Total \\
Total\ Requirements & \times\ Demand\ =\ Demand \\
Matrix & Vector & Vector
\end{array}
$$

$$
\begin{pmatrix}
1.321 & 0.726 & 0.584 \\
0.335 & 1.319 & 0.716 \\
0.530 & 0.345 & 1.262
\end{pmatrix}
\times
\begin{pmatrix}
100 \\
30 \\
60
\end{pmatrix}
=
\begin{matrix}
189 \\
116 \\
139
\end{matrix}
$$

Based on this new final demand we can calculate a new transactions matrix. Recall that the technical coefficients are $a_{ij} = X_{ij}/X_j$. It follows then that the elements of the transactions matrix are $X_{ij} = (a_{ij})\ (X_j)$. The X_j's are the elements of the total demand vector and the a_{ij}'s are known from the direct requirements table. For example, suppose we want the new X_{12} (i.e., sales from the agricultural sector to the housing sector). We would calculate:

$$X_{12} = (a_{12})\ (X_2) = (0.476)\ (116) = 55$$

Table 14.4 REVISED INPUT/OUTPUT TRANSACTIONS TABLE

| SELLING INDUSTRIES | PURCHASING INDUSTRIES | | | FINAL DEMAND | TOTAL DEMAND |
	AGRI-CULTURE (1)	HOUS-ING (2)	MANU-FACTURING (3)		
Agriculture (1)	11	55	23	100	189
Housing (2)	5	11	70	30	116
Manufacturing (3)	73	6	0	60	139

This and the other elements of the revised transactions matrix are given in Table 14.4.

We can see that a great deal of useful information about the interrelationships between sectors of the economy results from the application of input/output analysis. This tool is particularly useful in developing industry forecasts and for economic planning. However, there are some problems that we should mention. First, input/output analysis assumes that the technological coefficients are constant. If they are not, errors will pervade the system. As technology changes, we know these coefficients will change as well, and so they must be updated periodically. A further problem is that the use of such a system of analysis demands a great deal of data and data manipulation and can therefore be quite expensive.

Selected Readings

Bator, Francis M. "The Simple Analytics of Welfare Maximization." *American Economic Review* (March 1956), 22–59.

Coase, Ronald. "The Problem of Social Cost." *Journal of Law and Economics* (October 1960), 1–44.

Samuelson, Paul A. "A Diagrammatic Exposition of a Theory of Public Expenditures." *Review of Economics and Statistics* (November 1955), 550–556.

Scitovsky, Tibor. *Welfare and Competition*, 2d ed. Homewood, Ill.: Irwin, 1971.

QUESTIONS

1. Write a short explanation of the following terms or concepts that were used in this chapter:
   (a) contract curve
   (b) Edgeworth box
   (c) efficiency in exchange
   (d) efficiency in production
   (e) general equilibrium
   (f) input/output analysis
   (g) marginal rate of product transformation
   (h) marginal rate of substitution
   (i) marginal rate of technical substitution
   (j) Pareto optimum
   (k) production possibilities curve
   (l) technical coefficients
   (m) total requirements matrix

2. Use an Edgeworth box diagram to illustrate the efficient exchange of two goods (X and Y) between two individuals, given an initial allocation of the goods at the point W in the accompanying graph. You should draw at least four indifference curves for each consumer and indicate their ordinal ranking. Also, shade the area representing exchanges that would improve at least one consumer's satisfaction without reducing the other's, and construct the contract curve. Explain the diagram carefully.

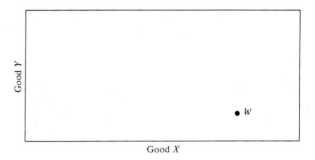

Good X

3. Use an Edgeworth box diagram to illustrate efficiency in the production of two goods (X and Y) using labor (L) and capital (K) inputs. Use the box shown as a basis with an initial allocation of L and K at the point U. Use at least five isoquants for each good with one isoquant for each good representing the maximum output of that good that is possible, given the amount of labor and capital defined by the size of the box. Show the contract curve and carefully explain its significance.

4. Based on the analysis of efficiency in production in Question 3, derive a production possibilities curve for the two goods X and Y and graph that curve on the axes shown. What is the slope of the production possibilities curve called? How does this slope relate to the marginal rate of substitution in Question 2 and to the marginal rate of technical substitution in Question 3? Draw an Edgeworth box for consumer exchange inside the production possibilities curve and use this complete diagram as the basis for an explanation of general equilibrium.

5. A representative input/output transaction table is shown. Assuming the economy to be in equilibrium, find the final demand and the total demand for industries A, B, and C. Write a one-sentence explanation of each of the values in this transactions table, including the values you filled in.

SELLING INDUSTRY	PURCHASING INDUSTRIES			FINAL DEMAND	TOTAL DEMAND
	A	B	C		
A	20	40	10		
B	10	50	40		
C	40	20	0		
Value Added	80	90	50		
Total	150	200	100		

6. Based on the transactions table in Question 5, complete the table of technical coefficients (the direct requirements table) shown. Write a one-sentence explanation for each of the values in this table.

SELLING INDUSTRIES	PURCHASING INDUSTRIES		
	A	B	C
A			
B			
C			

PART II
EXTENDED APPLICATIONS OF MICROECONOMICS

CHAPTER 15
AGRICULTURE

MARKET DEMAND
PRODUCTION AND COST
MARKET STRUCTURE
PRICE FLUCTUATIONS
AGRICULTURAL POLICY
SELECTED READINGS
QUESTIONS

The farmer has been a respected figure in American life ever since colonial days when agriculture was the mainstay of our fledgling economy. The austere couple, pitchfork in hand, illustrated in Grant Wood's *American Gothic* has symbolized the hard-working, self-reliant, ruggedness of the early American farmer and of farm life. Up in the predawn hours, the farmer labored long and hard, with little capital equipment, to supply the nation's food needs. At the mercy of nature's whims (floods, hailstorms, droughts, late spring or early autumn frosts, insect plagues, etc.), farm incomes were subject to wide and largely uncontrollable variations from year to year. The typical farm was a quite small family operation, being very labor intensive.

Today, agriculture has changed significantly. It is now "big business," not necessarily in the corporate conglomerate sense. In fact, large corporations that went into farming in the late 1960s, such as Ralston Purina, Gates Rubber, and Tenneco generally failed and cut back or withdrew entirely. However, the average size of the farm has increased to well over 400 acres. There are also farmers such as Eugene Smith of Lebanon, Indiana, who started farming on 450 acres with borrowed money in the late 1960s and doubled his net worth every year from 1968 to 1977, at which time he was farming 8000 acres, employing 16 workers, and still growing. The application of economic analysis has contributed to the ability of individual farmers to succeed despite the whims of nature and the agricultural industry's tendency to exacerbate its own supply and demand disequilibrium problems. In Smith's words, "I am proving that success involves knowing what the economics of farming is all about."[1]

In this chapter we will explore some economic aspects of the agricultural sector, including demand and supply shifts that may trigger price fluctuations, the consequence of a relatively price-inelastic demand for agricultural products, changes in production methods, some aspects of market structure and concentration in farming, as well as American agricultural policy.

MARKET DEMAND

The market demand for agricultural products is most significantly tied to the size of the population. As the United States and world populations have increased, there has been a steady rise in the total demand for virtually all farm products. Consider the use of farm products as raw materials for various types of production (e.g., cotton for textiles). We can expect that as the number of people increases there will be greater demand for most (if not all) products, and therefore a greater "derived demand" for the inputs used in the production process. Thus, as population increases, or if existing consumer preferences shift to favor more cotton fabrics, the demand for cotton will shift to the right.

Even when we think of just the most obvious use of agricultural production, food, we see a set of conditions that gives rise to an increasing demand. First, the existence of more people means more mouths to feed and correspondingly a greater demand for farm products. The total world population continues to increase yearly. In the United States the growth in population has leveled, but we have had a change in tastes and preferences that has stimulated agricultural demand. We have a stronger preference than we once did for a diet with relatively greater amounts of meat products than grain. Furthermore, we prefer the more tender meat from grain-fed animals to the somewhat tougher texture found in range-fed animals. Both of these combine to shift the demand for agricultural products, especially grains, to the right.

A typical shift in agricultural demand is illustrated in Figure 15.1. Along the demand D' more would be demanded at each price than along demand curve D. In our earlier discussion of demand, we have noted that demand shifts may be caused by increased populations, changes in tastes and preferences, changes in consumer incomes and changes in the prices of substitute or complementary goods. The examples given above represent illustrations of the first two of these causes.

In general, consumers' incomes have been rising. However, this has probably had little effect on the total demand for agricultural products. It may be true that as incomes rise, people spend more money on food, but

[1] "How the Family Farm Can Harvest Millions," *Business Week* (July 4, 1977), 68.

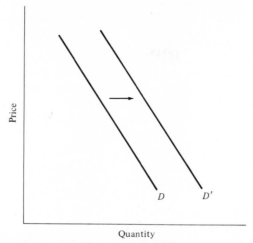

Figure 15.1 Increasing Demand for Agricultural Products An increase in the demand for agricultural products is represented by a rightward shift in the demand function, such as from *D* to *D'*. This could be caused by population growth, changes in consumers' tastes and preferences, an increase in consumers' incomes, increases in the prices of substitute goods, or decreases in the prices of complementary goods.

they probably do not consume very much more in the way of basic agricultural products. We have a tendency to purchase more fully prepared foods than the raw ingredients to make our own. For example, most households purchase bread that has been baked commercially and delivered to a food retailer where we purchase not just the raw inputs but also the convenience of not milling the flour, preparing the dough, and baking the bread. Other factors contributing to higher expenditures on food, but not agricultural products, include our tendency to buy foods that are almost completely prepared for us (such as TV dinners) and an increasing propensity to eat outside of the home (at a wide variety of eating establishments, from the ubiquitous McDonald's to the more elegant Matterhorn Room at the Lowell Inn in Stillwater, Minnesota). We can generalize to say that the income elasticity for agricultural products is positive but less than one. That is, there is an inelastic income elasticity for agricultural products (at least food products) and, therefore, the demand curve for these products will shift only very slightly due to increases in income.

How will changes in other prices influence the demand for agricultural products? Since there is virtually no substitute for food, we might expect that other prices will have little effect on the demand side of the agricultural market. Changes in relative prices between different farm products such as beef and lamb may cause shifts in the demand curves for those individual products but not a perceptible change in the total demand for agricultural production.

The situation changes considerably, however, when nonfood uses of farm output are considered. As the price of petroleum products continues to increase, agricultural substitutes become more attractive. Cotton and wool fabrics may increasingly replace synthetics that have a petroleum base. Vinyls in automotive and home furnishings may be replaced by these natural fabrics as well as by leathers. Handbags, shoes, wallets, and other vinyl products may similarly become more predominantly leather. Gasoline may potentially be replaced to a significant degree by gasohol, derived from a very wide range of agricultural products that can be grown in virtually any part of the United States. Thus, we can expect a positive cross-price elasticity between products with a petrochemical base and certain agricultural products (indicating that they are substitute goods). As the price of petroleum products becomes higher, we should expect the cross-price elasticity to become greater.

Agricultural producers may attempt to influence the position of their demand curve by exerting pressures to control export and import markets, as well. For example, wheat farmers may try to broaden their export market by breaking down trade barriers to potential export markets. Domestic beef and sheep ranchers may try to increase the demand for their output by lobbying to have import quotas established for Argentinian beef and Australian lamb, respectively.

A very important characteristic of the market demand for agricultural products is that it is inelastic with respect to its own price. That is, *the quantity demanded is relatively insensitive to price changes.* This has important ramifications in terms of agricultural policy and for the effect of price fluctuations on incomes received in the agricultural sector. If demand is inelastic, a decrease in price will result in lower total revenue (gross income) to the producers despite a greater quantity of sales, ceteris paribus. On the other hand, if agricultural prices increase, gross income to the farm sector will increase as well, since consumers will respond with only relatively slight reductions in the total quantity of agricultural products purchased.

PRODUCTION AND COST

Some of the resources used in agricultural production can be fairly readily transferred from one type of production to some alternative use. Perhaps the best example is farm labor, which can be used in producing corn or soybeans, wheat or barley, or even has use outside agriculture in other sectors of the economy. However, most of the resources used in agriculture are relatively specialized and are considerably less valuable in other forms of production. For example, the land in Montana's "Golden Triangle" has few, and not very attractive, uses outside of growing wheat. The same is true for much of the very expensive farm equipment used in modern agricultural production.

Thus, in the short run, we find that agriculture is not unlike most other forms of production in that there are certain resources that are fixed while others are variable. Following from the principle of diminishing productivity, the total-product, average-product and marginal-product curves can be expected to have the shapes depicted in the left two quadrants of Figure 15.2. These, in turn, give rise to the cost functions illustrated in the two right-hand quadrants of that figure (assuming that the cost per unit of the variable resource—labor, in this case—is constant).

There are more than 2 million farms in the United States, producing agricultural products of near-perfect homogeneity. Thus, agriculture provides a reasonably good example of a perfectly competitive market structure. Each firm (farm) is a "price taker," accepting a market-determined price and attempting to maximize profit (net income to the farmer) at that price.[2] The level of this price determines the profitability of the operation, given both the fixed and variable costs of production.

We know that the farmer should use more of a variable input until the marginal cost of production rises (due to diminishing marginal productivity) to the level of marginal revenue, which, for a "price taker" equals price (i.e., $MR = P$). Thus, as shown in Chapter 9, the farmer's marginal-cost curve (above AVC) and supply curve are identical ($MC = S$). As long as price is above the level of marginal cost represented by point A in the bottom right quadrant of Figure 15.2, the farmer makes an economic profit. If price is below that level, the farmer incurs a short-run economic loss; if price is just equal to that level, the farmer "breaks even." This is why the point A (the minimum point on the average-cost curve, and the point at which $MC = AC$) is referred to as the "break-even point."

In the short run, the farmer may wisely continue to produce even at prices below this "break-even" level. As Duncan and Harshbarger have pointed out: ". . . resources devoted to a type of agricultural production tend to be locked into that use in the short run, even though such use may be unprofitable. In the short run, the losses resulting from shifts to other types of production may exceed the losses from continuation of previous production patterns."[3] In terms of the bottom right-hand diagram in Fig-

---

[2] In actuality, the price that is taken by farmers for wheat, milk, beef, or other products is determined through a mixture of market forces and a variety of government programs. More will be said about these programs in subsequent sections, but the result to the individual farmer is the same. Price is determined outside the firm and is taken as given in operating the farm.

[3] Marvin Duncan and C. Edward Harshbarger, "A Primer on Agricultural Policy," *Monthly Review*, Federal Reserve Bank of Kansas City (September–October 1977), 6.

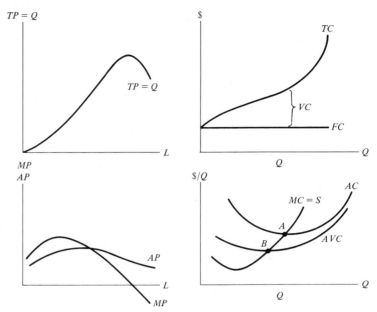

Figure 15.2 Agricultural Production and Cost Curves Since agriculture uses many specialized inputs that are fixed in the short run, the principle of diminishing marginal productivity operates such that short-run total product (*TP* = *Q*), average product (*AP*), and marginal product (*MP*) have the shapes depicted in the left-hand diagrams. With variable inputs having a constant cost per unit, this results in the U-shaped unit cost curves and related total-, fixed-, and variable-cost relationships shown in the right-hand diagrams.

ure 15.2, the farmer should continue to produce at prices less than the level represented by *A* as long as the price at least covers average variable cost. Thus the firm would continue to operate in the short run until price fell below the level represented by point *B*, which we call the "shutdown point." Above that price all of the variable costs are covered, and there is some money left to pay part of the fixed expenses, which must continue to be paid regardless of the level of production.

In the long run all factors of production are variable. We observe new farms being formed, often through consolidation of existing smaller farms, as well as farmers leaving the industry. The net result has been a decrease in the number of farms, an increase in farm size, and a change in the techniques of production from the highly labor-intensive smaller farms to more and more capital-intensive methods used on large farms.

In the decade from 1964 to 1974, the number of farms declined from 3.2 million to 2.3 million, while the average farm size increased from 352 to 440 acres. The average size of farm varies a great deal from one region to another, but average farm sizes have increased in all regions of the country. For example, in the East North Central Region (Ohio, Indiana, Illinois, Michigan, and Wisconsin) average acreage increased from 173 to 202 acres during this period, while in the Mountain Region (Montana, Idaho, Wyoming, Colorado, New Mexico, Arizona, Utah, and Nevada) the increase was from 1998 to 2262 acres.

Changes in the technology of agricultural production resulted in a decrease in the labor hours required on farms during that decade from roughly 7.5 billion to 5.5 billion labor hours while output increased. At the same time, the value of farm implements and machinery used increased from about 24 billion dollars to more than 44 billion dollars. During the period from 1950 to 1975 the indices of the physical quantities of resources used in agricultural production provide additional insight into the changing techniques of production. For labor the index dropped from 217 to 81; for mechanical power and machinery the index increased from 85 to 104; and for agricultural chemicals the index increased from 30 to 126 (for all three indices, 1967 = 100).

As farm labor has more land and capital to work with per unit of labor, we should expect the workers' productivity to rise. This can be seen by comparing the number of labor hours necessary to produce a given unit of agricultural output for different time periods. Some examples include:

Output and Unit of Measure	*1945–49*	*1971–75*
Corn: labor hours/100 bushels	53	6
Wheat: labor hours/100 bushels	34	9
Cotton: labor hours/bale	146	23
Tobacco: labor hours/100 pounds	39	14
Cattle: labor hours/100 pounds produced	4	1.6
Hogs: labor hours/100 pounds produced	3.0	0.9
Turkeys: labor hours/100 pounds produced	13.1	0.8

Such increases in labor productivity would result in upward shifts of the total product, marginal product, and average product functions in the left-hand quadrants of Figure 15.2. These shifts in turn would result in the average-variable-cost and marginal-cost curves declining in the right-hand diagrams of that figure. Further, in the upper right diagram the vertical distance between total cost (*TC*) and fixed cost, which represents variable cost (*VC*), would become less. Whether total cost and average cost would decline depends on the stability of fixed cost. If fixed costs stayed constant, *TC* and *AC* would decline, but if fixed costs (such as interest) did increase, these other costs could stay the same or increase.

As in other industries, technological changes in agriculture have tended to favor the use of more capital and less labor as indicated in some of the data given above. This change can be illustrated using the isoquant-isocost construct introduced in Chapter 7. As productive methods are developed that make labor relatively less productive and capital relatively more productive, isoquant curves will become less steeply sloped in general. In terms of the marginal rate of technical substitution of labor for capital ($MRTS_{L:K} = MP_L/MP_K$), we can say that one should expect that the $MRTS_{L:K}$ would decrease given a more capital intensive technology. That is, it would become more difficult to substitute labor for capital or, alternatively, it would be easier to substitute capital for labor. With a flatter isoquant, a given reduction in labor would require less additional capital to maintain the same output than would be true for a more steeply sloped isoquant. This is illustrated by the mapping of isoquant curves in the two panels of Figure 15.3. The left panel represents the initial technology, while the right panel depicts a new technology that is more capital intensive. The isocost lines in both panels are identical with respect to the total dollar outlay and the unit costs of capital and labor.

We see that the combination of inputs used to maximize output for the given cost uses relatively more capital and less labor after the new technology is introduced (K_N and L_N) than before (K_0 and L_0). The isoquant I_2^N can be presumed to represent a greater level of output than I_2^O since the former utilizes a more advanced technology and the same dollar expenditure on resources.

Another factor that may contribute to a shift to more capital relative to labor in agricultural production is an increase in the relative cost of

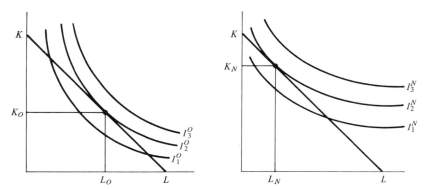

Figure 15.3 Effect of Labor Saving Technology Technological changes in agricultural production have been "labor saving," that is, have favored the use of more capital. Such changes in production are reflected in the change from the isoquant map on the left to the one to the right. In the latter the isoquants are relatively flatter, indicative of a lower marginal rate of technical substitution of labor for capital. With a constant isocost curve, we see that the equilibrium combination of labor and capital changes from L_0, K_0 to L_N, K_N, showing relatively greater use of capital.

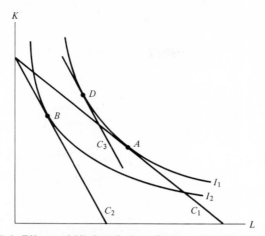

Figure 15.4 Effect of Higher Labor Cost on Production A firm wishing to produce output at the level represented by isoquant I_1 will use labor and capital in amounts determined by the tangency at *A,* assuming the relevant isocost curve is C_1. If the unit labor cost increases such that the isocost changes to C_2, the firm would find a new equilibrium at *B,* using more capital and less labor and producing less output (along I_2). Should the firm wish to maintain production at I_1, we can find the optimum levels of labor and capital inputs by drawing a new isocost (C_3) parallel to C_2 and tangent to I_1 at point *D.* Thus, with higher unit labor cost, the firm wishing to maintain I_1 units of output would use more capital and less labor.

labor. This is illustrated in Figure 15.4. Suppose that farmers are initially faced with the resource price ratio implied by isocost line C_1 and wish to produce a level of output represented by isoquant I_1. Then assume that unit labor costs rise, relative to the unit capital costs, such that the slope of the isocost becomes steeper. Recall that the negative of the ratio of the unit cost of labor (P_L) to the unit cost of capital (P_K) determines the slope of the isocost as we have drawn them (slope of isocost $= -P_L/P_K$). If no more dollars are spent on inputs, the equilibrium will shift from point A to point B in which case less output will be forthcoming (and, as our diagram is constructed, more capital but less labor will be used). If the original I_1 level of output is maintained, the farmer would have to move to a higher isocost (C_3) which will be tangent to I_1 above and to the left of point A. This new equilibrium, D, will definitely represent the use of a greater quantity of capital and fewer units of labor.

Before leaving this section on production and cost, let us look at a particular application of the use of these economic concepts in a decision context. The decision involves the choice of what mixture of protein supplement (PS) and corn (C) to use in order to achieve given levels of

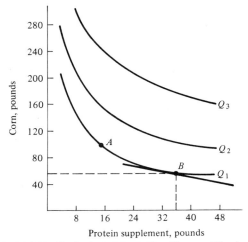

Figure 15.5 Weight Gain Isoquants for Hogs The isoquants Q_1, Q_2, and Q_3 represent three different levels of weight gain for hogs that can be obtained using different combinations of two feeds (corn and protein supplement). At A the $MRTS_{PS:C}$ is 3.62; at B it is 0.95. If the ratio of the price per pound of protein supplement to the price per pound of corn is known, one can determine the best mix of feeds by finding the point on an isoquant (for the desired weight gain) at which that price ratio equals the $MRTS_{PS:C}$. When the price ratio is 0.95, the optimum mix of feeds for a 40-pound weight gain Q_1 is found at B: roughly 36 pounds of protein supplement and 58 pounds of corn.

weight gain in hogs. Sonka, Heady, and Dahm have estimated equations for isoquant curves representing three levels of weight gain.[4] These are graphed in Figure 15.5 as Q_1, Q_2, and Q_3. The first represents a 40-pound gain from 60 to 100 pounds, the second represents a gain of 50 pounds from 100 to 150, and the third a gain of 65 from 150 to 215 pounds. Note that these isoquants, derived from careful empirical analysis, have the same characteristics as those discussed on a more conceptual level in Chapter 7.

For any of these levels of weight gain, one could use any of the combinations of corn and protein supplement represented along the relevant isoquant. That is, the inputs are substitutable along the entire range of the isoquants. We see, however, that the marginal rate of technical substitution of protein supplement for corn diminishes. Using the

[4] Steven T. Sonka, Earl O. Heady, and P. Fred Dahm, "Estimation of Gain Isoquants and a Decision Model Application for Swine Production," *American Journal of Agricultural Economics* 58 (August 1976), 446–474.

equations provided by Sonka et al., we can calculate the $MRTS_{PS:C}$ at any point. For example, at A it is 3.62. To the left of point A it would be greater and to the right of point A it would be smaller (along Q_1). The $MRTS_{PS:C}$ can be estimated by drawing a line tangent to an isoquant at the desired point and measuring the slope of the tangent.

In April 1971 the ratio of the price per pound of protein supplement to the price per pound of corn was 0.95, according to data in the article. Suppose you had hogs at that time that weighed 60 pounds and you wanted to "fatten them up" to 100 pounds. What combination of feeds would provide the 40-pound weight gain (Q_1) at the lowest cost? To find out, one would want to determine the combination of PS and C for which Q_1 has a slope of -0.95. This can be done mathematically from the equation of the isocost or in graphic form by drawing an isocost with a slope of -0.95 tangent to Q_1. This is done in Figure 15.5 and we see that the tangency occurs at point B which represents roughly 36 pounds of protein supplement and 58 pounds of corn. The same type of procedure could be used for other levels of weight gain desired (Q_2 or Q_3), as well as any other ratio of feed prices.

MARKET STRUCTURE

As we have noted above, the agricultural sector of the economy approximates fairly closely the economic notion of perfect competition. There is a very large number of sellers, over 2 million, no one of which is large enough in comparison to the industry to have any effect on the market price of the commodities produced. The products are classified and graded in such a manner that there is near-perfect product homogeneity. A bushel of hard red winter wheat from a wheat ranch near Great Falls, Montana, is the same in the eyes of the buyer as a bushel of hard red winter wheat from the Bismarck, North Dakota, area. There is essentially no advertising or branding of products and thus buyers are likely not to know the actual producing firm, and are not likely to care since the products are so homogeneous. It is relatively easy to enter the industry—although with rising land values and more sophisticated technology being used, the cost of entering is becoming greater, and thus entry is no longer as easy as when agriculture was more labor intensive. Further, there is an excellent information flow throughout the industry with regards to new techniques so that no one producer has an advantage over others.

The range of firm sizes is substantial in agriculture, with many small producers selling less than $2500 of farm products per year. Of those with sales greater than $2500 per year, the percentage distribution by number and value of sales was as follows for 1974:

ECONOMIC CLASS OF FARM (VALUE OF FARM PRODUCTS SOLD) ($)	PERCENT OF FARMS*	PERCENT OF SALES*
2,500– 4,999	17.1 (17.1)	1.2 (1.2)
5,000– 9,999	17.5 (34.6)	2.7 (3.9)
10,000–19,999	18.3 (52.9)	5.5 (9.4)
20,000–39,999	19.0 (71.9)	11.5 (20.9)
40,000–99,999	19.1 (91.0)	24.9 (45.8)
100,000 and over	9.0 (100)	54.2 (100)

SOURCE: Statistical Abstract of the United States.
* Cumulative percentages in parentheses.

We see that the smallest 17.1 percent of firms accounted for just 1.2 percent of industry sales, while at the other extreme the largest 9 percent of the firms had 54.2 percent of the sales. Thus, although the industry is reasonably competitive, sales are by no means equally distributed among firms. Large farms or ranches may be 50, 75, or 100 times the size of their smaller counterparts, as measured by either acreage or sales. But even so, these large agricultural firms are small relative to the total market and have no real market power.

In Figure 15.6, Lorenz curves are illustrated for the agricultural sector of the economy for 1964 and 1974. We see that for the latter year the

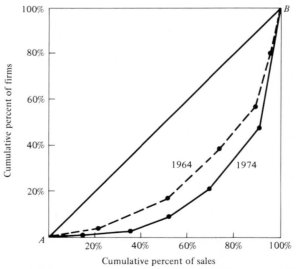

Figure 15.6 Lorenz Curves for the Distribution of Agricultural Sales These two Lorenz curves illustrate the growing inequality in the distribution of sales among firms in agriculture between 1964 and 1974. The Gini coefficient would have increased during this period because of the shift of the Lorenz curve away from the line of equality (*AB*).

Lorenz curve bows farther away from the line of perfect equality (*AB*) which is indicative of growing inequality in the distribution of firms by size. This is consistent with the observations made above concerning the changing character of agriculture, as measured by the number and size of farms as well as by the technology employed in production.

Even with such increasing inequality of sales among firms, we can expect the agricultural sector of the economy to follow the perfectly competitive model fairly closely, due primarily to the large number of firms involved, the homogeneity of products, and the relative ease of entry. Thus market prices will be determined by market supply and demand forces, as illustrated in Figure 15.7.

The demand curve *D* and supply curve *S* intersect at *A* to establish a market price P_1. This price is then taken as given by each producer and the individual firm sells whatever quantity it chooses to produce at that price. Recall that in a perfectly competitive market the supply curve *S* is the horizontal sum of all the individual firm's supply (or marginal cost) curves. Thus, as each firm reacts to the price P_1, exactly Q_1 units will be produced and offered for sale. Since consumers' demand tells us the quantities consumers are willing and able to purchase at each price, we know they will collectively purchase the Q_1 units at price P_1.

From what we have said earlier in this chapter about the demand for agricultural products, we should expect that over time there will be

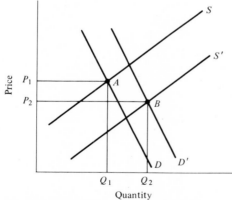

Figure 15.7 Free Market Price Determination in Agriculture Supply *S* and demand *D* determine the equilibrium price P_1 and quantity Q_1 for a perfectly competitive industry such as agriculture. If the supply function increases (perhaps due to technological advances) to *S'*, while demand increases less dramatically to *D'* (perhaps due to population growth), the equilibrium will move from point *A* to point *B*. Price would fall from P_1 to P_2, while the equilibrium quantity would increase from Q_1 to Q_2.

modest increases in demand. This may be due to a greater domestic population, more exports, increasing consumer incomes, new nonfood uses for the products, or any combination of these factors. However, in total, the rate of increase in demand over time is not great. A slight rightward shift of the demand curve in Figure 15.7, from D to D', represents this modest increase in demand.

On the supply side, the move to larger farms and greater use of mechanical as well as chemical aids in production has caused supply to increase more dramatically than demand. Such an increase in supply is illustrated by the shift from S to S'. This has resulted in lower real prices for agricultural products along with higher levels of production. This downward pressure on agricultural prices has resulted in considerable efforts on the part of "farm state" legislators to establish government policies to prop up farm prices.

PRICE FLUCTUATIONS

The perfectly competitive and decentralized nature of the agricultural industry has led to recurring and often substantial fluctuations in prices over time. As consumers we tend to be more aware of the upward fluctuations, but farm prices also fall relatively frequently. In farm markets, in fact, we often see several price changes of as little as a few cents (either up or down) in any given day of trading. This indicates that the market is quite sensitive to overall supply-and-demand conditions, such as weather changes or changes in export demand.

The lag time between when production plans are determined and when products are ready to market contributes to the high incidence of price fluctuations in agricultural markets. In their discussion of agricultural policy, Duncan and Harshbarger have stressed the nature of this problem[5]:

> Biological production processes are not amenable to quick and substantial shifts. It is typically not possible to stop a biological production process once it has started (a cow bred or a crop planted), without losing a substantial part of the variable cost of production. Consequently, production decisions and actions tend to be relatively irreversible. The time required to produce a crop is determined by the maturity date of the crop and the time required to produce cattle of slaughter weight will depend on growth rates and feeding practices. In the case of cattle, for example, about 38 months (over 3 years) are required to increase beef production—that is, from the time a heifer calf is born until that animal's first offspring can be sold as a 1,000-pound slaughter animal.
>
> Once a biological production process has been started, variability in final

[5] Marvin Duncan and C. Edward Harshbarger, "A Primer on Agricultural Policy," *Monthly Review,* Federal Reserve Bank of Kansas City (September–October 1977), 6.

production levels is determined by factors over which the producer has limited control. Animal and plant diseases can sharply reduce output. Weather conditions also have marked effects on production levels. For example, harsh weather during the winter and spring of 1976–77 limited the U.S. December–May pig crop to a 2 percent increase, despite a 5 percent increase in the number of sows farrowing (female pigs giving birth). Lack of adequate moisture and excessive heat during the growing season can sharply reduce production levels from crops.

To illustrate the fluctuation in prices, let us look at hog prices per hundredweight for selected years during the five-decade period from 1924 to 1974:

YEAR	PRICE ($)	YEAR	PRICE ($)	YEAR	PRICE ($)
1924	7.34	1949	18.10	1966	22.80
1926	11.79	1953	21.60	1967	18.90
1932	3.34	1956	14.50	1970	22.70
1936	9.37	1958	19.60	1971	17.50
1939	6.23	1960	15.30	1972	25.10
1942	13.04	1963	14.90	1973	38.40
1947	24.10	1965	19.60	1974	34.20

SOURCES: Wyllis R. Knight, "Agriculture" in Walter Adams, ed., *The Structure of American Industry*, 4th ed. (New York: Macmillan, 1971), 10; and *Statistical Abstracts of the United States*.

We see in these data considerable price fluctuation in both an upward and downward direction. Even in the year-to-year changes shown for the early 1970s there is a drop of 23 percent, followed by an increase of 43 percent, an increase of another 53 percent, then a drop of 11 percent.

Such fluctuations in price can be described by the cobweb effect discussed in Chapter 9. A shortfall of production in one period drives price upward. At the higher price each farmer, acting independently of others, takes steps to increase production. As this new production reaches market (from a year to three years later), there is a glut and price falls. Producers cut back and the cycle begins again. The relative inelasticity of demand for agricultural products tends to make these price fluctuations more severe than they would be if the quantity demanded were more elastic.

AGRICULTURAL POLICY

"Times have changed in the development of agricultural policy. It used to be that only farmers and the government were concerned over farm programs and little national attention was paid when we passed a farm bill. Today, agriculture touches everyone in America, and its importance is widely recognized. Our people have been reminded that milk does not come from plastic containers and that bread does not originate at the bakery."[6] In fact, as of 1975, the farmer's share of every dollar spent on milk at retail was 51 cents and for baked goods it was just 15 cents. On average, for all farm food products, the farmer's share of the consumer's dollar was 42 percent. Including backward and forward linkages, agriculture may account for as much as one-sixth of the nation's GNP.

Agricultural policy is a wide mixture of confusing and often contradictory programs that have generally ill-defined objectives. We have a network of land grant universities spending substantial public dollars in extension work, research, and other programs designed to help farmers get greater yields from given-sized farms. Meanwhile, other government programs may be paying those same farmers to hold land out of production or providing incentives for crop restriction. Thus while one arm of government is spending tax dollars to reduce crop acreage, another arm is spending tax dollars to show farmers how to increase output on the land they do plant. It is no wonder that few people really understand agricultural policy.

In this section we shall review some of the major types of agricultural policies and programs, beginning with the concept of a "parity price."[7] The parity price for an agricultural commodity is that price (in current dollars) that will give the commodity the same purchasing power—in terms of goods and services bought by farmers and certain production costs—as the commodity had during the 1910–14 base period. Although the actual calculations required to derive the parity prices are rather complicated, the basic concept of parity is fairly straightforward. To use a simple example, if—in the base period—50 bushels of wheat could have been sold and the proceeds used to purchase a ton of fertilizer, then the parity price of wheat at any given time is the price that would enable a farmer to purchase a ton of fertilizer with the proceeds from 50 bushels of wheat. Of course, in practice, parity prices are based on the average change in prices of all goods and services rather than on individual items.

Parity prices are frequently considered to represent "fair" product prices and have been used as a factor in determining government price support levels. However, when parity price standards are used as a measure to assure a specified net farm income, 100 percent of parity prices may actually yield a higher real net income to farmers than they would have had during the "golden years of agriculture"—the 1910–14 base period. This is true because the parity formula *does not take into account increases in farm efficiency,* as measured by an average index of produc-

---

[6] Statement by Senator Herman E. Talmadge, chairman of the Senate Agricultural Committee, *Farmland News* (June 30, 1977), 5, as quoted in Duncan and Harshbarger, 3.

[7] The remainder of this section is directly from or adapted from Duncan and Harshbarger, pp. 7–10.

tivity. As productivity increases, returns to resources used in production equivalent to 1910–14 can be obtained with lower than 100 percent parity levels.

The government supports some agricultural prices through loans to farmers granted through the Commodity Credit Corporation (CCC). A farmer can borrow from the CCC at the loan rate (or support price) using the commodity as collateral. If the market price is less than the CCC support price, the farmer simply defaults on the loan and the commodity is turned over to the CCC as full settlement of the loan. Commodities thus obtained by the government are typically used for domestic and international food aid programs. If the market price rises above the loan rate, the farmer may sell the commodity, repay the CCC and capture the price advantage of timely marketing. Thus the market mechanism is circumvented and the loan rate becomes the floor or lowest price for the commodity that the farmer needs to accept.

This concept can be illustrated and evaluated, using the diagram in Figure 15.8. Suppose that the market supply and demand functions for wheat are given by the curves SS' and DD', respectively. The free market price would be P_M and Q_M bushels would be produced and sold. Now suppose the CCC establishes a support or loan price at P_S. Consumers would only be willing and able to purchase Q_D bushels at that price, while producers would make Q_S bushels available. The difference (AB,

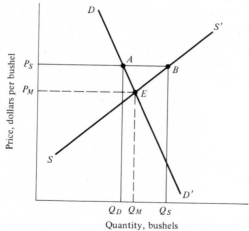

Figure 15.8 Effect of a Price Floor in Agriculture   In a free market, supply and demand would determine an equilibrium price, P_M, and quantity, Q_M. If a support price (price floor) is set at P_S, consumers will only purchase Q_D units while farmers are encouraged to produce Q_S units. The difference (AB or $Q_S - Q_D$) must then be purchased by the government at a cost of AB times P_S to taxpayers.

or $Q_S - Q_D$ bushels) would be purchased by the CCC at a cost of AB times P_S dollars to taxpayers.

Under a price support system, the effective demand function becomes DAB since if price falls to a level below A (or P_S), the farmers can sell all that is produced to the government at the support price. Should market forces (such as a decrease in supply, or an increase in demand, or both) establish a price above P_S, the farmer simply takes the market price and repays the CCC loan. Thus the support price is frequently referred to as a "price floor," since it provides a level below which price to the farmer cannot fall.

If the demand for the commodity in question is inelastic, total revenue to the producer will be greater under the support price than if a lower market price prevailed. That is, the area defined by P_S times Q_D is greater than the area P_M times Q_M. Since most agricultural products are characterized by an inelastic demand, it is not hard to see why such price support programs have been very popular within the agricultural community.

During the 1920s, the U.S. government—at the urging of farmers—developed programs for farmers that included reducing the acreage of certain major crops in order to limit production, and thus to raise farm prices. Such a program under which individual acreage allotments were assigned to farmers based on their previous acreage, production, and sales records was enacted into law with the Agricultural Adjustment Act of 1933. Acreage allotments in some form have been around ever since.

The chief objective of acreage allotments is to establish and maintain levels of production of certain agricultural commodities such that the market can absorb the output at prices considered to be "fair" to producers. Each year the secretary of agriculture, after determining the acreage necessary to supply domestic requirements, projected export sales, and normal carryover of the crop, announces a national acreage allotment for each crop covered by such legislation (e.g., corn, barley, wheat, cotton, peanuts, rice, and some kinds of tobacco). The national allotment is then allocated among states and individual farmers on a proportional basis.

The secretary of agriculture has the authority to set aside allotments as may seem appropriate, given market demand and supply factors. For example, on August 1, 1979, Secretary of Agriculture Bob Bergland announced that after two days of secret meetings the United States had given the Soviet Union permission to purchase an additional 10 million metric tons of U.S. wheat in the following 14 months. At that time he also announced that for the first time in three years there would be no major restriction on how much U.S. wheat growers could plant. It was estimated at the time that this would save U.S. taxpayers $660 million in farm subsidies and administrative costs.

Acreage allotment, or other crop restriction programs, can be evaluated with the help of a diagram such as the one in Figure 15.9. The

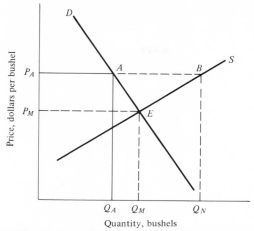

Figure 15.9 Effect of Acreage Allotments in Agriculture Supply and demand in a free agricultural market would establish an equilibrium price, P_M, and quantity, Q_M. The government can help farmers raise price by establishing acreage allotments to curtail supply. If supply is reduced to Q_A, the effect will be to raise price to P_A, the price consumers are willing and able to pay for Q_A units. Farmers would have the incentive to produce Q_N units at a price P_A and so some penalty may be adopted if acreage allotments are violated.

market supply and demand curves are S and D, respectively. The free market equilibrium price and quantity would be P_M and Q_M. If P_M is not judged to be a fair price, a higher price can be established by curtailing supply via acreage allotments. If supply is reduced to Q_A through such a program, the price would rise to P_A, the price consumers are willing and able to pay for Q_A units, as described by the market demand function. The effective supply function becomes Q_AABS. Farmers have incentive to produce beyond Q_A units since at the relatively high price P_A they would normally choose to produce Q_N units. Thus for allotment programs to be effective, there must be some penalty for planting more than one's allocated acreage. For consumers the cost is a higher commodity price and fewer units available than would be true with a free market. For taxpayers there is the additional cost of administering the program, but there is no cost for buying surplus production or supplementing market prices.

Selected Readings

Al-Zand, O. A., and Z. A. Hassan. "The Demand for Fats and Oils in Canada." *Canadian Journal of Agricultural Economics* 25:2 (July 1977), 14–25.
Arzac, E. R., and M. Wilkinson. "A Quarterly Econometric Model of United

States Livestock and Feed Grain Markets and Some of Its Policy Implications." *American Journal of Agricultural Economics*, 61:2 (May 1979), 297–308.

Duncan, Marvin, and C. E. Harshbarger. "A Primer on Agricultural Policy." *Monthly Review*, Federal Reserve Bank of Kansas City (September–October 1977).

Ike, Donald N. "Estimating Agricultural Production Functions for Some Farm Families in Western Nigeria." *Developing Economies* 15:1 (March 1977), 80–91.

QUESTIONS

1. Write a short explanation of the following terms or concepts that were used in this chapter:

    (a) acreage allotment
    (b) break-even point
    (c) income elasticity
    (d) isocost
    (e) isoquant
    (f) labor productivity
    (g) "labor-saving" technology
    (h) Lorenz curve
    (i) marginal rate of technical substitution
    (j) market demand
    (k) market price
    (l) parity price
    (m) perfect competition
    (n) price elasticity
    (o) price floor
    (p) price support
    (q) price taker
    (r) product homogeneity
    (s) production cycle

2. Why do you think the total demand for most agricultural products is inelastic with respect to both price and income? What relation do these elasticities have to the "farm problem" of declining real income of farm families? Does the relatively inelastic demand for wheat in total seem inconsistent with the notion that an individual wheat farmer faces a perfectly elastic demand? Explain.

3. Suppose that farmers can use two types of fertilizer (A and B) that can be substituted for one another along a typical isoquant curve (Q), as shown in

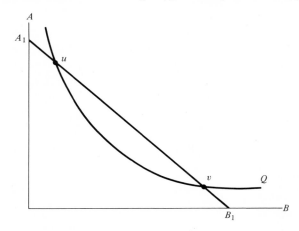

the accompanying illustration. The ratio of prices of the two fertilizers is $P_B/P_A = 1.1$. Two points along the isoquant are marked U and V.

(a) At which of these points is $(MP_A/P_A) > (MP_B/P_B)$ and at which is $(MP_A/P_A) < (MP_B/P_B)$?

(b) At which of these points will the $MRTS_{B:A}$ be the greatest? Why?

(c) Draw in an isoquant representing the maximum output possible, given the $1.1:1$ price ratio and the cost level represented by the isocost line A_1B_1. Indicate the amounts of A and B to use by constructing lines from this isoquant to each axis.

(d) What will the $MRTS_{B:A}$ be at this combination of inputs? Why?

4. There has been a movement toward larger farms and a decrease in the number of farms in the United States. What factors do you think have been contributing to this trend? Do you believe that this is a desirable or undesirable event? Why?

5. Explain whether you might expect to find diminishing marginal productivity for the following variable agricultural inputs:

(a) labor

(b) fertilizer

(c) water

(d) pesticides

(e) capital equipment

In each case, explain what you would expect to happen to the marginal productivity of the variable input if twice as many acres of land were available.

6. Fluctuations in agricultural prices and output are common. Consider, for example, the following data from the mid-1970s for the United States production of two crops.

YEAR	SOYBEANS		WHEAT	
	PRODUCTION*	PRICE	PRODUCTION*	PRICE
1973	1548	5.68	1711	3.95
1974	1216	6.64	1782	4.09
1975	1547	4.92	2122	3.56
1976	1288	6.81	2142	2.73
1977	1762	5.88	2036	2.33

* Millions of bushels.

What factors do you think would contribute to such fluctuations? How does this relate to the cobweb phenomena discussed near the end of Chapter 9?

7. What factors have contributed to the increasing demand for agricultural products produced in the United States? What factors have caused supply to shift? Given the initial supply and demand curves shown, illustrate the effect of these changes on price and output.

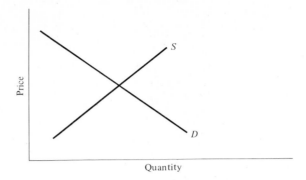

Quantity

8. The marginal cost, average cost, and average variable cost functions for a perfectly competitive firm are illustrated in the left-hand graph below. Market supply and demand curves are shown in the right-hand graph, with the equilibrium price being determined at P_1.
   (a) Explain why this price and the corresponding quantity for the firm (Q_1) determine what is called the "shutdown point?" What can you say about the firm's profit at this price?
   (b) Suppose that market demand increases such that the firm reaches the "break-even point." Draw such a demand curve (D_2) and label the corresponding price P_2. Show that price on both graphs and label the "break-even" quantity for the firm Q_2.
   (c) Now suppose that demand increases further to D_3. What happens to the firm's profit? Given the perfectly competitive nature of agriculture, what adjustment would you expect in this market? Illustrate the adjustment on the given graphs.

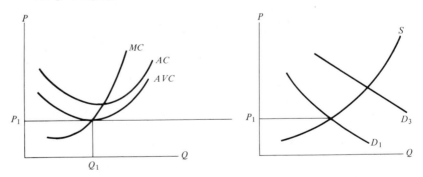

9. The following graph illustrates an initial equilibrium (E) combination of labor (L), and capital (K) in agricultural production, for a given isocost curve and the isoquant Q_o. There has been a trend toward more capital-intensive production in part due to new "labor-saving" technology. Draw in three new isoquants representing such a labor-saving technological change. Explain why you have drawn these new isoquant curves as you have in relation to Q_o and show a new equilibrium, assuming the isocost curve remains fixed.

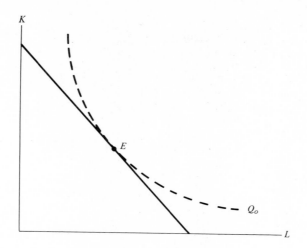

10. In Figure 15.5 we have illustrated the optimum combination of protein supplement and corn to feed hogs at different weight-gain levels. Suppose the
ratio of the price of protein supplement to the price of corn was 8.33. What
would be the optimum mix of feeds for the weight gain given by isoquant Q_1?
If that price ratio fell to 3.62, the optimum would be at point A on Q_1. What
would be the best mix of feeds to use at the 3.62 price ratio if one were
concerned with the weight gain represented by Q_2?

11. For eight classes of farm size (increasing from 1 to 8), the accompanying table
represents the percentage distributions of the number of farms and the cash
receipts received for 1970 and 1978. Complete the table by filling in the
cumulative percentage columns for each year. Also, plot the Lorenz curve for
each of these years on the grid provided on the following page. What do these
two Lorenz curves indicate about the equality of distribution of cash receipts
among firms in agriculture for 1970 and 1978?

SIZE CLASS	1970 FARMS %	1970 FARMS CUM. %	1970 RECEIPTS %	1970 RECEIPTS CUM. %	1978 FARMS %	1978 FARMS CUM. %	1978 RECEIPTS %	1978 RECEIPTS CUM. %
1	39.8		2.8		34.3		0.9	
2	14.3		3.4		10.4		1.1	
3	13.6		6.5		10.5		2.2	
4	13.2		12.3		11.1		4.6	
5	11.1		19.5		12.1		9.9	
6	6.1		22.1		14.6		25.0	
7	1.3		10.8		4.6		17.0	
8	0.6		22.6		2.4		39.3	

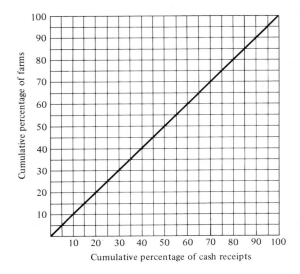

CHAPTER 16
TAX POLICY
AND
SOCIETY

PRINCIPLES OF TAX ANALYSIS
THE PERSONAL INCOME TAX
SALES AND EXCISE TAXES
CORPORATE TAXES
GOVERNMENT EXPENDITURES: THE OTHER SIDE OF THE COIN
SELECTED READINGS
QUESTIONS

We have all heard it said that "there are only two things about which we can be certain: taxes and death." It is our purpose in this chapter[1] to investigate only the former. Everyone in our society is impacted by tax policy in some way(s). Most persons pay taxes in various forms, such as income taxes or sales taxes, and most also receive benefit(s) from the expenditure of those tax dollars by various levels of government; for example, the use of highways, state or national parks, and public libraries.

More than two decades ago Richard Musgrave identified three types of effects that government tax and expenditures policies have on society: allocative effects, distributive effects, and stabilization effects. Allocative effects relate to the way in which resources are allocated among competing uses in the economy. For example, the decision to build a fleet of submarines means that fewer resources are available for the production of other goods and services; or a tax on a particular product may result in

---

[1] In this chapter we shall look only at a few examples of how microeconomic analysis may be used to evaluate tax policy. Readers interested in additional applications and/or a more complete analysis should refer to either of the following fine texts: (1) Neil M. Singer, *Public Microeconomics: An Introduction to Government Finance*, 2d ed. (Boston: Little, Brown, 1976); and (2) Edgar K. Browning and Jacquelene M. Browning, *Public Finance and the Price System* (New York: Macmillan, 1979).

lower consumption of that good and thus allocation of fewer resources to its production. The distributive effects refer to how a given level of production of goods and services is distributed among members of the society; that is, how the real income generated in the economy is divided. For example, the social security system redistributes income on an intergenerational basis through which younger working members of society pay taxes that go to provide benefits for older retired persons. The stabilization aspects of tax policy involve effects on the aggregate level of employment, total production, and the overall level of prices. This final category is more within the domain of macroeconomics. Therefore, our emphasis in the sections that follow will be on the allocative and distributive effects of tax and expenditure policies.

PRINCIPLES OF TAX ANALYSIS

There are many possible sources of tax revenue available to the various levels of government, each of which will have a somewhat different impact on economic activities. Taxes can be (and are) levied at almost any point in the overall flow of economic activity, as described in Chapter 1. The simple circular flow of economic activity as first presented in Figure 1.1 is reproduced here as Figure 16.1, with the addition of blocks indicating points at which taxes are likely to be imposed.

A tax levied at block 1 would represent a tax on personal income. Federal and state (and the occasional local) income taxes, as well as the employee portion of the social security payroll tax are examples of taxes at this point in the circular flow. A tax at block 2 would be levied on firms' productive inputs, such as a value-added tax, or the employer's portion of the payroll tax. Corporate income taxes can also be considered as occurring at this point. As business enterprises produce goods and services for sale to consumers, a tax may be levied on that flow of output. Thus block 3 represents another common point of taxation (most states and many localities use such sales taxes as a source of revenue). A tax at block 4 would be an expenditures tax based on total household purchases of goods and services. Such a tax is not very common because its use involves a very complete record-keeping process on the part of households. Each household would have to prepare the equivalent to a firm's balance sheet and income statement on an annual basis in order to accurately determine the year's actual expenditures. It is generally believed that this is unnecessarily burdensome and complex. Experiments with an expenditures-based tax in other countries, such as India, have been less than successful.

We must be careful in considering various taxes to differentiate between the statutory incidence of the tax (i.e., the blocks identified in Figure 16.1) and the effective incidence. The individual or business upon

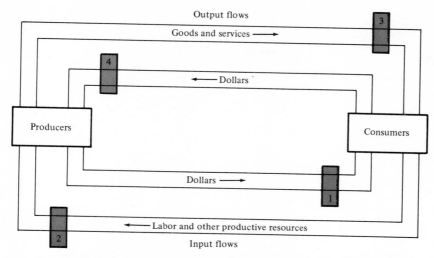

Figure 16.1 Taxes in the Circular Flow Model The circular flow of resources, products, and money in the economy can be used to indicate points at which various taxes are levied. For example, block number 1 could represent the personal income tax and the individual's contribution to social security. Block 2 would include such taxes as a value-added tax and the employer's portion of social security. Blocks 3 and 4 would represent a sales tax and an expenditures tax, respectively.

which the tax is levied may be able to shift some part, or perhaps all, of the burden of the tax to others. Tax shifting may be in either, or both, of two directions; forward or backward.

Let us first consider an illustration of forward shifting. Suppose that corn is produced in a constant-cost, competitive industry such that the supply curve S is perfectly horizontal and that the market demand for corn is given by the demand curve D in Figure 16.2. The market equilibrium price ($P_1 = \$2.50$) and quantity ($Q_1 = 5.8$ billion bushels) would be determined by the intersection of demand and supply at E_1. Now suppose that the government imposes a tax T of 10 cents per bushel on corn producers. This would mean that farmers would only be willing to supply any given amount of corn at a price that is 10 cents per bushel higher than before the tax. Thus the supply curve is effectively shifted upward by the amount of the tax, and a new equilibrium is achieved at E_2. The price consumers must pay is now $\$2.60$ per bushel and, consequently, under these conditions, the entire burden of the tax is shifted forward to consumers.

The ability to shift a tax forward in such a complete way is possible only when supply is perfectly elastic (as in Figure 16.2) or when demand is perfectly inelastic (a vertical demand function), or when both condi-

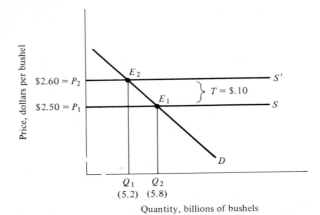

Figure 16.2 Tax Shifting: Perfectly Elastic Supply A tax on corn production of 10 cents per bushel is shifted entirely to the consumer if the supply function is perfectly elastic (horizontal). Without the tax, supply S and demand D intersect at E_1 with a market price of $2.50 established. Adding the 10-cent-per-bushel tax shifts the supply curve to S', and the equilibrium moves to E_2 with a price of $2.50.

tions exist. A more likely case is one in which neither demand nor supply is perfectly inelastic or elastic, such as the situation that was depicted in Figure 2.5. As a general rule, we can say that a greater share of the tax burden can be shifted forward when demand is more inelastic and/or supply is more elastic than when the opposite is true. Therefore, if we want to levy a tax such that the statutory incidence is the same as the effective incidence, we would prefer a relatively inelastic supply and a relatively elastic demand.

A tax is said to be shifted backward if the burden of the tax can be moved back toward the factors of production rather than ahead to consumers. Suppose, for example, that farmers faced with the 10-cent-per-bushel tax on corn have to absorb some of the incidence of the tax because the supply function is positively sloped as in Figure 16.3 (rather than horizontal as in Figure 16.2). It may very well be reasonable to expect that farmers would shift part (or all) of the tax burden (not already shifted forward to consumers) backward to suppliers of fertilizer or labor in the form of lower prices (wages). If indeed the supply of labor is relatively inelastic, it is likely that the market wage for farm labor would be reduced.

The examples given above comparing forward and backward tax shifting also illustrate some of the differences between partial equilibrium and general equilibrium analysis of tax incidence. In the partial equilibrium analysis of forward shifting we implicitly assumed that ev-

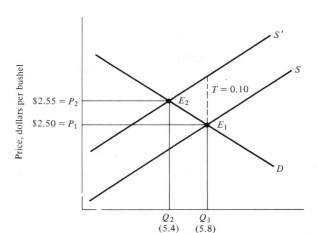

**Figure 16.3 Tax Shifting: Neither Supply nor Demand Perfectly
Elastic**   With a positively sloped supply curve and a negatively
sloped demand curve, part of the tax is shifted to consumers, but
part is absorbed by the producer or shifted backward to factors of
production. A pretax supply curve (S) and the demand establish
an equilibrium at E_1 at the price of $2.50. Adding a 10-cent-per-
bushel tax, shifts the supply function to S' giving a
new equilibrium at E_2 and a price of $2.55. In this case half the tax
is shifted forward while the remainder will be absorbed by others,
such as some backward shifting in the form of lower wage rates.

erything other than the effect on the price of corn was held constant.
However, in looking at secondary effects on the farm labor market we
opened the doors of general equilibrium analysis by investigating how
other markets may be impacted. We really only cracked that door a bit.
There would be a number of other secondary, and tertiary, effects in
various markets. For example, as corn production is reduced, we might
expect to see greater demand for soybeans resulting in upward pressure
on price in that market, which would itself trigger further effects. One
can see from this brief example how complex a full general equilibrium
analysis could become, and why in using economic models we tend more
toward partial equilibrium analysis even though only a few relationships
of major importance can be evaluated. This is, of course, the very essence
of using models—that is, to simplify very complex situations such that
only the most essential elements are considered.

In considering the desirability of a particular tax burden, we come
face to face with equity considerations. The question of what constitutes
an equitable, or "fair," tax system goes beyond the bounds of purely
economic analysis. Political, sociological, psychological, and philosoph-
ical issues bear heavily on such a question. There are, however, two

criteria for judging alternative taxes, in terms of the equity of the tax incidence, which have a long history of application by economists. They are the "benefits received" and the "ability to pay" principles of taxation.

Individuals do obtain some benefit from government expenditures financed by tax revenues, and conceivably those benefits could be identified and measured. Following the benefits principle of taxation, the persons who benefit most from the expenditures should contribute the most in the form of tax revenues. As you can well imagine, the problems with such a system are immense. For many government expenditures, it is very difficult, if not impossible, to identify the incidence of benefits (much less *measure* them), and we have seen that it is not always clear without thorough analysis where the incidence of a tax ultimately falls. Further, we may not want to match benefits with tax payments in many cases. For example, we have collectively made the decision in the United States that we do not want to deprive the children of poor families the benefits of education just because their families may not contribute very much to the tax revenues that support the educational system.

Nonetheless, there are some taxes that do follow the benefit principle reasonably well. Consider, for example, the federal tax on gasoline. Historically this tax has been "earmarked" (set aside) for the highway trust fund for use in the construction and maintenance of a highway network. The people that drive the most presumably get the most benefit from the roadways and are also the ones that pay the most dollars in gas taxes. "User charges," such as tolls on highways or bridges and fees at campgrounds, are essentially taxes that follow the benefit principle quite closely.

The ability-to-pay principle is used to evaluate the concept of fairness from the single perspective of taxes paid, rather than from a dual perspective including both taxes and benefits. In this view, government expenditures are determined on the basis of the desirability of programs, and then the necessary revenues are collected quite apart from any attempt to tie the revenue source with the program benefits. It is assumed that a person with greater income, or wealth, should provide a larger share of tax revenue to the public sector than a poorer person. We have no completely satisfactory way to measure the utility of money for an individual, much less to make interpersonal comparisons of the marginal disutility of paying taxes. However, the conventional wisdom is that it is less burdensome for a high-income person to pay x dollars in taxes than it is for an individual with a lower income to pay the same amount.

The ability-to-pay principle is often described as providing both horizontal and vertical equity in a tax system. Horizontal equity would be achieved if persons with the same set of economic circumstances (e.g., income, family size, etc.) pay the same level of taxes. Vertical equity, on the other hand, implies that persons in different economic circumstances should have different tax liabilities. In the United States we favor the ability-to-pay principle to the extent that we have shown a general preference for a progressive tax structure (one in which the *percent of income paid in taxes increases as income increases*). However, we have a sufficient number of nonprogressive taxes and "tax loopholes" that on balance our tax structure is not very progressive, and may even be regressive (the opposite of progressive) in some income ranges.

THE PERSONAL INCOME TAX

The federal personal income tax was established after passage of the Sixteenth Amendment in 1913 which gave Congress the power to use personal income as a tax base. This tax has grown in importance over the years, averaging well over 40 percent as a source of federal revenue during the past two decades (this does not include the employees' portion of social security taxes, which would add another 15 percent or more). Probably the most important reason for reliance on the income tax is that we favor the ability-to-pay principle of taxation, and income is generally regarded as a superior measure of that ability. We have, in fact, extended that reasoning to the extent that we favor a progressive income tax structure, with marginal rates reaching as high as 90 percent during the 1940s. The tax reform of 1964 set a maximum marginal rate of 70 percent, although the maximum rate now applicable to labor income is just 50 percent.

Even though we may agree to use income as a tax base, it is difficult to establish a definition of taxable income that is acceptable to everyone. We begin with adjusted gross income (AGI) which includes wage and salary income, rents, royalties, dividends, interest on savings of various forms, 50 percent of long-term capital gains, and all of any short-term capital gains. There are potentially important sources of income that are not included in AGI, however. Examples include interest paid by state or local governments (interest on municipal bonds), income in kind (housing provided to a university president, food produced and consumed by a farm family), fringe benefits provided for employees (health insurance, contributions to pension programs), and the flow of consumption benefits from owner-occupied housing. These exclusions, and others, are often considered to be "loopholes" in the tax structure—generally by people who cannot, or do not, take advantage of the particular provision. However, there is some reason for such "loopholes" to exist. In the case of not taxing interest on state and local government bonds, the purpose is to provide a mechanism for those governmental units to raise money for public projects in a way that is less costly than it would be otherwise.

Once AGI is determined, taxable income is found by subtracting an allowance based on household size (exemptions) and some types of deductions (standard or itemized). The income tax rates are then applied to this measure of taxable income. Because itemized deductions may vary a great deal among taxpayers, considerable horizontal *inequity* can result. Let us consider two examples that are not at all uncommon.

First, suppose that a young woman and a young man are both employed with each earning $20,000 per year, all of which comes from a salary (i.e., their individual AGIs are $20,000). Assuming that they both take the standard deduction and have no dependents, their taxes would be as follows:

	Woman	*Man*
AGI	$20,000	$20,000
− Personal exemption	750	750
− Standard deduction	2,200	2,200
= Taxable income	$17,050	$17,050
Tax liability	$ 3,473.50	$ 3,473.50
Effective average tax rate of AGI	17.4%	17.4%
Marginal tax bracket	31%	31%

Now consider what would happen if this couple decided to get married, assuming no change in their income and that they still have no other dependents. Their tax calculations would be:

	Couple
AGI	$40,000
− Personal exemption	1,500
− Standard deduction	3,200
= Taxable income	$35,300
Tax liability	$ 8,702
Effective average tax rate of AGI	21.8%
Marginal tax bracket	42%

We see that their is a considerable "tax penalty" for this couple being married as opposed to another couple who lived together without marriage. Such a horizontal inequity should not exist unless one can justify it on some other grounds. The degree of this marital tax penalty will vary at different income combinations; but in this example it would cost the couple $146.25 per month in *disposable* income (i.e., 1755 ÷ 12).

As a second example of how the personal income tax structure may create horizontal inequity, let us assume that there are two married couples, as described above, that are identical in terms of economic factors except that one couple rents a house for $500 a month while the other couple is buying a house with a $500 a month payment (including principle, interest, and property taxes). Depending on the mortgage rate, length of the mortgage, and property tax level, the amount of the $500 house payment which goes to pay the principle will vary but a likely figure especially on the early years would be something like $50. Thus, $450 per month qualifies as an itemized tax deduction ($5400 per year). Suppose that each couple gives $500 per year to charities (the church, the colleges they attended, etc.); that they both have other interest payments of $35 per month, or $420 per year (on a car they've financed, charge cards, etc.); that both couples have $350 per year of eligible sales tax deductions; that both couples pay $1600 per year in state income tax; and that both have $150 that qualifies as a medical deduction. Thus, both couples have $3020 in potential itemized deductions, other than those related to housing. Since this is less than the standard deduction, the renters would take that option and have the same tax liability calculated for the "couple" above. The home buyers would have an additional $5,400 in itemized deductions, and thus their tax would be calculated as:

	Couple (Buying a Home)
AGI	$40,000
− Personal exemption	1,500
− Itemized deductions	8,420
= Taxable income	$30,080
Tax liability	$ 6,696
Effective average tax rate of AGI	16.7%
Marginal tax bracket	36%

We see that there is considerable incentive within the tax structure for persons to purchase a home rather than to rent. In this example, the effect on disposable personal income is $167 per month, or an effective reduction in housing cost of that amount for the couple that is buying a home rather than renting. If we make the assumption that the overall quality of the two housing options is equivalent, this provision of the income tax structure creates a clear horizontal inequality.

Why should the federal government subsidize my purchase of a home? There may be many answers to this question, but certainly one of them is that they seek to promote home ownership and residential construction. The housing industry is one of the key sectors of the economy in terms of the general level of production and employment. Every new residence that is constructed stimulates demand for furniture, appliances, draperies, carpeting, lighting fixtures, and so on. The increased demand in these sectors further stimulates other sectors of the economy, and thus the multiplier effect can be substantial.

By permitting certain housing-related expenses to be used as deductions in computing federal income taxes, the government effectively reduces the cost of housing to homeowners. This has clear ramifications in terms of resource allocation that can be evaluated using a graph such as the one illustrated in Figure 16.4. The axes in the graph measure units of housing, H, on the horizontal axis and all other goods (money not spent on housing), G, on the vertical. Measuring housing units is not an easy task and there can be considerable disagreement about quantitative, as well as qualitative aspects of such a measure. However, for our purpose, it is sufficient to simply identify some representative unit, perhaps square feet of living space. The indifference curves I_1 and I_2 are just two of an infinite number from the consumer's utility function for square feet of housing versus other forms of consumption. These are independent of the price of housing, and thus tax policy, since they depend solely on the consumer's preference structure.

The budget constraints in Figure 16.4 are influenced by anything that impacts on the effective price of housing to the consumer. The line MN represents the budget constraint assuming that the homeowner bears the entire housing expense with no tax preferences. The vertical intercept M represents the consumer's money income since that is the amount

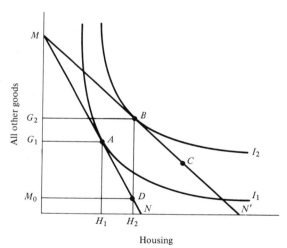

Figure 16.4 Effect of Tax Preferences on Home Ownership
By allowing various tax advantages for home ownership, the government reduces the effective cost of housing to homeowners, shifting their budget constraint from *MN* to *MN'*. The result is that more units of housing are purchased than would be true otherwise (H_2 rather than H_1), and homeowners would move to a higher level of satisfaction (I_2 rather than I_1). The cost to the government is $G_2 - M_0$ (= $B - D$).

available for other consumption if no housing is purchased. The absolute value of the slope of MN represents the price per square foot of housing (P_H), since the price of the composite good (money) on the vertical axis is unity, and, as we have seen before, the slope of the budget constraint in general would be $-P_H/P_G$. Under these conditions the consumer would opt to consume H_1 units of housing and G_1 of other goods, given the tangency equilibrium at A.

If part of the housing expense can be shifted to others due to tax preferences, the effective price per unit of housing would be $P_H - T$ (where T represents the reduction in federal income tax per unit of housing). This results in a counterclockwise rotation of the budget constraint around point M. Thus, the effective budget constraint for the home buyer thus becomes MN'. The new equilibrium amount of housing consumed will be H_2 units, determined by the equilibrium at point B. We see that generally more housing will be consumed if there is a tax preference than would be true otherwise; that is, $H_2 > H_1$. Of course, if housing were a Giffen good, H_2 would be less than H_1, but this is unlikely for most consumers. As diagramed, $G_2 > G_1$ as well. This result is not as general as the effect on housing consumption. Movement from an equilibrium at A to one at B, with the related changes in H and G, implies that as the effective price of housing declines, consumers will use some of the "savings" to purchase more of other goods and services (entertainment, clothes, travel, etc.). As we have seen above, this savings can be considerable ($167 per month in our example, or more than 30 percent of housing cost). How much of this money will be spent on other goods rather than more housing depends on the price elasticity of demand for housing.

In the example illustrated by Figure 16.4, the demand for housing would be inelastic. We can see that this is true by examining how much is spent on housing before and after the change in the effective price of housing. At the initial equilibrium (A), G_1 dollars are spent on other goods, and thus $M - G_1$ must be spent on housing. Given the tax preferences and a new equilibrium at B, G_2 dollars are spent on other goods, so $M - G_2$ is spent on housing. Since $(M - G_1) > (M - G_2)$, less must be spent on housing after the effective price reduction than before. If price declines and total expenditure (total revenue in terms of our earlier discussion of elasticity) also declines, demand must be inelastic. Were demand for housing elastic, the new equilibrium would occur at a point such as C in Figure 16.4.

The cost to the government for providing this subsidy to a homeowner can also be determined from this graph. If H_2 units were purchased at the market price, the consumer would spend $M - M_0$ dollars, since H_2 units correspond to point D on the original budget constraint, MN. However, the consumer only spends $M - G_2$ dollars, and thus the remainder $G_2 - M_0$ ($= B - D$) is the cost to the government.

Before leaving our discussion of personal income taxes, let us consider the effect such levies may have on a person's work effort and the supply of labor in general. To simplify the analysis somewhat, we shall assume that the tax rate is proportional rather than progressive. In Figure 16.5 three diagrams are illustrated, each representing a different possible effect of such a tax on the number of hours a person works. In each diagram income is measured on the vertical axis while hours of leisure

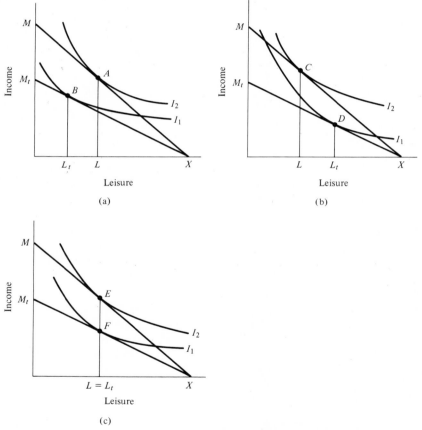

Figure 16.5 Effect of Income Tax on Work versus Leisure
Indifference curves representing a person's preferences between earning income (i.e., work) and leisure. The budget constraints represent pretax pay rates (MX) and posttax pay rates (M_tX). It is seen that a tax on earnings may or may not affect a person's work effort. (a) In this case the aftertax work effort is greater (leisure is less). (b) In this case the work effort is less (leisure is greater). (c) In this case a tax on earnings has no influence on hours worked (leisure is constant).

are measured along the horizontal increasing from left to right. Thus, hours worked is represented by the distance from X to any point to the left of X, increasing from right to left.

The indifference mappings in each panel of Figure 16.5 reflect an individual's preference structure for the trade-off between leisure and income (and thus the purchasing power to buy goods and services). The budget constraints identify various combinations of income and leisure available to the individuals, given a constant rate of pay. The slope of the three budget constraints labeled MX is the pretax pay rate. The effect of a tax on earned income is to reduce the "take-home" pay rate such that the budget constraint becomes flatter. This is represented by the budget constraints labeled M_tX.

For the individual in Figure 16.5(a) the tax would encourage more work and less leisure. The person's equilibrium changes from the initial point A with L hours of leisure ($X - L$ hours of work), to point B with L_t hours of leisure ($X - L_t$ hours of work). The price of leisure is now less, so we know that the substitution effect will be to increase the consumption of leisure. However, for this individual the income effect is such that more hours would be worked (less leisure consumed) after the tax than before.

Figure 16.5(b) illustrates the opposite result. The income effect in this case reinforces, or is dominated by, the substitution effect, with the result that more leisure is consumed and thus the work effort is reduced. When it is suggested that higher taxes on income may decrease work incentives, it is this type of preference structure between income and leisure that would have to prevail. In this situation the pretax equilibrium is at C, with L hours of leisure, or $X - L$ hours of work, resulting. The aftertax equilibrium is at D, with leisure increased to L_t and work reduced to $X - L_t$.

It is frequently argued that the supply of labor is very inelastic with respect to the rate of pay. If it were perfectly inelastic, a tax on earned income would not affect the work effort in either direction. This case is illustrated in Figure 16.5(c), in which the pretax equilibrium (E) results in the same work effort as the aftertax equilibrium (F); that is, $L = L_t$.

SALES AND EXCISE TAXES

An excise tax is a form of consumption tax that is levied on a particular commodity or group of commodities. Common examples include the federal excise tax on alcoholic beverages, tobacco, tires, air transportation, and gasoline, as well as state excise taxes on these and other products. The immediate effect of an excise tax is to raise the price of the taxed commodity. How much of that increase falls on consumers and how much on producers depends on the relative price elasticity of demand for the products. The shifting incidence of an excise tax is explained by Figures 2.5, 16.2, and 16.3, as well as the discussion surrounding those figures. In general, it is fair to say that most excise taxes are levied on products for which demand is relatively inelastic, and thus most of the burden falls on consumers.

Let us go a little deeper into the analysis of excise taxes than we have with the simple supply-and-demand approaches referred to above. Suppose that we want to evaluate the federal excise tax on beer. We can do so using an indifference curve/budget constraint mapping such as that depicted in Figure 16.6, in which beer consumption is measured on the horizontal axis and all other goods (money) on the vertical axis. Three relevant indifference curves are illustrated for a given consumer, where $I_1 > I_3 > I_2$. The budget constraint for this consumer with no tax on beer is given by MX, the slope of which (in absolute value) represents the pretax price of beer. The consumers' original equilibrium is at E_1, with B_1 units of beer consumption.

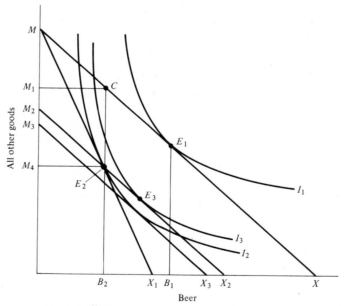

Figure 16.6 The Efficiency of an Excise Tax An excise tax on beer rotates the consumer's budget constraint from MX to MX_1 and causes the consumer's equilibrium to shift from E_1 to E_2, decreasing beer consumption from B_1 to B_2. The amount of tax collected is $M_1 - M_4$ dollars. If the same tax revenue was collected using a lump-sum tax, the consumer's equilibrium would be at E_3 and the loss of satisfaction would be less since $I_3 > I_2$.

Imposing an excise tax on beer rotates the budget constraint clockwise about point M to the line MX_1. With this posttax budget constraint, the consumer's equilibrium shifts to E_2, with beer consumption falling to B_2. Such a reduction in consumption is consistent with our earlier supply-and-demand analysis of an excise tax, but using this diagram we can evaluate additional consequences of the tax.

First, we clearly see that the individual beer consumer is at a lower level of satisfaction, since $I_2 < I_1$. We might ask ourselves whether the same amount of tax revenue could have been collected with less loss of consumer satisfaction. To do so we must identify the amount of revenue collected through the tax. When the consumer purchases B_2 units of beer, the total expenditure is $M - M_4$ dollars. However, only $M - M_1$ goes to the seller of the beer. This can be seen by recognizing that if the consumer purchased B_2 units at the pretax price, only $M - M_1$ would be spent (see point C on budget constraint MX). It follows that the amount of tax collected is $M_1 - M_4$ dollars.

Suppose the government levied a lump-sum tax on this consumer equal to $M_1 - M_4$ dollars rather than using the excise tax on beer to generate that revenue. The price of beer would not be affected, but the consumer's budget contraint would shift to M_2X_2 (which is parallel to MX since the price of beer is not changed). Constructing M_2X_2 through point E_2 means that it represents $C - E_2$ $(= M_1 - M_4)$ less purchasing power than the original budget constraint. Thus a lump-sum tax equal to the tax revenue from the beer excise tax would result in the consumer facing the budget constraint M_2X_2. But note that if the revenue were collected by such a lump-sum tax, the consumer would reach a utility-maximizing equilibrium at E_3 and achieve a higher level of satisfaction than if the revenue were derived from the excise tax (i.e., $I_3 > I_2$). This difference (between I_3 and I_2) is referred to as the *welfare cost* of using an excise tax, in comparison to the benchmark of a lump-sum tax that generates the same revenue.

A dollar measure of this welfare cost can be derived from Figure 16.6 as well. We have seen that the tax revenue collected by the excise tax described above is $C - E_2 (= M_1 - M_4)$. This is also equal to the distance MM_2 $(= CE_2$, because they are opposite sides of a parallelogram). A lump-sum tax of $M - M_3$, leaving the price of beer unchanged, would reduce the consumer's utility to I_2, the same as resulted from the excise tax on beer that generated only $M - M_2$ dollars of revenue. Thus, the distance M_2M_3 represents the dollar measure of the welfare cost of using the excise tax. It is also worth noting that use of the lump-sum tax has less impact on resource allocation than the excise tax since it interferes less with the functioning of the price system.

A sales tax is very similar to an excise tax except that it is levied on a wide variety of goods at a uniform rate. The results of a general sales tax, however, are different than those for selective excise taxes. A broad-based sales tax may not affect the price that consumers pay and may be more likely to be shifted backward to factors of production (who are, of course, also consumers). Assume that a constant-percentage sales tax is applied to every industry. All firms would then have less money available from sales to pay for productive resources, and so the demand for those resources would be reduced. This would result in a lower rate of resource compensation since all industries are taxed, and thus resources cannot avoid the impact of the tax by moving to other uses. (For a more detailed analysis of this shifting incidence of a general sales tax, see the Browning and Browning reference in footnote 1, especially pages 283–286.)

CORPORATE TAXES[2]

There are four areas of tax policy that bear heavily on investment decisions by a firm: the corporate income tax; investment tax credits; the allowable service lives for depreciating capital; and the rate at which capital gains are taxed. The corporate income tax rate is the percentage corporations apply to taxable income for determining tax liability. This rate has been changed frequently to stimulate or restrain economic activity, with the most recent proposal being for a reduction to 18 percent on the first $25,000 of taxable corporate income, to 20 percent on the second $25,000, and to 44 percent on income over $50,000.

Investment tax credits were first introduced to the tax structure in 1962 at a rate of 7 percent (3 percent for public utilities). An investment tax credit represents the proportion of the cost of a capital good that can be used as a direct reduction in tax liability. For example, if a firm had a tax liability of $100,000 but had invested in $200,000 of qualifying machinery, with a 7 percent tax credit, the tax liability would be reduced to $86,000—that is, $100,000 − 0.07 ($200,000). Since 1966 the investment tax credit was removed twice to help slow down economic activity, but in 1975 the credit was raised to 10 percent (including public utilities), with a scheduled reduction to 7 percent in 1981 (to 4 percent for utilities). There are restrictions on the types of expenditures that qualify for the tax credit. It applies only to machinery and equipment (except for specific exceptions), and for full credit the service life for such assets must be at least seven years. Also, it is worth noting that there must be a sufficiently large tax liability for the tax to offset. If there is not, the tax credit may be applied against taxes paid in the three previous years or passed forward for seven years.

[2] This section is based on Carl J. Palash's "Tax Policy: Its Impact on Investment Incentives," *Quarterly Review*, Federal Reserve Bank of New York (Summer 1978), 30–36.

The depreciation allowance is the deduction (from sales revenue) for wear and obsolescence of capital goods and structures that may be taken as an expense each year. There are three standard methods of calculating depreciation allowances that are widely used: straight-line, double declining-balance, and sum-of-years'-digits. These differ in the amount that shows up as an expense each year, and thus they influence the taxable income of the firm. Table 16.1 shows the pattern of depreciation allowances under each of these methods for an asset worth $10,000 with a ten-year service life and a salvage value of zero. The straight-line method distributes the value of the asset evenly over the service life. Therefore, in the example given, 10 percent of the $10,000 is expensed in each of ten years.

The double declining-balance method applies twice the straight-line rate to the *undepreciated* value in each year. In the example, the double declining-balance rate is 20 percent applied to $10,000 the first year ($2000), to $8000 the second year ($1600), and so forth. A taxpayer using this method may switch to straight-line (on the undepreciated balance) at any time. In the example such a switch is made in the seventh year.

The sum-of-years'-digits method determines the depreciation rate as the ratio of the service years remaining to the sum of the numbers from 1 to 10 the service life. In this example, the sum of the numbers from 1 to 10 is 55. Therefore, in the first year, the depreciation rate is 10/55, in the second year it is 9/55, in the third year 8/55, in the fourth year 7/55, and so on.

We can see from Table 16.1 that the double declining-balance and sum-of-years'-digits depreciation methods allow larger amounts of de-

Table 16.1 COMPARISON OF THREE DEPRECIATION METHODS FOR A $10,000 ASSET WITH A 10-YEAR SERVICE LIFE AND ZERO SALVAGE VALUE

YEAR	STRAIGHT-LINE	DOUBLE DECLINING-BALANCE	SUM-OF-YEARS'-DIGITS
1	$ 1,000	$ 2,000	$ 1,818
2	1,000	1,600	1,636
3	1,000	1,280	1,455
4	1,000	1,024	1,273
5	1,000	819	1,091
6	1,000	655	909
7	1,000	655.5	727
8	1,000	655.5	545
9	1,000	655.5	364
10	1,000	655.5	182
Total	$10,000	$10,000	$10,000

preciation in the early years and thus would reduce the firm's tax liability in those years. Therefore any tax policy that permits accelerated depreciation will encourage greater investment. The dollar amount of depreciation allowances can also be effected by policy measures which influence the service life of assets over which depreciation is calculated. The shorter the service life, the greater each year's depreciation expense. Therefore, a shorter service life will provide more incentive for investment than a longer one.

If an asset, such as property or common stock, is sold for a greater value than its acquisition cost, the increase in its value is referred to as a "capital gain." In order to qualify as a capital gain, rather than ordinary income, the asset must be held for 12 months or more. The tax that is levied on the increased value of an asset, called a "capital gains tax," is not incurred until the asset is sold and the increased value is realized. The advantage of not treating money gained from the sale of an asset as ordinary income (corporate or personal) is that capital gains are taxed at a lower rate.

Having reviewed the major areas of tax policy that affect corporate investment decisions, let us now focus our attention on how these effects can be analyzed using some basic microeconomic principles. We will begin with the corporate income tax. Firms view the tax as a cost of doing business, and money that goes to pay taxes is not available for other alternative uses.

> A reduction in the corporate tax rate increases a firm's aftertax earnings . . . [and] . . . raises the expected net aftertax return from an investment in corporate plant, equipment, or other useful capital goods. These new capital goods, together with labor, materials, etc., allow a firm to increase its output and sales. With a lower tax rate, a firm is permitted to keep a larger fraction of the profit from this new endeavor and thus is given an incentive to expand. (Palash, p. 33).

Thus, the lower corporate income tax would result in firms having more money to spend on various inputs than would be true at a higher tax rate. In Figure 16.7 this effect is illustrated by the two isocost curves, C_1 and C_2. Both isocost curves represent combinations of labor and capital that can be employed after netting out the corporate income tax. Therefore C_2 would depict the *effective resource isocost curve* at a lower tax rate than along C_1. At some initial corporate income tax, the firm would have C_1 dollars to spend on productive inputs and would maximize production by employing K_1 and L_1 units of capital and labor, respectively. Output would be Q_1. If the tax rate were reduced, C_2 dollars would be available to hire inputs. The firm could now increase production to Q_2 and employ capital and labor at higher levels (K_2 and L_2).

The effect of more liberal depreciation allowances (either accelerated methods of calculation or shorter service lives) has a very similar

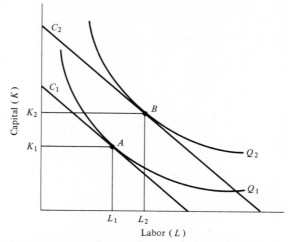

Figure 16.7 Reduction of the Corporate Income Tax   A reduction in the corporate income tax would make more money available to purchase various inputs such that the "effective resource isocost curve" would shift from C_1 to C_2. Output would be increased from Q_1 to Q_2 and it is likely that more labor and capital would be employed (certainly more of at least one input would be used). The increase in resource use is represented by movement from K_1 to K_2 and L_1 to L_2. The effect of more liberal depreciation allowances would have a similar effect.

influence on the firm's decisions. By changing the timing of the tax liability, reducing payment during the early years of an asset's service life, more liberal depreciation allowances increase the funds available for employing productive resources immediately. Actually, the cumulative dollar amount of the firm's tax liability is unchanged, so more liberal allowances amount to "an interest-free loan from the government" (Palash, p. 34). In Figure 16.7 this would again result in a shift of the effective resource isocost curve from C_1 to C_2 and a movement of the firm's equilibrium position from A to B.

Investment tax credits, by reducing the tax liability when a firm buys an eligible capital good, lower the effective cost of new capital. This may be represented by a more steeply sloped isocost curve, as in Figure 16.8 (movement from C_1 to C_2). Without an investment tax credit the firm would be an equilibrium at A, using K_1 units of capital and L_1 units of labor, producing Q_1 amount of output. An investment tax credit will stimulate production to Q_2 by reducing the effective cost of new capital to the firm. Given the production function inherent in the isoquants of Figure 16.8, the firm would increase both capital and labor usage (from K_1 to K_2 and from L_1 to L_2, respectively). This is not a necessary result, although it is quite likely. The lower effective cost of capital will certainly

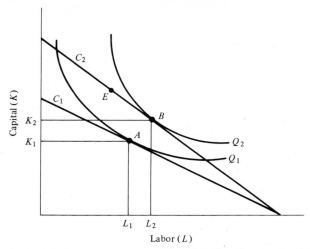

Figure 16.8 Effect of an Investment Tax Credit An investment tax credit reduces the cost of capital to the firm relative to the cost of labor and causes the isocost curve to become more steeply sloped. This is represented by movement from isocost C_1 to isocost C_2. Thus additional output is stimulated as the equilibrium moves from A (along Q_1) to B (along Q_2). A decrease in capital gains taxes is likely to have the same effect since it would also reduce the cost of obtaining new capital.

increase production and the use of at least one of the inputs. It is *possible* that a new equilibrium would result at a point such as E, in which case less labor would be employed than at A.

The effect of a decrease in the capital gains tax can be evaluated in a similar manner, but the path is less direct.

> A reduction in the tax rate on realized capital gains . . . affects mostly individuals but can also influence a firm's decision to invest. Because the aftertax value of realized capital gains is increased, stock ownership is made more attractive to investors. Stock prices would be bid up, enabling corporations to obtain more new money per extra share issued and thus make the financing of new investment easier and less costly. (Palash, p. 34)

Thus the result for the firm is movement from an isocost such as C_1 to one like C_2 resulting in greater output (Q_2 rather than Q_1) and greater employment of at least one productive resource.

GOVERNMENT EXPENDITURES: THE OTHER SIDE OF THE COIN

We too often complain about the taxes we pay without stopping to consider the benefits society obtains as those tax dollars are spent. Federal government expenditures include functions such as: national defense

(125,830); international affairs and finance (8,213); general science, space and technology (5,457); agriculture (4,269); natural resources and environment (11,456); energy (7,878); transportation (17,609); education, training, employment and social services (30,210); health (53,379); income security (179,120); administration of justice and general government (8,800); and, community and regional development (7,281)—where values in parentheses are *millions of dollars* for 1980. In addition, we derive benefit from expenditures by state and local governments for functions including: education (102,805); highways (23,104); public welfare (34,564); health and hospitals (22,542); and, police and fire (14,674)— where values in parentheses are *millions of dollars* for all states in 1977.

Government expenditures are generally classified as being either "exhaustive" and "nonexhaustive." Exhaustive expenditures are those that remove resources from the production of private sector goods. That is, these expenditures involve a reallocation of resources away from the private sector in favor of the public sector. Examples of exhaustive expenditures include national defense, administration of justice and general government, highway construction, and education. The allocative effects of such expenditures can be evaluated with the help of a production possibilities curve as shown in Figure 16.9. The production possibilities curve ($Y_0 X_0$) represents the maximum possible output for the economy and how it may be allocated among public or private goods. Every dollar spent on producing national defense (an example of Y) means that there is one less dollar available to allocate for private goods. At Y_0 all of the economy's resources are allocated to public goods, while at X_0 all resources are used for private goods. Neither of these extreme positions is likely, so we can expect to have production take place at some intermediate position along the production possibility curve.

If the current level of production was at point D, some resources would be unemployed and more public goods could be produced without changing the level of private goods (movement from D toward B). Alternatively, the Y_1 level of public goods could be maintained with production of private goods increasing toward A. Movement from D to any point between A and B would be most likely, but exactly where is not easy to determine. The particular combination of goods to be produced in each sector would best be determined at a point such as C, where the social welfare function W is just tangent to the production possibility curve. However, this decision is made within the context of the political system that may result in a less than perfect interpretation of the relative position of the social welfare function.

Nonexhaustive government expenditures consist of transfers of income from one segment of society to another, such as social security payments or unemployment compensation. These types of government expenditures do not directly reallocate resources since the money stays

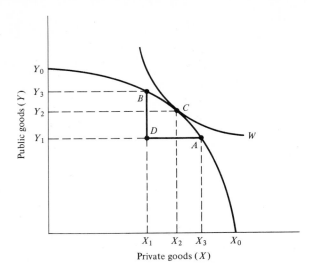

Figure 16.9 The Socially Optimal Product Mix The production possibilities curve from Y_0 to X_0 represents the maximum possible production of public and private goods in the economy. From an interior point such as D, we could move to any point between A and B by utilizing resources more fully. Once on the production possibilities curve, a decision in favor of more of either type of good necessarily means less of the other can be produced. Ideally the best position on the production possibilities curve, and thus the optimum allocation of resources, would be at the point where the social welfare function W is just tangent to the production possibilities curve.

within the private sector. However, it is quite likely that reallocations of resource use in the economy will result, since the individuals receiving the transfer are likely to have different spending preferences from the individuals who contribute more to the taxes that support the transfer payments.

Many government transfers are in the form of "in-kind" income rather than money income. Food stamp programs are an excellent example. In Chapter 6 we discussed "Subsidies: Money or Goods in Kind," including an evaluation of both housing subsidies and food stamp programs. In both cases it was clear that it would be more efficient for the government to give unrestricted money transfers rather than use programs geared to particular forms of consumption (see Figures 6.5 and 6.6, as well as the surrounding discussion). The general case of excise-type subsidies (i.e., subsidies tied to a particular form of consumption) can briefly be reviewed using Figure 16.10. The vertical axis measures "all other goods" (money), whereas the horizontal axis measures the subsidized good, X. The original budget constraint is BC_M, the slope of which is determined by the market price of X. The consumer is in equilibrium at A, purchasing X_1 units of X.

If we now subsidize the purchase of X, the budget constraint becomes BC_S, which is flatter because the effective price of X is less. The consumer would reach a new equilibrium at B, purchasing X_2 units of X. The market value of those X_2 units is the distance $M - M_1$, but the consumer only pays an amount equal to $M - M_2$ due to the subsidy. Thus the cost to the government is $M_2 - M_1$.

By shifting the original budget constraint (BC_M) upward by an amount equal to the government's cost $(M_2 - M_1$, or $B - D)$, we can evaluate the welfare effect of the excise subsidy. This new budget constraint BC'_M is parallel to BC_M, since it represents an income supplement

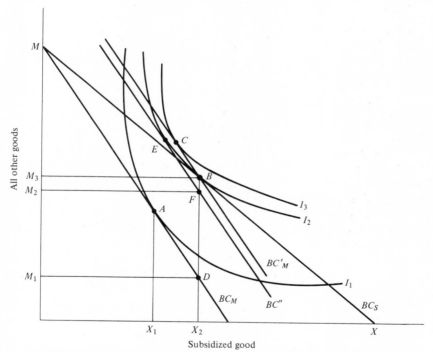

Figure 16.10 The Efficiency of an Excise Subsidy An excise subsidy for the good X causes the consumer's budget constraint to rotate from BC_M to BC_S with the consumer's equilibrium position moving from A to B. The subsidy program costs the government $M_2 - M_1$ dollars, which if allocated to the consumer as an income supplement rather than an excise subsidy, would increase consumer satisfaction by a greater amount (see the equilibrium at C). The welfare loss of using the excise subsidy rather than a cash grant is measured by the dollar amount of $M_2 - M_3$.

to the consumer rather than a change in the effective price of X. Given BC'_M, the consumer would reach an equilibrium at C, which lies on a higher indifference curve than B and thus provides greater satisfaction to the consumer *at equal cost to the government.* The difference between I_3 and I_2 is then a measure of the welfare cost of using an excise subsidy rather than a cash grant of an equal dollar cost to the government.

A dollar measure of the welfare cost can be determined by seeing what amount of a cash grant would bring the consumer to the same level of satisfaction as the excise subsidy (i.e., to indifference curve I_2), and then comparing the two costs. If we draw a budget constraint BC'' parallel to BC_M but tangent to I_2, we see that the consumer's equilibrium is at E. The cost to the government is $M_3 - M_1$ through the cash grant rather than $M_2 - M_1$ using an excise subsidy. Thus, it cost the government $M_2 - M_3$ more dollars to use the latter to arrive at the same level of consumer satisfaction. $M_2 - M_3$ is then a dollar measure of the welfare cost involved.

Another interesting aspect of evaluating public expenditures relates to the determination of the optimal level of provision of a public good. Public goods are those which are jointly consumed by all members of society and are characterized "nonrival consumption" and "nonexclusion." Nonrival consumption means that one person's consumption of the good does not limit consumption by others. Nonexclusion refers to the fact that it would be impossible, or prohibitively expensive, to exclude anyone from consuming the good. The best example is probably national defense, although such things as police or fire protection, highways, and flood control projects are also illustrative.

In determining the optimum level of provision for such goods, the objective is to equate the marginal cost of production with the marginal benefit from consumption of the good. Suppose for simplicity, there are just two consumers and that their demand curves for some public good are given by D_1 and D_2 in Figure 16.11. If we add their demand curves vertically, we obtain the total demand curve of the society for the public good in question. Recall that a consumer's demand curve represents the marginal value that consumer places on each unit of the good. In the case of public goods (due to nonrival and nonexclusive consumption) we must then add demand curves vertically to determine the benefits of all members of society (D_T). Note that this is different from finding the market demand for private goods, which are not characterized by nonrival and nonexclusive consumption. For private goods individual demand curves are summed horizontally to get the market demand (see Figure 4.7 and the surrounding discussion). The demand curve D_T represents the marginal benefits of the public good, including all members of the society.

Now suppose that the marginal cost of producing this public good is

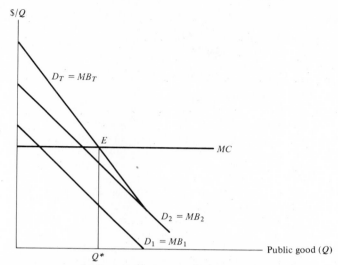

Figure 16.11 The Demand for a Public Good   For a public good, the total demand for society is found as a vertical summation of individual consumer demands. For a two-person case, $D_1 + D_2 = D_T$, as shown. Demand measures individual's evaluation of marginal benefit, and therefore the optimum level of production of a public good is where the marginal cost of production (*MC*) equals the sum of all individual marginal benefits (MB_T), such as at point *E*.

given by the line labeled *MC* (although a constant marginal cost is used for simplicity, this is not necessary). The optimum level of output (Q^*) is determined at point *E*, where $MB_T = MC$. Each individual would be able to consume the Q^* units since his or her consumption will not interfere with consumption by others (nonrival consumption).

Selected Readings

Allingham, M. "Inequality and Progressive Taxation: An Example." *Journal of Public Economics* 11:2 (April 1979), 273–274.

Guthrie, R. S. "Measurement of Relative Tax Progressivity." *National Tax Journal* 32:1 (March 1979), 93–95.

Lawler, Patrick J. "Payroll Taxes: A Two-Edged Sword?" *Voice*, Federal Reserve Bank of Dallas (May 1980), 1–12.

Modigliani, Franco, and C. Steindal. "Is a Tax Rebate an Effective Tool for Stabilization Policy?" *Brookings Papers on Economic Activity* 1 (1977), 175–203.

Wildasin, D. E. "Local Public Goods, Property Values, and Local Public Choice," *Journal of Urban Economics* 6:4 (October 1979), 521–534.

QUESTIONS

1. Write a short explanation of the following terms or concepts that were used in this chapter:

   (a) ability-to-pay principle
   (b) backward shifting
   (c) benefits-received principle
   (d) capital gain
   (e) corporate taxes
   (f) excise tax
   (g) exhaustive expenditures
   (h) forward shifting
   (i) marginal tax rate
   (j) nonexhaustive expenditures
   (k) personal income tax

   (l) private goods
   (m) progressive tax
   (n) proportional tax
   (o) public goods
   (p) regressive tax
   (q) sales tax
   (r) tax incidence
   (s) user charges
   (t) vertical equity
   (u) welfare cost

2. Suppose that an excise tax is levied on each of the goods for which market demand-and-supply functions are graphed.

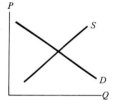 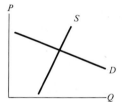 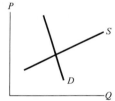

   (a) Show the effect of an equal excise tax graphically for all three situations.
   (b) In which case is the greatest portion of the tax shifted to consumers in the form of a higher price?
   (c) In which case would the equilibrium quantity decrease the most?
   (d) Of what relevance are the concepts of price elasticity of demand and of supply to the incidence of an excise tax?

3. Prepare a list of six goods or services that you consume and that are provided through the public sector. Estimate the "value" to you of each of these. Why aren't the goods on your list purchased through the private market economy?

4. The personal income tax structure in the United States provides for various deductions or exemptions based upon such things as: interest on a car loan, property taxes paid, the number of children in a household, mortgage interest paid, and payment of medical insurance premiums. Evaluate the reasons for and desirability (or undesirability) of having such deductions. Do these contribute to the equity of the income tax? Explain.

5. Suppose that a tax on earned income is imposed such that an individual's budget constraint rotates, as illustrated. The person has a pretax equilibrium at E. Draw in a new indifference curve (I_2) to illustrate the case in which the tax provides sufficient disincentive for work that the individual actually reduces the number of hours worked.

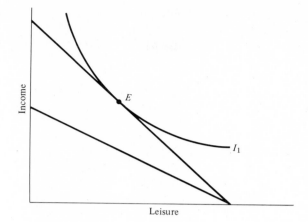

6. The accompanying graph depicts a college student's equilibrium consumption of wine and "all other goods."

(a) Show the effect that an excise tax on wine would have on the student's budget constraint.

(b) Now draw in another indifference curve to show a new equilibrium for the student.

(c) For the new equilibrium you have found, discuss the effectiveness of the tax as: (1) a source of revenue, and (2) as a deterrent to consumption.

(d) For your diagram, is the demand for wine price elastic? Why or why not?

7. Use the isoquant mapping shown to illustrate the effect of reducing the effective corporate income tax rate.

(a) Explain why the changes you show in output (Q), labor hired (L), and capital used (K) are or are not reasonable to expect.

(b) Would it make any difference to your analysis whether the reduced tax liability came from a reduction in the stated tax rates or from an investment tax credit? Explain and show both on your graph.

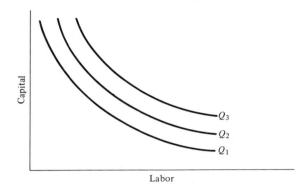

8. The accompanying graph represents a consumer's equilibrium consumption of solar generating equipment (X) and "all other goods." Suppose that the government wants to encourage people to use solar energy and so provides an excise subsidy for solar generating equipment.

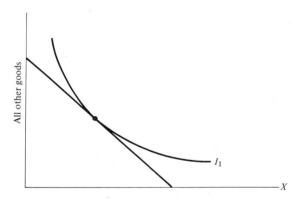

(a) Show the effect that such a subsidy would have by making the appropriate changes in the budget constraint and drawing another indifference curve to illustrate the consumer's new equilibrium.

(b) For your solution, would you say that the demand for solar equipment is price elastic? Why?

(c) Use your graphic solution to determine the cost of this excise subsidy program to the government.

9. Make a list of four types of government expenditures which are exhaustive and four which are nonexhaustive. What determines whether each of these is exhaustive or not?

10. In the graph shown, two individual demand curves for a hypothetical good
    (X) are illustrated.

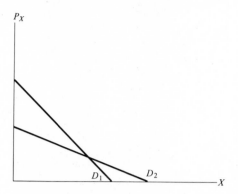

(a) Construct the total demand curve for X assuming that it is a private good
    and that these are the only two consumers.
(b) Construct the total demand curve for X assuming that it is a public good
    and that these are the only two consumers.
(c) Explain why your answers to (a) and (b) differ.

CHAPTER 17
ECONOMICS AND THE ENVIRONMENT

FORMS OF ENVIRONMENTAL POLLUTION
EXTERNALITIES
THE DEMAND FOR ENVIRONMENTAL QUALITY
BENEFIT/COST ANALYSIS
CONTROLLING EXTERNALITIES
SELECTED READINGS
QUESTIONS

The environmental awareness that developed during the 1960s and 1970s will be heightened as we move through this decade. Discussion about environmental issues will intensify as energy problems become even more acute and we are forced to re-evaluate the use of less environmentally desirable energy resources, or alternatively accept a lower standard of material well being. Analysis of environmental problems necessitates a multi-disciplinary study including the biological and chemical sciences, the behavioral sciences such as sociology and psychology, and the social sciences. Microeconomic theory has a great deal to contribute to such analysis because the fundamental processes or decisions which lead to environmental problems are of an economic nature (e.g., decisions involving the goods we want to consume as well as those related to how such goods will be produced). The tools of microeconomics, particularly the use of marginal analysis, can help to evaluate questions regarding environmental problems and can contribute to finding solutions that are socially desirable at the lowest cost.

FORMS OF ENVIRONMENTAL POLLUTION

The principal types of pollution that are the focus of attention in today's society are air and water pollution. Although our discussion in this chapter will use these areas as examples, the analyses are applicable to other forms of pollution as well. These include such things as thermal pollution, noise pollution, congestion, and pollution from discarded physical objects (beer cans, fast-food containers, rubble from old buildings, junked vehicles, etc.). In general, we can think of pollution as the accumulation of factors that are harmful or undesirable. This is a very broad definition, which serves to allow for a wide variation in what can be considered as a pollutant. Note that to qualify as pollution the accumulation must interfere with some desired objective of people. If we do not desire clean waterways, then using rivers as a sink in which chemicals are dumped should not be viewed as pollution. Similarly, noise is not a pollutant unless it reaches a level at which it interferes with our ability to enjoy life or perform certain desired functions.

Since air and water pollution are the most widely recognized forms, let us briefly review some attributes of each. Water pollution is divided into wastes that are biodegradable and those that are not readily (if at all) degradable. Organic waste materials from petroleum refining, agricultural production, and food processing, as well as domestic sewage, are examples of *biodegradable pollutants*. Bacteria and other microorganisms feed on such waste and break them down to natural organic compounds. This process involves the use of oxygen that is dissolved in the water and is also necessary for the existence of higher-level life forms in the water (such as fish). This is called an aerobic process, and in the process of degrading wastes nutrients are created that stimulate the growth of algae. The algae may eventually "take over" the lake or river as they thrive, whereas higher life forms are reduced due to a lack of dissolved oxygen.

The most generally accepted measure of water pollution is the level of biological oxygen demand (BOD) that results from dumping a waste product into our water resources. BOD measures the amount of dissolved oxygen that is used for a given amount of waste in five days at 20° Celsius (another time period or temperature may be used, but these are common). Such a measure allows us to compare the relative deleterious effects of different types of biodegradable waste products. A ton of waste from one activity may result in a far different level of pollution than an equal weight of waste from another activity. A measure such as BOD provides a means by which these differences can be evaluated.

The ability of a water resource to respond to a given BOD depends on several factors. Turbulent water can accommodate a larger BOD than still water because the more turbulent water absorbs more oxygen from the air. Water temperature also influences the capability of handling a given BOD. The warmer the water, the less oxygen it can absorb through aeration and the faster the bacteria will use the dissolved oxygen. Thus a warm-water lake in Oklahoma would have less ability to respond to a given BOD than a cool mountain stream in the northern Rockies. A third, and more obvious factor affecting the ability of water to purify itself, is the volume of the body of water. Clearly Lake Superior can handle a larger BOD than Atwood Lake (in Ohio), even after adjusting for temperature differences.

As the level of dissolved oxygen declines, aerobic life forms become more difficult to support and anaerobic types begin to dominate. Anaerobic processes give off waste products that are themselves undesirable, particularly methane and hydrogen sulfide. A previously clean body of water can become very darkened and may develop a bad stench, making it unfit for recreation, unable to support higher life forms, and costly to purify for other uses.

Nondegradable water pollutants are those that are not degraded by natural water biological processes. Such pollutants include heavy metals, various salts, and chlorides. Mercury poisoning from eating fish from waters in which mercury has been dumped has been a significant problem. Some classes of nondegradable pollutants are further classified as *persistent*. These include synthetics of various kinds (e.g., synthetic detergents), pesticides (e.g., DDT), and, in the extreme, radioactive wastes.

As an example of wastes in a major body of water, consider the following *partial* list of substances found in the water of the Ohio River near Cincinnati: various organic wastes, ammonia, arsenic, barium, boron, cadmium, chlorides, copper, fluorides, iron, lead, magnesium nitrates, phosphorus, selenium, silver, sulfates, zinc, organic chemicals, and radioactive substances.[1] The diverse nature of such pollutants creates a complex water quality problem that is all too common throughout the world.

Just as water resources have been too frequently viewed as a free dump for waste products, so also the air has been seen as a sink into which other forms of waste could be freely dumped. The four major sources of air pollution include: private residences, factories and utilities, trash incinerating facilities, and motor vehicles. The pollutants include carbon monoxide, sulfur oxides, hydrocarbons, nitrogen oxides, and particulate matter. Over 50 percent of all air pollution results from our heavy use of motor vehicles.

Motor vehicles emit carbon monoxide, which affect human health (especially heart and lung functions), and hydrocarbons and nitrogen oxides, which combine to form what has come to be called "smog." This smog causes eye irritation, respiratory and heart diseases, and corrosion of physical facilities. The compound growth rate in motor vehicle registrations in the United States has been well above 3 percent per year. This

[1] Joseph J. Seneca and Michael K. Taussig, *Environmental Economics* (Englewood Cliffs, N.J.: Prentice-Hall, 1974), 123.

growth in motor vehicle use is alarming when we couple it with the high level of pollutants emitted from such vehicles.

The stationary sources of air pollution are responsible for most of the sulfur oxides and particulate matter. Sulfur trioxide and water combine in the environment to form sulfuric acid, which can then fall to earth in the form of rain, causing corrosion and damage to vegetation. Particulate matter includes soot, ash, dust, and smoke. The city of Pittsburgh in the 1940s and early 1950s represents an example of extreme air pollution from stationary sources, especially the steel factories and related industry. It was not uncommon for residents to have to sweep porches twice a day to keep them reasonably free from soot and ash. Fortunately we can also look at Pittsburgh as an example of a metropolitan area that has made very real and substantial progress in cleaning up the environment, to the extent that today it is a relatively clean and inviting city.

Once pollutants are in the air we are forced to rely on natural processes for cleaning. Some chemical reactions may contribute to ridding the air of undesirable elements, but the primary methods by which the air becomes cleansed are through dispersal (air movement) and precipitation. The lack of air movement is one of the reasons that the Los Angeles area has such a severe air pollution problem (coupled, of course, with excessive use of motor vehicles).

In some respects air pollution is a more difficult problem than water pollution. First, whereas water pollution comes from thousands of sources (principally industrial and municipal), air pollution comes from literally millions of sources. Every, or nearly every, home emits some pollutants into the air and all of the motor vehicles streaming along our highways spew forth pollutants resulting from incomplete combustion, not to mention the emissions from aircraft, factories, and utilities. Second, we take air directly from the atmosphere for use, whereas water in most cases is piped to us for consumption. Since the water must be handled anyway, it is easier to purify to the desired level than is the air, which we must take pretty much as it comes (although some people do wear masks for certain activities such as jogging and the market for residential air cleaners is strong in some parts of the country).

EXTERNALITIES

An externality results when some of the costs and/or benefits of an activity accrue to individuals who are not directly involved with the activity. The externality is considered negative when it is a cost of some type that is shifted to third parties and positive when a benefit is shifted. In the case of negative externalities the social cost of the activity exceeds the private cost. As we shall see, this results in extension of the activity beyond what is socially optimal since the vast majority of economic decisions are based solely on private cost. On the other hand, activities that result in positive externalities have social benefits that exceed the private benefits and as a result tend to be underrepresented in the economy.

Such negative or positive externalities may result from the production or the consumption side of the marketplace. Let us consider an example of each. The faculty member whose office is next to mine frequently tunes his radio to a station that plays classical music. The sound spills over into my office and I receive benefit from his consumption of the classical music. This is an example of a positive externality resulting from a consumption activity. If my benefits were included in the determination of how many hours of classical music were consumed, the radio would be on more frequently than it is at present. Although this example of the consumption of music leads to a positive externality, such an activity could also lead to a negative externality. Consider your life in student housing at a time when you are studying for a major midterm examination. If a neighbor is playing a stereo at a loud volume, you might well find the noise distracting and irritating rather than providing a benefit to you. There are costs to you in lost sleep, a lower grade, increased stress, and so on, which are not part of the decision calculus in determining how long and/or loud to play that stereo. Thus the neighbor is likely to consume stereo music beyond what would be socially optimal.

On the production side both positive and negative externalities may also be found, although the latter are more frequently identified. Let us begin with an example of a positive externality resulting from a form of production. Suppose that I own some rental housing a few blocks from campus and that I decide to put new siding on the two houses I own in the block. In doing so I am adding to the value of these houses by increasing their useful life, making them more resistant to harsh weather, and increasing the satisfaction my tenants get from living there. These are private benefits which will yield a greater stream of earnings to me for years to come and thus provide incentive for me to make such improvements. However, there are additional benefits to other parties in the neighborhood such that the social benefits exceed the private benefits. By making these improvements to two (of the ten) houses on the block I have significantly improved the character of the area. Other persons living nearby benefit from having a nicer neighborhood in which to live. Even persons who just drive, walk, or pedal by receive some additional satisfaction. But since such external benefits are not included (or are included at a low weight) in the decision process, fewer such improvements take place than would be socially desirable.

Examples of negative externalities resulting from production activities frequently appear in daily news media. We read and hear about radioactive wastes being improperly disposed of in the state of Washington, emissions of radioactive gases at Three Mile Island in Pennsylvania, the dumping of asbestos fibers into Lake Superior, pollution of the Yellowstone River by industries in Billings, Montana, air pollution alerts in major cities, like Los Angeles, due to automotive exhaust and industrial emissions, and so forth. These are all situations in which some part of the total cost of an activity is shifted to other members of society resulting in social costs which are greater than private costs. The result is that these pollution-generating activities are extended beyond what would be a socially optimal level.

Let us now consider an analytical framework within which we can determine the socially optimal level for any of these activities. In Figure 17.1 we have drawn a marginal-benefit (MB) and a marginal-cost (MC) curve for some economic activity. The marginal-benefit curve is negatively sloped to illustrate the principle that for most things the additional benefit received from successive units eventually declines regardless of whether we are considering a consumption or a production situation. The marginal-cost function is positively sloped to show that additional units can generally be made available only at higher incremental cost.

As long as $MB > MC$, it would be desirable to extend the activity further. However, if $MB < MC$, the level of the activity should be reduced. The optimum level (Q_S) is, therefore, where $MB = MC$. If all costs are included in MC (such that social costs equal private costs) and all benefits are included in MB (such that social benefits equal private benefits), the level shown as Q_S will be optimal from a societal perspective. This will be true if there are no externalities, either positive or negative (and no monopolistic influences), so that the marginal private

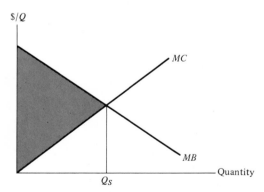

Figure 17.1 The Socially Optimal Output   For nearly all economic activities the marginal benefits (MB) will decline and marginal costs (MC) will increase as quantity increases. If all benefits and all costs are included, the socially optimal quantity is at Q_S, where $MB = MC$. The net benefit to society (excess of benefits over costs) is the shaded area below MB and above MC.

benefits and marginal private costs are identical with marginal social benefits and marginal social costs, respectively.

The total benefit to society of having the Q_S units is the area under the marginal-benefit curve between the origin and Q_S. The total cost to society for Q_S units is the area under the marginal-cost curve between the origin and Q_S. Therefore, the difference in these areas represents the net benefit to society resulting from the production and consumption of Q_S. This is shown as the shaded area in Figure 17.1. This general type of model provides a foundation on which we can build in order to evaluate the influence of externalities.

Let us first consider the case of a negative externality, such as the dumping of waste products into a river or stream rather than disposing of them in some other manner. In analyzing this case initially we will assume that there are no concurrent positive externalities resulting from the activity. In Figure 17.2 we see that the marginal private benefit (*MPB*) equals the marginal social benefit (*MSB*), which reflects the lack of any positive externality. All of the benefits accrue to the firm that dumps the waste materials into the river.

However, the marginal private cost (*MPC*) does not reflect the entire incremental cost to society. As the firm produces more output and dumps additional amounts of waste into the river, part of the full cost of producing the product is shifted to other members of society. Since fish life in

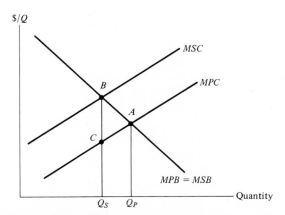

Figure 17.2 Negative Externalities In the case of a negative externality the marginal social costs (*MSC*) are greater than the marginal private costs (*MPC*). If there are no positive externalities, marginal private benefits (*MPB*) equal marginal social benefits (*MSB*). If the external costs are ignored, production would be at Q_P, where *MPC* = *MPB*. However, this is greater than the socially optimal level Q_S, at which all costs are considered and *MSC* = *MSB*.

the river may be destroyed, people who once used the river for recreational fishing must now go elsewhere for those recreational benefits, and so they bear part of the cost. The river may well become too polluted to be enjoyed as a place to swim or water ski (it may even be a health hazard to do so) and people must use alternative facilities—which must have been more costly, or of lower quality, or people would have used them in the first place. In addition, communities that withdraw water from the river downstream from the source of the pollutant will have to spend more money purifying the water for human consumption. Thus, residents of those communities will incur additional cost for water consumption either through higher direct charges or higher local taxes.

It follows then that the marginal social cost (MSC) will be above the marginal private cost curve, as illustrated in Figure 17.2. If only private costs and benefits are included in the polluting firm's decision process, production of Q_P units would result. However, if social costs are considered, the optimum rate of production is seen to be Q_S units. Since $Q_S < Q_P$, we see that the existence of a negative externality will be likely to lead to excessive production of the good involved and therefore to a misallocation of society's resources.

Later in this chapter we shall consider some alternative methods for correcting such a market failure. At this point, however, let us briefly consider one possibility. Suppose that the government were to levy a tax in the amount BC per unit on the firm involved. This would shift the firm's marginal-cost function (MPC) up to MSC. The firm would then find Q_S to be the optimum level of production.

Now let us turn to a situation in which a positive externality results from the production of some good. In this case we will assume that no negative externalities are involved such that $MPC = MSC$ (i.e., all costs are internalized). The marginal social benefits (MSB) will exceed marginal private benefits, as illustrated in Figure 17.3.

If the firm evaluates only MPB and MPC in determining the rate of output, Q_P units will be produced. However, if the additional benefits that others receive are also considered, the optimum level of output would be determined by the intersection (or equality) of MSC and MSB. This would result in Q_S units of output. The firm might be encouraged to expand production to this socially optimal level if a subsidy of BC dollars per unit were provided. This would generate additional private benefits to the firm and shift the marginal private benefit function upward until $MPB = MSB$. We see in Figure 17.3 that the existence of positive externalities can be expected to lead to too low a level of production ($Q_P < Q_S$) and therefore a misallocation of society's resources.

It is, of course, possible that both positive and negative externalities could exist simultaneously. If so, the results in terms of resource alloca-

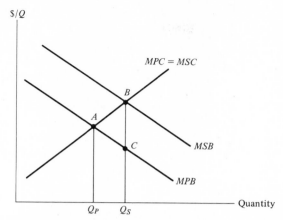

Figure 17.3 Positive Externalities When a positive externality exists, the marginal social benefits (*MSB*) are greater than the marginal private benefits (*MPB*). With no negative externality, marginal private costs (*MPC*) are equal to marginal social costs (*MSC*). If the external benefits are not considered, the rate of output would be Q_P, which is less than the socially optimal level Q_S, where $MSB = MSC$.

tion will depend on the relative magnitude of the two externalities. Three possible cases are illustrated in Figure 17.4. In Figure 17.4(a) the negative externalities dominate the positive ones such that the private sector would tend to overproduce (i.e., $Q_P > Q_S$). A tax of AB dollars per unit would shift MPC up enough that $MPC = MPB$ at the socially optimal level of production Q_S. Note that this is less than the tax that would have been appropriate in Figure 17.2, in which no positive externalities existed. If the same size tax were used here as in Figure 17.2 (equal to the vertical distance between MSC and MPC), the firm would choose to produce Q_1 units, which is less than the socially optimal level Q_S.

In Figure 17.4(b) the positive and negative externalities exactly offset each other. When the firm equates MPB with MPC, the socially optimal level of production is obtained because $Q_P = Q_S$. No interference with the market system would be necessary to correct for misallocation of resources in this case.

In Figure 17.4(c) we have illustrated the case in which the positive externalities dominate the negative ones. The firm would be led to produce at too low a rate of output ($Q_P < Q_S$). A subsidy of AB dollars per unit would encourage the firm to expand production to the socially optimal level, Q_S. If a subsidy equal to the entire difference between marginal private benefits and marginal social benefits was to be used (as in Figure 17.3), the firm would overproduce since $Q_1 > Q_S$.

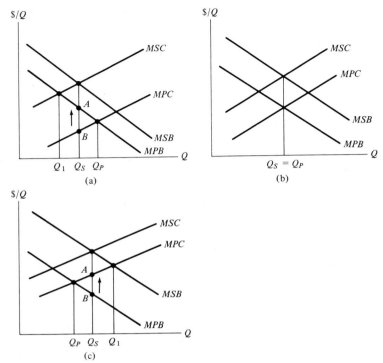

Figure 17.4 Interaction of Positive and Negative Externalities
If both positive and negative externalities exist simultaneously,
the socially optimal level of output (Q_S) may be less than, equal to,
or greater than the optimal level considering only private costs
and benefits (Q_P). (a) In this case the negative externality
dominates and $Q_S < Q_P$. A tax of AB would lead to the socially
optimum output. (b) If the two externalities exactly offset each
other, $Q_S = Q_P$ without any tax or subsidy. (c) In this case the
positive externality dominates, such that $Q_S > Q_P$. Here a subsidy
of AB would lead to the socially optimum output.

THE DEMAND FOR ENVIRONMENTAL QUALITY[2]

Our demand for environmental quality is different from our demand for
most goods or services in a substantial way. Most of the things we consume can be classified as *private goods* because we obtain property
rights to the goods and can therefore exclude others from obtaining benefits from those goods. For a pure private good, we can completely
eliminate any and all joint consumption that would yield benefits to
others. An example might be our consumption of a candy bar. Other
things we consume may have some degree of publicness, in the sense

[2] This section is based on Seneca and Taussig, op. cit., 90–97.

that some of the benefits spill over to others. For example, if I install a yard light, I receive the bulk of the benefit, but some benefits do accrue to my neighbors and others who walk by my house at night.

One could array all goods and services along a continuum from purely private goods (like a candy bar) to *purely public goods*. Perhaps the most common example of a pure public good is national defense. Once the government determines the desired level of national defense to be provided, that amount is available to all of us, and my consumption does not diminish the ability of others to benefit from the same level of defense. I obtain no property right to national defense and I cannot prohibit others from consuming it equally. That is, I cannot, nor can anyone else, exclude any other person from consumption. The marginal cost of providing national defense to one more person is virtually zero, while the cost of excluding anyone from consumption would be very high.

Environmental quality is also an example of a public good, or at least has attributes of being a public good. If a high degree of air quality is provided for one person, it is equally available to all others. Further, the marginal cost of extending that level of air quality to one more person is very nearly zero. With water quality, some exclusion may be possible, and thus water quality is not as close to being a pure public good as is air quality.

In the case of private goods, we have seen that the market demand is found as the horizontal summation of all individuals' demand functions (see Chapter 4, especially Figure 4.7). Thus, at each level of value (price) we find how many units each consumer would be willing and able to purchase, and then we add these amounts for all consumers to determine the market demand at that price. For example, if there are five consumers for a product who would purchase 10, 15, 5, 30, and 25 units at a price of \$7.95, the market demand at that price would be 85 units ($= 10 + 15 + 5 + 30 + 25$). Doing the same thing for all possible prices would yield the market demand schedule or curve.

For public goods, individuals cannot vary in the quantity they choose to consume. A given level of national defense, or air quality, is provided, and we all consume that level. As illustrated in Figure 17.5, the demand curve for a public good is the vertical summation of individual consumer demands, rather than a horizontal summation as for private goods. If Q_o is the level of the public good that is made available, consumer 1 (represented by demand D_1) would have a willingness to pay (or valuation) equal to P_1. The second individual in this hypothetical two-person case is represented by the demand curve D_2 and has an individual valuation of P_2 for Q_o units. Thus, for the entire society the valuation of Q_o units is P_T ($= P_1 + P_2$).

The demand curve for public goods can be expected to have a negative slope just as the demand for a private good does since both types of

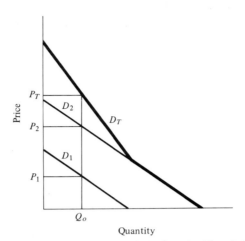

Figure 17.5 The Demand for a Public Good The demand curve for a public good (D_T) is the vertical sum of all individual demand functions for the good (D_1 and D_2 for this two-consumer example). If Q_o is the quantity of the public good provided consumer 1 values that amount at P_1, whereas consumer 2 values it at P_2. Thus, P_T (= $P_1 + P_2$) is the total value society places on having Q_o of the public good, such as environmental quality.

goods are likely to be subject to diminishing marginal utility. Consider the case of air quality. At low levels of air quality, we would value a unit of additional quality highly since we would see a connection between air quality and health fairly readily. However, as the air quality is improved, the benefit we perceive from additional units becomes less. Once the air is as fresh and clean as it is at Logan Pass in Glacier National Park, there is little additional benefit to be gained from greater air quality.

This approach to estimating the value of a public good may actually provide just the minimum possible value. This is because individuals' willingness to pay is bounded by their income and stock of assets even though the potential value of the public good might be much more. My ability to pay for the minimum level of air quality that will support life is limited by my income and assets. However, there is no price that would compensate me for the loss of life should that level of air quality not be available.

It is obviously very difficult to estimate individual demand functions for environmental quality since there is no market mechanism that generates price signals. There are methods to approximate the appropriate values through nonmarket techniques, but they are subject to considerable potential error of either overstatement or understatement of the true valuation of the public good.

BENEFIT/COST ANALYSIS

In the market for private goods and services the price system acts as a rationing device, providing signals that eventually determine what goods (and what quantities) will be produced. For a public good, such as environmental quality, there is no price mechanism, and therefore allocation decisions must be made through political and/or bureaucratic channels. Before 1965 there was little explicit recognition of the importance of using a systematic approach to such decisions involving government expenditures. During the Johnson administration, the Planning-Programming-Budgeting System (PPBS) was established to provide for a systematic evaluation of government expenditures using benefit/cost analysis. While the success of the system has not reached everyone's expectations, it has provided an improved framework for economic decisions in the public sector.

Benefit/cost analysis is essentially a way of thinking and problem solving that incorporates a systematic and analytical process into the decision process. As the term implies, benefits are compared to costs in evaluating an expenditure program. If benefits (B) exceed costs (C), the project is at least worthy of further consideration. Most frequently this comparison is expressed as the "benefit-to-cost ratio" or the "B/C ratio." Thus if $B/C > 1$, the project is desirable.

In general, if two projects that are mutually exclusive and both have B/C ratios greater than one, the project with the higher ratio is the more desirable. An example would be the decision whether to construct a second Panama Canal—and, if so, at which of two sites, A or B. If only one B/C ratio is greater than one, the decision would be to build the canal at that location. Thus, if $(B/C)_A > 1$ but $(B/C)_B < 1$, the canal should be built at A. But if both ratios exceed one and $(B/C)_B > (B/C)_A$, the preferable site is B.

Some types of expenditures will not be as "lumpy" as such a major project as building a canal, but rather may involve a continuum of levels. Environmental quality is in the latter class. We have options ranging, at least conceptually, from such an impure environment that human life could not be maintained to a level of purity represented by water that is pure H_2O and air that is pure O_2 (neither such pure water nor such pure air would probably be desirable, however). For such continuous cases, the B/C ratio is still important but the additional benefits and costs of expanding the level of environmental quality become more important. In particular we need to evaluate the relationship between the marginal social benefit and the marginal social cost of successive units of environmental improvement.

Figure 17.6 illustrates representative marginal social benefit (MSB) and marginal social cost (MSC) curves. The MSB curve is the social

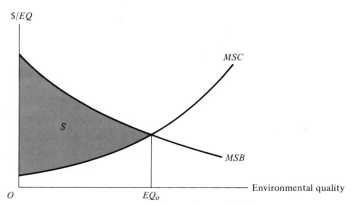

Figure 17.6 The Optimum Environmental Quality The demand curve for environmental quality is the marginal social benefit curve (*MSB*). The optimum level of environmental quality is EQ_o, where *MSC = MSB*. The maximum net benefit to society is the difference between the area under *MSB* and the area under *MSC* between *O* and EQ_o. This is represented by the shaded area *S*.

demand function for environmental quality and is derived in the same manner as D_T in Figure 17.5. The area under the *MSB* curve up to EQ_o is the total benefit accruing to society if EQ_o units of environmental quality are available. This area corresponds to *B* in the *B/C* ratio. The *MSC* curve represents the additional cost of providing successive units of environmental quality, and thus the area under *MSC* up to EQ_o is the total cost of providing EQ_o (this cost corresponds to *C* in the *B/C* ratio). The difference between these areas is the net benefit to society of having the level of environmental quality identified as EQ_o. This difference is $S = B - C$ and must be positive if $B/C > 1$. The shaded area in Figure 17.6 represents *S*.

For any level of environmental quality less than EQ_o, $MSB > MSC$ and thus *S* can be increased (or the *B/C* ratio increased) by increasing the level of environmental quality toward EQ_o. Beyond EQ_o, $MSC > MSB$, and thus those additional levels of environmental quality reduce *S* (or reduce the *B/C* ratio). Thus, using benefit/cost analysis we see that the socially optimal level of environmental quality is where $MSB = MSC$.

There are four major problems in using benefit cost analysis that we should note. First, and perhaps most critical, is that many (if not most) projects yield benefits and costs that extend years into the future. These future benefits and costs must be converted to their present values in order to be properly compared. This is because there is a positive time preference for money; a dollar today is worth more than a dollar one year from now.

The present value (*PV*) of any stream of values is the sum (Σ) of the value in each year (R_t) divided by one plus the appropriate discount rate (r_t) to the tth power, where t represents a particular year. Thus

$$PV = \sum \frac{R_t}{(1 + r_t)^t}$$

Since both benefits and costs have some time flow, we must calculate the present values for each: PVB and PVC, respectively. If the costs include some initial capital outlay K in the first year, the benefit/cost ratio becomes

$$\frac{B}{C} = \frac{PVB}{PVC} = \frac{\Sigma B_t/(1 + r_t)^t}{K + \Sigma C_t/(1 + r_t)^t}$$

where B_t is the benefit in year t and C_t is the cost in year t.

The social discount rate (r_t) becomes critical in calculating such a benefit/cost ratio. The higher the discount rate, the lower the present value of benefits and costs. Depending on the values of B_t and C_t in each year, varying r_t may determine whether a project passes the $B/C > 1$ test. Many people argue that in practice too low a discount rate is used and that the true social value of many projects are overstated as a result. Frequently the discount rate used is perhaps one-half the current market rate for money in the private sector. Since the private sector market rate may represent the true opportunity cost of money, many economists believe such a rate should be used in benefit/cost calculations. This entire problem is severely compounded by our inability to accurately forecast interest rates. For example, at year end 1978, few people would have predicted a prime interest rate of 16 percent during 1979; yet after the Federal Reserve actions in October 1979 interests increased dramatically. It is common, therefore, to settle on some present social discount rate and use that rate for all years involved in calculating the present values (even though doing so may dramatically influence the results if there are significant changes in interest rates over the life of the project).

A second problem with B/C analysis involves the identification and measurement of benefits and costs. The difficulties are generally most severe on the benefit side since there are usually some market prices for the components of the cost side. What are the benefits of cleaning up Lake Erie? There are industrial benefits involving the fishing industry, benefits to people who would use the lake for swimming and water skiing, benefits to boaters who would sail and/or cruise the lake, benefits to those who would take advantage of sports fishing, benefits to communities that use the lake water for consumption, and so on. Not only is it often hard to identify all possible beneficiaries of environmental quality, but once they are identified, it is difficult to quantify their potential benefits.

A third, but somewhat related, problem is that most benefit/cost analysis can only be readily evaluated in a partial equilibrium framework. Secondary and tertiary effects are even more difficult to identify and measure, and so are often ignored completely. Finally, income distribution aspects such as public or social programs are generally not considered. The impact of an environmental quality program on social welfare may depend on whether the money to pay for the program comes from persons at the high end of the income distribution or from those at the lower end, as well as on how the benefits are distributed among groups. Some attempts have been made to assign weights to benefits and costs (generally favoring low-income groups) but the value judgments involved in such weightings go a long way toward reducing the objectivity of the entire benefit/cost analysis.

CONTROLLING EXTERNALITIES[3]

In this final section of the chapter, we will review four of the alternative types of policies that are frequently considered for adjusting for or controlling negative externalities. The four are: strict regulation, compensating victims, providing a subsidy for cutting back on pollution, and the use of effluent charges to reduce pollution. Before discussing these we should first refine our understanding of the marginal social costs and the marginal social benefits from increasing the level of environmental quality, *for a given level of production in the economy.*

We have shown the *MSB* function to be negatively sloped but have not commented on its likely shape. As shown in Figure 17.7(a) at low levels of environmental quality (*EQ*), *MSB* will be very high. If we begin at zero with such a low *EQ* that human life cannot be supported, the marginal social benefit of improving the environment is essentially infinite. But as *EQ* increases, *MSB* can be expected to diminish. If we designate *EQ** as a pristine pure level of environmental quality, we can say that beyond that level there would be no additional benefit from further increase in *EQ*. Thus, *MSB* falls to zero at that point. It seems reasonable that society would value the initial life-supporting improvements in *EQ* much more highly than subsequent units and that *MSB* would decline more readily at first than it would as *EQ** was approached. Therefore, it is likely (though not necessary to our analysis) that the *MSB* curve will be convex to the origin as illustrated in Figure 17.7(a).

In earlier diagrams we have shown *MSC* to have a positive slope but have not discussed its shape in any more detail. In Figure 17.7(b) we have drawn the *MSC* curve as also being convex to the origin. At very low

---

[3] This section is based in part on Matthew Edel, *Economies and the Environment* (Englewood Cliffs, N.J.: Prentice-Hall, 1973), chap. 5, 85–111.

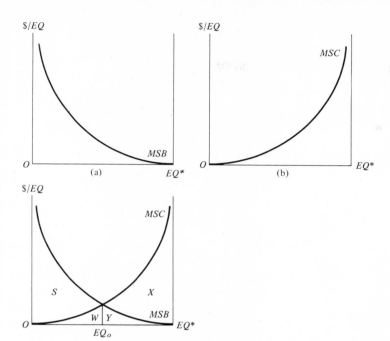

**Figure 17.7 Society's Net Benefit from the Optimum
Environmental Quality** If *EQ** represents a complete level of
environmental quality, (a) the *MSB* curve reaches zero at that level
but (b) *MSC* increases very rapidly as *EQ** is approached. (c) The
socially optimal level of environmental quality is EQ_o, where
MSB = MSC. *S* represents the net benefit of reaching EQ_o. Area *Y*
is the potential benefit of increasing environmental quality from
EQ_o to *EQ**; however, the cost of doing so is *X + Y*.

levels of *EQ*, increasing quality slightly would be relatively inexpensive.
However, as *EQ** is approached, the additional cost of further units of
purification would become astronomical. Suppose, for example, that
Lake Erie were somehow cleaned to its pristine state, and then someone
accidentally spilled one quart of motor oil into the 9940-square-mile
lake. Further, assume that wind and water currents quickly spread the oil
evenly over this vast surface area. The cost of recovering every last drop-
let of oil would be unthinkably high. Thus we might draw the *MSC*
function as exploding upward as it approaches *EQ**. (Throughout this
section, we assume that *MSC = MPC*; i.e., all costs are internalized.)

In Figure 17.7(c) we have drawn both the *MSB* and *MSC* functions
with the shapes indicated by the discussion above. As mentioned in connection with Figure 17.6, environmental quality should be improved
until *MSB = MSC*—that is, to EQ_o. This implies that there is some opti-

mal level of pollution equal to $EQ^* - EQ_o$. If the government were to regulate the level of environmental quality, the most socially desirable level would be at EQ_o. Some people might argue that an amount greater than EQ_o would be desirable since benefits would continue to accrue to society. Some may even desire to extend EQ to EQ^*. Doing so, however, would generate additional costs in excess of additional benefits. Starting at EQ_o and moving to EQ^* would yield total additional benefits equal to the area Y but increased costs equal to the area represented by $X + Y$. If X happened to be greater than S, society would actually be worse off at EQ^* than at zero.

Another approach to achieving an optimum level of environmental quality would be to require that polluters compensate victims for damages. This could be accomplished by allowing victims to sue for damages. The polluter could avoid paying damages of the amount represented by $S + W$ in Figure 17.7(c) by spending W on environmental quality (i.e., increasing EQ to EQ_o). Such action would be rational for the polluter since the net savings would be equal to S. However, improving EQ beyond EQ_o would not be reasonable. Consider increasing to EQ^*. The cost would be $X + Y$, but the potential savings in damages would only be equal to Y. Thus polluters would be willing to risk paying possible damages of up to Y rather than improve EQ beyond EQ_o.

A third method of encouraging the achievement of EQ_o would be to provide subsidies to polluters to clean up the environment. We can evaluate a subsidy program by referring to Figure 17.8. We know that the

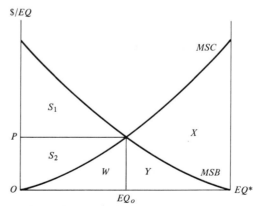

Figure 17.8 Obtaining the Optimum Environmental Quality with Subsidies The government could encourage firms to reduce pollution, or increase environmental quality (*EQ*), by offering a subsidy to clean up the environment. Since the cost of reaching the optimum at EQ_o is the area W, any subsidy in excess of W would be sufficient. However, the subsidy must be less than $S_1 + S_2 + W$, which is the total benefit to society of reaching EQ_o.

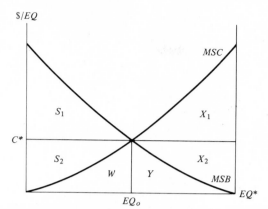

Figure 17.9 Obtaining the Optimum Environmental Quality with Effluent Charges If a per-unit effluent charge of C^* is established, firms would find it less expensive not to pollute up to EQ_o since $C^* > MSC$. Beyond EQ_o, firms would find it less expensive to pollute since $C^* < MSC$ to the right of EQ_o.

optimal level of environmental quality is EQ_o. It would cost the polluters W dollars to reach the level EQ_o, and so any subsidy greater than W would be sufficient to encourage them to do so. As long as the subsidy is less than $S_1 + S_2 + W$ (= the total benefit to society), it would be worth giving. Some people argue in favor of a per-unit payment, P, equal to the value at which $MSB = MSC$. This would provide a monetary benefit to the polluter of $S_2 + W$ in exchange for obtaining EQ_o at a cost of W. The polluter would, of course, increase EQ as long as $P > MSC$.

Finally let us briefly look at effluent charges using the same form of analysis as for the other methods of achieving an optimal level of environmental quality. This can be done with the help of Figure 17.9. If we were to set an effluent charge, we would want to do so such that EQ_o units of environmental quality resulted. That is, we would want the effluent charge (C) to equal MSC at EQ_o. Such a charge is indicated by the horizontal line at C^*. Firms would choose to incur costs of W to improve EQ to EQ_o rather than pay the effluent charges of C^* times EQ_o $(= S_2 + W)$. However, beyond EQ_o, the tax or charge per unit of C^* would be less than MSC, and thus pollution would occur in the amount $EQ^* - EQ_o$. Total charges paid would equal $C^*(EQ^* - EQ_o)$ or the area $X_2 + Y$ (which is less than the cost of total cleanup by the area X_1). The money collected in these effluent charges could be used in part to compensate victims and in part to reduce other taxes. Only Y dollars would be necessary for compensation, where Y equals the area under the MSB curve between EQ_o and EQ^*. Thus X_2 dollars would be available for tax relief or some other social program.

Selected Readings

Denison, Edward F. "Pollution Abatement Programs: Estimates of Their Effect Upon Output Per Unit of Input, 1975–78." *Survey of Current Business* (August 1959), 58–59.

Freeman, A. Myrick. "Distribution of Environmental Quality." In Allen V. Kneese and Blair T. Bower, eds., *Environmental Quality Analysis*. Resources for the Future, Inc., 1972, pp. 243–278.

Johnson, Manuel H., and James T. Bennett. "An Input-Output Model of Regional Environmental and Economic Impacts of Nuclear Power Plants." *Land Economics* 55:2 (May 1979), 236–252.

Mills, Edwin S. *The Economics of Environmental Quality*. New York: Norton, 1978. (See especially chap. 2, "The Microeconomic Theory of Discharges and Environmental Quality," pp. 35–67, and chap. 3, "Welfare Economics and Environmental Policy," pp. 68–96.)

QUESTIONS

1. Write a short explanation of the following terms or concepts that were used in this chapter:

    (a) benefit/cost analysis

    (b) BOD

    (c) marginal social benefits

    (d) marginal social costs

    (e) negative externality

    (f) positive externality

    (g) present value

    (h) private good

    (i) public good

    (j) social discount rate

    (k) socially optimum output

2. Make a list of several positive and several negative externalities that have had an impact on you personally. In each case suggest some economic measure that could be used to either eliminate the externality or act as a compensatory agent.

3. A community of 80,000 people had to close 5 of 18 elementary schools in 1980 because of declining population in the relevant age group. A social agency (AYI) was interested in using one of the buildings as a youth center and the school district was willing to give them the facility on a zero cost lease as long as the agency maintained the building. AYI's funding was on a 75 percent state match to 25 percent locally raised money. In order to get the state funds, they had to justify projects on a benefit cost basis. AYI estimated the benefits and costs over a 10-year period as shown in the accompanying table.

BENEFITS	PVB_1	PVB_2	COST	PVC_1	PVC_2
10,000			5,000		
10,000			5,000		
10,000			10,000		
20,000			15,000		
20,000			15,000		

BENEFITS	PVB_1	PVB_2	COST	PVC_1	PVC_2
30,000			15,000		
20,000			15,000		
10,000			20,000		
10,000			20,000		
5,000	___	___	30,000	___	___
Totals 145,000			150,000		

The flow of benefits reflects the relative distribution of teenagers that would be primary users of the facility, and the increasing costs reflect the fact that the building is currently in good condition but will need various repairs over time.

On the basis of the given data, the state refused to grant matching funds since costs were greater than benefits. Would it make any difference if present values (PVB and PVC) had been used? Complete the table, first assuming that the appropriate discount rate is 10 percent (PVB_1 and PVC_1), and then using a rate of 5 percent (PVB_2 and PVC_2). How does the choice of discount rate influence the benefit/cost ratio? Would any of the conclusions about the project be changed if AYI had to spend an initial $2,000 to get the facility started?

4. Explain why marginal social costs may exceed marginal private costs in some types of production and why there may be situations in which marginal social benefits are greater than marginal private benefits. Illustrate each with an example and show the relationships graphically.

5. In the very early years of the development of automobiles, an article in *Scientific American* noted that the car would eventually make our cities much cleaner and quieter places in which to live and work. Today, the automobile is the focus of attention relating to negative externalities, two of which are air pollution and congestion. The marginal private costs and benefits from using a car are illustrated. Use this graph as the basis for evaluating the problem and for showing how you might "solve" the problem.

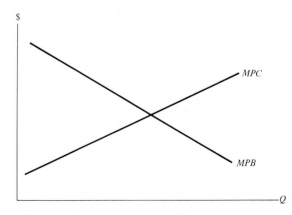

6. On the graph shown, indicate the optimum level of production of the good Q from a social point of view. Shade in the area that represents the net benefit to society of producing the optimum Q you have shown.

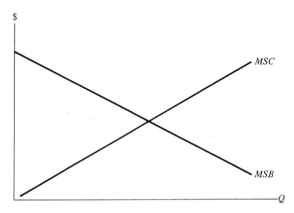

7. Owners of residential property are taxed on the basis of the "market value" of their property (after various adjustments to arrive at a taxable value). As an individual owner makes improvements to the property, the amount of property tax increases. Implicit in such a taxing scheme is the assumption that all of the benefits are internalized to the property owner. List five types of property improvements that would have external effects as well and propose a method of encouraging such positive externalities through the tax system.

8. The graph that appears as Figure 17.9 is reproduced (in part) here to be used as the basis for answering the following questions. (Add whatever additional notations and lines that are useful in answering the questions.)

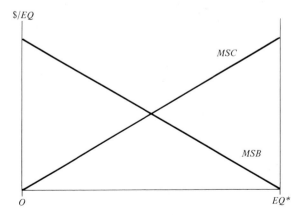

(a) If EQ represents environmental quality, how should EQ^* be interpreted?
(b) What is the optimal level of environmental quality (label it EQ_o)? Why?
(c) Under what circumstances would society be less well off at EQ^* than at O?

(d) If you wished to use an effluent charge to achieve the optimum level of environmental quality, at what level should the charge be set? Explain why this would lead to the optimum result.

(e) How could a subsidy be used to encourage firms to reduce pollution or increase environmental quality (EQ) to the optimum level?

9. "Governmental tinkering with the economy to control the environment imposes high costs to society in the form of increased product prices as well as due to a decrease in economic freedoms. We would be better to allow the market system to function freely." Comment on this statement.

CHAPTER 18
INFLATION
AND
UNEMPLOYMENT

SOME BACKGROUND ON UNEMPLOYMENT
TYPES OF UNEMPLOYMENT
SOME BACKGROUND ON INFLATION
TYPES OF INFLATION
TRADITIONAL UNEMPLOYMENT AND INFLATION POLICIES
SELECTED READINGS
QUESTIONS

Unemployment and inflation have been among the most vexing economic problems we have had to face in recent years. There was a time, not very long ago, that economists and politicians alike were convinced that we could control these events with relative precision through the use of the macroeconomic measures of fiscal and monetary policies. There was much talk of "fine-tuning" the economy during the middle sixties. As we moved into the early seventies, it became increasingly clear that these measures were not performing as well as anticipated—or were not being correctly administered. In either case we found ourselves faced not with the usual trade-off between inflation and unemployment but with both the rate of inflation and the rate of unemployment simultaneously near "double-digit" levels. In 1975 the inflation rate was 9.1 percent, down from 11.0 percent the year before, while the unemployment rate climbed to a post–World War II high of 8.5 percent.

The Employment Act of 1946, which established the Council of Economic Advisors, proclaimed the federal government's responsibility for maintaining full employment, price stability, and economic growth. During the following two decades macroeconomic policies appeared to work relatively well. We experienced inflation of less than 3 percent per year on average and unemployment averaged less than 5 percent. During the 1970s, it was quite another matter. Inflation averaged about 7.2 percent through the decade (11.3 percent for 1979) while unemployment averaged roughly 6.2 percent. New terms were coined to describe the economy: "sloom," a mix of slump and boom; "excession," an expansionary recession; "stagflation," stagnation accompanied by inflation.

It became clear that traditional macroeconomics was not capable of explaining concurrent high rates of inflation and unemployment, nor did macroeconomic policies seem able to stabilize the economy. Many people have begun to look to microeconomics for answers to these perplexing problems. There appear to be some aspects of both unemployment and inflation that might more properly be evaluated as microeconomic problems.

SOME BACKGROUND ON UNEMPLOYMENT

Periods of unemployment have plagued the economy at various times throughout history. In the United States we have had at least six different "official" recessions with relatively high rates of unemployment since World War II: in 1948–49, 1953–54, 1957–58, 1959–60, and 1974–75; at this writing the "peekaboo recession" that began in 1979 has not been officially assigned an end date nor has its severity been fully determined. During the 1974–75 recession, which was the most severe since the Great Depression of the thirties, unemployment reached a peak of 9.2 percent in May of 1975. The costs of such unemployment include personal, social, and economic dimensions. Unemployed persons are not contributing to the production of our GNP, and thus there is some forgone production the cost of which, in economic terms, is an opportunity cost equal to the difference between the full employment level of GNP and the actual GNP.

The personal and family costs of unemployment are perhaps the most important particularly when the head of the household is unemployed. When paychecks stop coming in, families must worry about how to make housing payments, car payments, and how to maintain food purchases. Family arguments and tension are likely to result. Self-respect and self-confidence suffer. Harassment by bill collection agencies often compounds the stress caused by being unemployed. Even after a job is obtained, the struggle to get back on a firm financial footing continues. These personal costs can be very damaging and frequently long-lasting. Additional social costs can grow out of these personal costs. Unemployment *may* lead some persons to illegal activities to support themselves and their families. Idle time itself may lead some people to engage in crime. Further social costs may be realized if medical care is reduced and a higher incidence of disease results.

As we can see from the data presented in Table 18.1, unemployment is not evenly distributed among segments of the work force. The unem-

Table 18.1 LABOR FORCE AND UNEMPLOYMENT RATES FOR SELECTED YEARS BY RACE, SEX, AND AGE

		UNEMPLOYMENT RATES									
	CIVILIAN LABOR FORCE (000)	ALL WORKERS	WHITE			NON-WHITE			ALL MALES 20 YEARS AND OVER	ALL FEMALES 20 YEARS AND OVER	ALL PERSONS 16–19 YEARS
YEAR			TOTAL	MALES	FEMALES	TOTAL	MALES	FEMALES			
1950	62208	5.3	4.9	4.7	5.3	9.0	9.4	8.4	4.7	5.1	12.2
1955	65023	4.4	3.9	3.7	4.3	8.7	8.8	8.5	3.8	4.4	11.0
1960	69628	5.5	4.9	4.8	5.3	10.2	10.7	9.4	4.7	5.1	14.7
1961	70459	6.7	6.0	5.7	6.5	12.4	12.8	11.9	5.7	6.3	16.8
1962	70614	5.5	4.9	4.6	5.5	10.9	10.9	11.0	4.6	5.4	14.7
1963	71833	5.7	5.0	4.7	5.8	10.8	10.5	11.2	4.5	5.4	17.2
1964	73091	5.2	4.6	4.1	5.5	9.6	8.9	10.7	3.9	5.2	16.2
1965	74455	4.5	4.1	3.6	5.0	8.1	7.4	9.2	3.2	4.5	14.8
1966	75770	3.8	3.3	2.8	4.3	7.3	6.3	8.7	2.5	3.8	12.8
1967	77347	3.8	3.4	2.7	4.6	7.4	6.1	9.1	2.3	4.2	12.8
1968	78737	3.6	3.2	2.6	4.3	6.7	5.6	8.3	2.2	3.8	12.7
1969	80734	3.5	3.1	2.5	4.2	6.4	5.3	7.8	2.1	3.7	12.2
1970	82715	4.9	4.5	4.0	5.4	8.2	7.3	9.3	3.5	4.8	15.2
1971	84113	5.9	5.4	4.9	6.3	9.9	9.1	10.8	4.4	5.7	16.9
1972	86542	5.6	5.0	4.5	5.9	10.0	8.9	11.3	4.0	5.4	16.2
1973	88714	4.9	4.3	3.7	5.3	8.9	7.6	10.5	3.2	4.8	14.5
1974	91011	5.6	5.0	4.3	6.1	9.9	9.1	10.7	3.8	5.5	16.0
1975	92613	8.5	7.8	7.2	8.6	13.9	13.7	14.0	6.7	8.0	19.9
1976	94773	7.7	7.0	6.4	7.9	13.1	12.7	13.6	5.9	7.4	19.0
1977	97401	7.0	6.2	5.5	7.3	13.1	12.4	14.0	5.2	7.0	17.7
1978	100420	6.0	5.2	4.5	6.2	11.9	10.9	13.1	4.2	6.0	16.3
1979	102908	5.8	5.1	4.4	5.9	11.3	10.3	12.3	4.1	5.7	16.1

SOURCE: *Economic Report of the President* (Washington, D.C.: GPO, 1980), pp. 234, 237, 238.

ployment rate is consistently higher for nonwhites than for whites; for women than for men; and for teenage workers than for those 20 years of age and older. The unemployment rate for this latter group is typically 2.5 to 3 times as high as the general level of unemployment. The unemployment rate for blacks generally is about twice as high as for white members of the work force. The differences in unemployment rates by sex, age, and race occur for several reasons. One important factor is the relative skill level and educational background of the groups. Discriminatory hiring (and training) patterns with deep historical roots also contribute to these differences.

In Chapter 13 we investigated the determinants of the supply of and demand for labor in the economy. We found that we would generally expect the supply of labor to be a positively sloped function in relation to the wage rate. We also found that the demand for labor by businesses is a negatively sloped function of the wage rate and that it is determined largely by the marginal productivity of labor. These relationships are illustrated in Figure 18.1. At point E the supply of labor S_L and demand for labor D_L are equal at the equilibrium wage, W_E, with L_E units of labor employed. If the supply-and-demand functions represent the free, unencumbered choices of individuals and firms in competitive markets, a full employment equilibrium results because all those who are willing and

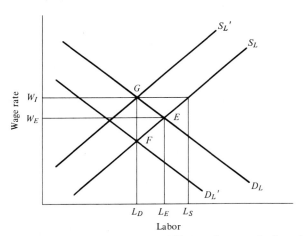

Figure 18.1 The Labor Market and Unemployment   In a free labor market the demand for labor would be D_L and the supply of labor would be S_L, with the equilibrium wage at W_E and L_E the level of employment. With S_L constant, a shift of demand to D_L' would reduce employment to L_D. A decrease in supply to S_L' would also reduce employment to L_D. If with S_L and D_L the government imposed a minimum wage at W_I, only L_D labor would be demanded, but L_S would wish to work. The difference would represent unemployed workers.

able to work at the prevailing wage will be employed. Given these supply-and-demand relationships anything that artificially pushes the wage above W_E (such as a governmentally imposed minimum wage) will result in unemployment (this may be a significant factor in explaining the high teenage unemployment rate). Suppose the wage were set at W_1. The amount of labor willing and able to work at that wage is L_S, but at that wage only L_D units would be demanded. The difference, $L_S - L_D$, can be considered unemployed because they would prefer to work at the existing wage, W_1, but would not be hired.

Anything that would cause the demand for labor to shift to the left, such as monopsonistic influences, could also result in unemployment. Suppose such a shift were to D_L', with supply remaining S_L. The new equilibrium would be at point F with L_D units of labor employed. The distance $L_E L_D$ can then be considered as a measure of the resulting unemployment. This same amount of unemployment could be caused by interference with purely market forces on the supply side. Suppose demand is given by D_L, but supply is reduced to S_L' (perhaps by ruling segments of the work force ineligible through arbitrary discrimination according to sex or race). The result again would be unemployment of $L_E - L_D$; although, since the wage is bid up to W_1 due to the shortage of labor, we could consider $L_S - L_D$ the better measure of unemployment in this case.

The actual measurement of unemployment in the economy is the responsibility of the Department of Labor. Unemployment is usually reported as the percentage of the civilian labor force that is unemployed at any given time. The civilian labor force (or work force) is defined as all people employed outside of the armed forces plus all other persons who are in the 16-to-64 age group who are actively seeking work but are currently unemployed. The Department of Labor determines the unemployment rate from figures collected monthly in surveys conducted by the Bureau of the Census. More than 1000 interviewers contact 50,000 households located throughout each of the 50 states. Individuals in those households who are 16 or over and did any work for pay or profit in the week before the survey are considered employed. Anyone in this age group who actively sought work in the 30 days preceding the survey and is presently available for work, but not employed, is counted as unemployed.

Because the data collected include a wide geographic spread, they provide insight into how various regions of the country are impacted by differential unemployment rates. In fact, data are published for some 150 major labor areas. In the area data we find some labor markets that are nearly always well below the national rate of unemployment; examples include the Denver-Boulder labor market in Colorado; Cedar Rapids, Iowa; Raleigh-Durham, North Carolina; Tulsa, Oklahoma; and Houston,

Texas. Other areas are consistently above the national rate, including San Diego, California; Bridgeport, Connecticut; New Bedford, Massachusetts; Flint, Michigan; Jersey City, New Jersey; Buffalo, New York; and El Paso, Texas. In addition to these geographic differentials and the demographic differentials that show up in Table 18.1, the unemployment rate will differ by industry or type of occupation. The latter is more difficult to identify because many workers are not tied to a particular industry. However, in some cases there is at least some rough basis for estimating unemployment for such groups. For example, as we began the decade of the 1980s, the overall unemployment rate was 6.2%, whereas for steelworkers it was about 9.6% and for auto workers it was more than 15%.

TYPES OF UNEMPLOYMENT

If we are concerned about unemployment from a policy perspective, it would be nice if we could consider all unemployment as a homogeneous mass that could be attacked with a single type of unemployment policy. To a significant degree we have tended toward this view in terms of the types of national policies we seem to consider to reduce unemployment rates. There is a tendency to look first at tax cuts or increased government expenditures (fiscal policy measures) to combat unemployment. These are broad-based policies that are not generally directed toward specific types of unemployment. There have been, and are, some programs aimed at particular types of unemployment (such as The Job Corps or CETA), but the fiscal policy measures are usually the first to be considered in the political arena. This makes some sense, by the way, in terms of the microeconomic theory of behavior. The marginal benefit (votes generated) to members of Congress is usually higher if they support a tax reduction that provides some benefit to most of their constituents than if they support a jobs program that benefits relatively few of their constituents, while the cost (votes lost) from supporting either program is probably small and essentially the same.

If we break the overall rate of unemployment down into major categories, we might better identify particular causes and thus develop more appropriate policies to deal with the problem. It is useful to divide total unemployment into three or four major types, some of which are of greater concern than others. First, some people are unemployed because they *temporarily* cannot find work that matches their qualifications, but they have a job skill that allows them to expect to find employment fairly quickly. They may even know that a particular job will be open soon and be waiting for that position. We refer to this type of unemployment as *frictional unemployment*. A closely related type of unemployment is what we classify as *seasonal unemployment*. Many people in ski resort

areas may be unemployed during the off-season, many farm workers are
not employed during the winter months, a golf pro in Milwaukee may be
unemployed during a portion of the year, and so forth. It is difficult to
estimate what portion of the total unemployed labor force is in these
classifications. However, most economists would agree that between 4
and 5 percent of unemployment is either frictional or seasonal. Because
these types are temporary, they are not as major a concern as the other
types in terms of policy considerations.

Unemployment also results when there is a low level of demand for
goods and services in the economy. During the depression of the thirties,
when unemployment rose to as high as 25 percent, most of the unemployment was because there was such a low demand. This type of unemployment is usually called *demand-deficiency* or *cyclical unemployment*.
If we use a general measure of the level of prices and measure goods and
services in real terms (constant dollar terms), we can illustrate the aggregate demand (*AgD*) and aggregate supply (*AgS*) functions for the economy as shown in Figure 18.2. Suppose that the level of output that would
be necessary to maintain full employment is the level labeled O_F. If
aggregate demand and supply are in equilibrium at a lower rate of output, such as O_E, there will be unemployment in the economy. Because
O_E is less than O_F, we say that there is a deficiency in aggregate demand.

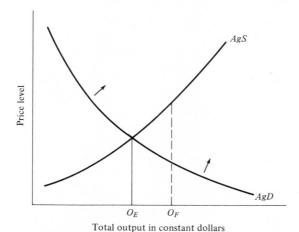

Total output in constant dollars

Figure 18.2 Demand, Supply, and Inflation Using a general
measure of prices and output in real terms, we can graph
aggregate supply (*AgS*) and aggregate demand (*AgD*) as shown.
The equilibrium is at O_E level of output. The level of output
necessary to generate full employment is O_F. In this case there is
insufficient aggregate demand to maintain full employment. The
resulting unemployment, called "demand-deficiency
unemployment," could be reduced by programs that would shift
aggregate demand in the direction indicated by the arrows.

Government policies to increase demand will increase employment as firms respond to the increased demand for goods and services. For example, a general income tax cut could be expected to increase aggregate demand, as indicated by the arrows in Figure 18.2. This is one form of macroeconomic policy that might well be used to help to stimulate economic activity in order to reduce unemployment. Other traditional macroeconomic policies used to combat unemployment, such as expansionary monetary policies (reduction of the discount rate and reserve requirements or buying bonds in the open market) or fiscal policies (tax reductions or increased government spending) would also result in a shift of the aggregate demand curve outward.

The final type of unemployment is *structural unemployment*, which results when there are imbalances between the supply of and demand for labor in various submarkets, even though in the aggregate the quantity available may equal the quantity demanded. One dimension of structural unemployment is geographical. As noted in the last paragraph of the preceding section, some labor markets will exhibit far higher unemployment rates than others. For example, the labor market in Houston or Tulsa may be quite tight, perhaps an unemployment rate of less than 4 percent, while in Flint or Jersey City there may be people with the skills that are needed in Houston or Tulsa but who cannot find employment due to high local unemployment, perhaps 7 to even 15 percent. Broad-based monetary and fiscal policies are not as useful as policies that would either encourage firms to locate where the unemployed workers are or encourage people to relocate to areas where jobs are more plentiful. For the former, tax reductions for firms may provide some incentive for them to locate in areas with high unemployment. Tax policy already provides some help to individuals who relocate by allowing moving expenses as an adjustment to income for income tax purposes. Government policies to improve the information flow concerning job vacancies would reduce the cost of job search and thus make moving to a new location easier for individuals. Government backed low interest "moving loans" or even "moving grants" could also help reduce this type of unemployment.

Another structural aspect of unemployment relates to factors that directly affect the supply of or demand for labor. Let us first consider some of the factors on the supply side. Odd as it may seem, some things that reduce the supply of labor as well as some which increase the supply of labor may cause an increase in the reported unemployment rate. Figure 18.3 illustrates supply-and-demand conditions in some particular labor market. For the present discussion, we shall keep the demand for labor fixed at the level indicated by D_L. The labor supply curve labeled S_L will be our benchmark supply function.

In many fields of employment it is very difficult to obtain the training and skills necessary to enter employment. Many trade unions have very

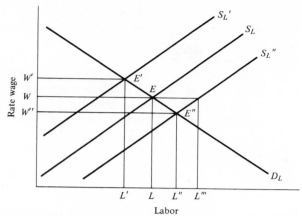

Figure 18.3 Effect of Entry Restrictions on the Labor Market
The curves S_L and D_L represent benchmark levels of the
labor supply and labor demand functions respectively. The
equilibrium wage rate would be W and L units of labor would be
employed. If entry into a job market is restricted such as by a tight
trade union, the AMA, government licensing, or discrimination, the
supply would move to S_L'. Although the wage rate would go up,
employment would drop from L to L'. If the labor force increases
such that supply increases from S_L to S_L'', we would expect wages
to fall to W'' and employment to increase to L''. However, wages
tend to be inflexible downward, and thus only L units will be
demanded at the fixed wage W, while L''' would be willing and
able to work at that wage. The difference ($L''' - L$) would
represent unemployment.

restrictive apprenticeship programs that are not tied to minimum necessary qualifications. They often make the apprenticeship period unnecessarily long. This practice, along with restricted entry into the programs,
limits the supply of labor in that type of employment but helps to keep
wages high for those who are employed. Trade unions are not the only
ones that are guilty in this regard. Governments may restrict entry to a
trade by issuing only a certain number of licenses, such as for electri-
cians, plumbers, and taxi drivers. The American Medical Association and
medical schools may also be guilty of artificially restricting the supply of
physicians by imposing constraints on the number of medical school
openings for new students and, many believe, by making the entire apprenticeship program longer than necessary. Discrimination by race
and/or sex also may reduce the supply of labor, either in total or in particular fields. For example, for years it has been very difficult for women
to become commercial airline pilots. Only in the late 1970s did women
make their first inroads in this occupation.

Referring to Figure 18.3, the labor market equilibrium without such restrictions would be at E, with the wage rate at W and L persons employed. If the supply of labor is restricted, due to one or more of the factors discussed above, the labor supply function would be S_L'. While the wage would increase to W', fewer persons would be employed. If the demand for labor is inelastic, this would result in higher total wage payments (but to fewer people). However, if the demand for labor is elastic, the result would be that total wage payments would be less, even though those that are fortunate enough to be employed would obtain higher wages. This type of restricted entry into various forms of employment accounts for much of the differential in unemployment rates between white males and white females, or nonwhite workers of either sex, as shown in Table 18.1.

Let us now turn to a situation that may result when the supply of labor increases. In the past 20 years there has been a dramatic change in the number of women entering the labor force. In 1960 the labor force participation rate for women was just over 37 percent (compared to 83 percent for men) but by 1979 it had jumped to 51 percent (compared to 78 percent for men). This represents a significant increase in the total supply of labor in the economy, which can be illustrated by a shift in the labor supply function from S_L to S_L''. If wages were completely flexible, we would expect wages to fall to W'' and the amount of employment to rise to L''. However, wages tend to be flexible only in an upward direction. Various institutional forces, such as minimum wage laws and collective bargaining, restrict downward movement in wages and thus, even with the increased supply, wages would remain at W. If the demand for labor is stable, the level of employment would stay at L, despite the fact that L''' amount would be available at that wage due to the increase in supply. The difference, L''' minus L, would represent additional unemployment.

In Table 18.1 we have seen that the unemployment rate was 5.5 percent in 1960 and 5.8 percent in 1979. But we should ask if a comparison between those years is really fair. One *might* conclude that the employment situation was worse in 1979 than in 1960. However, since many more people were in the labor force in 1979, this conclusion may be erroneous. If we were to look at "employment as a percent of the population" rather than unemployment, we would get a different picture of the condition of the labor market. In 1960, 54.9 percent of the population were employed, whereas by 1979 that rate had increased to 59.3 percent. Thus, despite a higher reported unemployment rate, a higher percentage of a growing population were employed in 1979 than in 1960. If we took the additional women out of the 1979 labor force, the unemployment rate for that year would be much lower than the reported figure. It may, therefore, make more sense to use the percent of the population that is employed when evaluating this aspect of the "health" of the economy than to use the traditional unemployment rate.

Now let us turn to the demand side of the labor market. We will make the not unrealistic assumption that current conditions in the labor market are described by the demand function D_L and the supply function S_L in Figure 18.4. Due to various institutional forces, the wage rate is W', which is above the market-clearing equilibrium level W. At this wage the supply of labor exceeds the demand for labor, and thus there is unemployment.

If the demand for labor could be increased to D_L', the market would be in equilibrium, with full employment, at the wage W'. Recall, from Chapter 13, that the demand for labor depends on labor's marginal productivity (MP_L). If MP_L could be increased, the demand for labor will shift outward. There are policies that could cause MP_L to rise. First, and perhaps most obvious, training programs to develop skills that are needed in production will increase labor's marginal product by providing a better base of human capital. Persons who are unemployed because they lack a marketable skill may be trained through a vocational education program. Information about the skills that are needed most in the economy can be made more readily available, particularly to young people who are making decisions about the type of education and/or training they will seek. Programs to retrain workers whose skill is no longer needed can also be implemented. For example, an unemployed

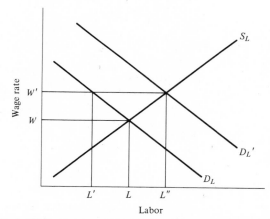

Figure 18.4 Reducing Unemployment by Increasing the Labor Demand   Current demand for labor and supply of labor functions are described by D_L and S_L, respectively. If institutional forces keep the wage at W', above the market-clearing wage W, unemployment ($L'' - L$) results. Policies that would shift the demand for labor to D_L' by increasing the marginal productivity of labor would eliminate unemployment and raise the market-clearing wage to W'. Such policies could include training programs and tax incentives for investment.

history teacher might be aided in the effort to obtain additional training in accounting, which is a more marketable skill.

The marginal productivity of labor is generally not independent of the amount of capital and other resources that labor has to work with. If more money were allocated to investment in the economy's capital stock, we should expect the productivity of labor to increase. In recent years the United States has been lagging in the rate of growth in productivity as measured by output per labor hour. If you look ahead to Table 18.2, you will see an index of output per labor hour in the next to the last column. Since 1970 the increase in output per man-hour has been very low, averaging only a little over 1.3 percent per year. Looking at comparable international data on the average percent of national income used for investment and the average percentage increase in productivity during the 15-year period ending in 1977, we find the following:

Country	Average Percent Used for Investment	Average Percent Increase in Productivity
Japan	33	8
West Germany	25	5
United States	12	2.5

As we discussed in Chapter 16, many aspects of United States tax policy could be more favorable to capital accumulation. Greater investment tax credits, more accelerated depreciation allowances, elimination of the double taxation of dividend income, exempting some savings interest from taxable income, and reducing the progressivity of the personal income tax have all been suggested as means to stimulate investment. One would expect that this would lead to an increase in productivity and a shift of the labor demand function such as from D_L to D_L' in Figure 18.4.

SOME BACKGROUND ON INFLATION

The cost that inflation imposes on the economy is more subtle, but no less real, than the cost incurred due to unemployment. Inflation is a sustained general increase in the level of prices; that is, the average level of prices is rising. During an inflationary period, however, some prices may actually be falling. Perhaps the most obvious example is the dramatic drop in the price of calculators during the 1970s even though the general level of prices increased by 98 percent through that period.

Inflation is generally measured by one of several price indices such as the consumer price index, the wholesale price index, or the implicit price deflator. The consumer price index (*CPI*) is by far the most widely

Table 18.2 SELECTED SERIES RELATED TO THE RATE OF INFLATION

| YEAR | CONSUMER PRICE INDICES | | | | | | PRIME INTEREST RATE | PRIVATE BUSINESS SECTOR | |
	CONSUMER PRICE INDEX (ALL ITEMS)	RENT	FOOD	NEW CARS	MEDICAL CARE	FUEL OIL, COAL AND BOTTLED GAS		INDEX OF OUTPUT PER HOUR OF LABOR (ALL PERSONS)	INDEX OF COMPENSATION PER HOUR
1950	72.1	70.4	74.5	83.4	53.7	72.7	2.07	61.0	42.4
1955	80.2	84.3	81.6	90.9	64.8	82.3	3.16	70.3	55.8
1960	88.7	91.7	88.0	104.5	79.1	89.2	4.82	78.7	71.9
1961	89.6	92.9	89.1	104.5	81.4	91.0	4.50	81.1	74.6
1962	90.6	94.0	89.9	104.1	83.5	91.5	4.50	84.8	78.1
1963	91.7	95.0	91.2	103.5	85.6	93.2	4.50	88.1	81.0
1964	92.9	95.9	92.4	103.2	87.3	92.7	4.50	91.6	85.3
1965	94.5	96.9	94.4	100.9	89.5	94.6	4.54	95.0	88.7
1966	97.2	98.2	99.1	99.1	93.4	97.0	5.63	98.0	94.9
1967	100.0	100.0	100.0	100.0	100.0	100.0	5.61	100.0	100.0
1968	104.2	102.4	103.6	102.8	106.1	103.1	6.30	103.3	107.6
1969	109.8	105.7	108.9	104.4	113.4	105.6	7.96	103.5	114.9
1970	116.3	110.1	114.9	107.6	120.6	110.1	7.91	104.2	123.1
1971	121.3	115.2	118.4	112.0	128.4	117.5	5.72	107.7	131.4
1972	125.3	119.2	123.5	111.0	132.5	118.5	5.25	111.4	139.7
1973	133.1	124.3	141.4	111.1	137.7	136.0	8.03	113.6	151.2
1974	147.7	130.6	161.7	117.5	150.5	214.6	10.81	110.1	164.9
1975	161.2	137.3	175.4	127.6	168.6	235.3	7.86	112.4	181.3
1976	170.5	144.7	180.8	135.7	184.7	250.8	6.84	116.4	197.2
1977	181.5	153.5	192.2	142.9	202.4	283.4	6.83	118.6	213.0
1978	195.4	164.0	211.4	153.8	219.4	298.3	9.06	119.2	231.2
1979	217.4	176.0	234.5	166.0	239.7	403.1	12.67	118.1	252.8

SOURCE: *Economic Report of the President* (Washington, D.C.: GPO, 1980), pp. 246, 259, 260, 261, 262, 278.

used and is reported monthly as an indicator of the general level of inflation. Table 18.2 includes data for the consumer price index for every year back to 1960 as well as for 1955 and 1950, with 1967 as the base year. The index value of 217.4 for 1979 means that prices in 1979 were 217.4 percent of the prices in 1967. Thus, if a bundle of goods cost $80 in 1967, they would have cost $173.92 (= 80 × 2.174) in 1979. To calculate the amount of inflation between any two time periods, we use the following format:

$$\frac{\text{Amount of}}{\text{inflation}} = \frac{\text{2nd-period } CPI - \text{1st-period } CPI}{\text{1st-period } CPI}$$

Thus, if we wanted to know the amount of inflation that we incurred from 1977 to 1979, we would find: (217.4 − 181.5)/181.5 = 0.198, or 19.8 percent. Thus, goods that cost $100 in 1977 would have cost $119.80 in 1979.

The consumer price index is based on a typical market basket of goods for an average family and various goods are assigned a weight based on the importance of each item to consumers as determined by the proportion of total expenditures going for that item. For example, a typical family spends about 19.2% of their income on food, and so food is given that weight in determining the CPI. About 400 items are included in the market basket used by the Bureau of Labor Statistics in their survey of several thousand retail stores and service establishments. We would not expect the rate of increase in prices to be equal for all these items and, as shown in Table 18.2, there are considerable differences indeed. We have provided the indices for just five subgroups from which we can see some of the variation that exists. Rent and new cars have increased in price more slowly than the CPI, but food, medical care, and fuel oil and bottled-gas prices have risen more sharply. The latter had a particularly high rate of price increase (35.1%) in the last year alone.

Inflation causes uncertainty in the marketplace for both consumers and business people. Shortly after World War I, Germany was the victim of runaway inflation. Prices were so uncertain that people would spend as rapidly as possible to avoid price increases. It is said that people eating in restaurants paid their bill as they ordered rather than waiting until they finished because by then prices might have gone up. People demanded to be paid at the end of each day's work so they could make purchases immediately rather than lose purchasing power during the normal interval to the next weekly, biweekly, or monthly pay period. Such rapid inflation would also create uncertainty for business, which would be likely to reduce investment and thus slow down economic growth.

Inflation that is less extreme, perhaps 2 to 3 percent, could actually stimulate the economy. During a mildly inflationary period (such as the early 1960s), money wages tend to lag behind price increases. Thus, the prices of goods that producers sell are high in relation to their cost for labor. The producer earns higher real profits and therefore is likely to expand production and hire more people. The newly employed will increase their spending, and the total demand in the economy will rise. This results in increased economic growth and prosperity. However, when inflation rises to higher rates, perhaps above 5–6 percent, it may actually contribute to unemployment. Lagging wages in this more extreme case may result in workers having reduced real incomes, and therefore they may cut back on purchases. This reduction in total demand may in turn result in reduced production and increased unemployment.

Inflation may distort economic decisions in other ways as well. As prices increase at different rates, if the price increases do not represent natural economic forces, consumer and producer reactions will alter the distribution of goods and the allocation of resources in a way that is likely to be inefficient. Another distortion of the economy may result due to speculation, especially when the rate of price increase is rapid for particular commodities. Some people will buy up large quantities of the good hoping to resell at a much higher price. This can further bid up the price for some period until the bubble finally bursts. An example of this process can be seen if we look back at the rapidly rising price of antifreeze in 1974. Many people stocked their garages with antifreeze hoping to make a considerable profit, but most were simply stuck with lots of antifreeze, while others found stores out of stock. This type of speculation is generally nonproductive and causes distortions in the market distribution of goods. The speculation in gold at the turn of this decade is another example. Gold prices rose by more than *10 percent a day* at several times. Many people took money out of banks, credit unions, and savings and loan associations to speculate in this "gold boom." This further aggravated already tight credit conditions for consumer loans and home mortgages.

TYPES OF INFLATION

Inflationary pressures in the economy are often separated into two basic types based on their causes. The first type is *demand-pull inflation*. The phrase "too many dollars chasing too few goods" is often used to describe this kind of inflation. "Too many dollars" means that the total demand in the economy is too high, while "too few goods" means that the total supply in the economy is too low in relation to that demand. Figure 18.5 illustrates demand-pull inflation using the simple aggregate demand (AgD) and aggregate supply (AgS) graph introduced earlier in this chapter.

Curves AgD_1 and AgS_1 in Figure 18.5(a) represent the levels of demand and supply at some initial point in time. Curve AgD_2 represents an

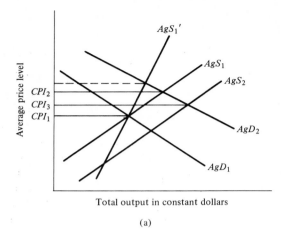

(a)

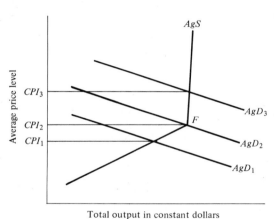

(b)

Figure 18.5 Demand-Pull Inflation (a) The original aggregate demand and aggregate supply functions are AgD_1 and AgS_1 respectively. If demand increases to AgD_2 but the supply function remains the same, the price level will rise from CPI_1 to CPI_2. If supply were more inelastic, say AgS_1', prices would increase even more (see dashed line). If aggregate supply also increases but less than the increase in aggregate demand, inflation will be less (rise from CPI_1 to CPI_3). (b) We see here that increases in AgD will increase CPI but also increase output until a point is reached where the economy is using all possible resources, at which point AgS becomes perfectly inelastic (vertical). Any further increases in AgD are purely inflationary. Both (a) and (b) thus illustrate demand-pull inflation.

increase in demand. If supply does not increase, the price level would rise from CPI_1 to CPI_2. The degree to which prices rise depends on the relative price elasticity of supply. The more inelastic the supply function, the greater the increase in price for any given increase in aggregate demand. For example, compare the price level at the intersection of AgS_1 with AgD_2 and at the intersection of AgS_1' with AgD_2 (where AgS_1' is the more inelastic supply function). It may be that during periods of increasing aggregate demand, aggregate supply could also increase. But as long as the increase in AgD is greater than the increase in AgS, inflation will still result. For example, suppose aggregate demand increased from AgD_1 to AgD_2 while aggregate supply increased from AgS_1 to AgS_2. There would still be inflation as the CPI moves to CPI_3.

Now consider another case depicted in Figure 18.5(b). Here the aggregate supply function is drawn with a sharp kink at point F, where it becomes perfectly inelastic. This could represent the full employment level of output for the economy. Increases in aggregate demand up to that kink would stimulate greater real production as well as higher prices. However, further increases in aggregate demand, such as to AgD_3, will be purely inflationary, and no additional real output will result.

Typically, we have experienced demand-pull inflation at the end of wars and military conflicts. The tremendous amounts of resources tied up in fighting wars create large increases in demand when a country returns to a civilian economy. The inflation experienced in 1947–48 following World War II, the 1950 inflation following the Korean conflict, and the inflation from 1965 to 1970 during the Vietnam War are all examples of demand-pull inflation.

The inflation from 1965 to 1970 was a little different from the other two examples. During World War II and the Korean conflict, total demand in the economy was suppressed to some extent as efforts were taken to curtail personal consumption expenditures in the domestic economy. Ration books and product shortages during World War II were signs of suppression in the domestic economy. However, during the Vietnam War, high defense spending was accompanied by continued high consumer demand as well as additional government spending on the social programs of President Johnson's "Great Society" programs. Much of this spending was financed by increasing the national debt rather than through tax collections. The result was a steady rise in inflation.

Even so, by 1970 the economy had edged into a recession. In December of that year, unemployment reached 6.2 percent. Typically in the past, unemployment resulted in decreased aggregate demand and reduced inflationary pressure. However, inflation did not decline, and we were faced with the twin problems of simultaneously unacceptably high rates of both inflation and unemployment.

This continuing inflation was, at least partially, composed of a second type—*cost-push inflation*. Cost-push inflation results not from pressures on the demand side but rather from different kinds of pressures on the supply side. During the middle to late 1960s the general inflation in the economy started to put further pressure on the costs of industrial production. Workers and unions demanded pay increases to make up for the real income they had lost due to the effects of inflation on their current and expected purchasing power. Cost-of-living adjustments were negotiated into nearly all contracts. Consequently labor costs continued to increase fairly rapidly. If you look back to Table 18.2, you find in the last column an index of compensation per hour. Comparing this index to the *CPI* in the same table, you can see that since 1967 compensation has increased more rapidly than the general rate of inflation (the 1979 indices were 252.8 and 217.4 respectively).

This is not to imply that the entire amount of cost push inflation is the fault of labor. Other business costs have also been rising during recent years, perhaps most notably the cost of various forms of energy. We have seen that the consumer price index for fuel oil, coal, and bottled gas was at 403.1 in 1979. Business firms are obviously also affected by higher energy costs. The "Producer Price Index for Intermediate Materials, Supplies, and Components" under the subgroup "Processed Fuels and Lubricants" for 1979 was 360.9 (1967 = 100). The "Producer Price Index for Crude Materials for Further Processing" for the subgroup "Fuel" was 568.2 in 1979 (1967 = 100). These rising costs are also reflected in price increases paid by consumers.

Another factor that may be contributing to cost-push inflation is the concentration of economic power in the hands of large corporations and large unions. These large economic units are able to increase prices and wages through the exercise of monopolistic and monopsonistic powers, as we have seen in Chapters 10, 12, and 13. Large corporations have, on the other hand, provided a strong base of capital equipment, which increases labor productivity and potentially has kept prices below what they would have been otherwise. If we look at what has been happening to interest rates, there may be some cause for concern about future increases in the capital stock. The prime rate (the rate charged by banks to their best corporate customers) has a long-run positive trend, and since about 1970 has been quite high (see Table 18.2). Early in 1980 the prime rate reached the extraordinarily high level of 20%. This could be both an effect of inflation and inflationary expectations as well as a cause of further inflation as this cost of doing business is passed on to consumers in the form of higher prices.

In general cost-push inflation can be explained with the help of a graph like that shown in Figure 18.6. In this analysis we will hold aggregate demand constant at AgD. We will take AgS_1 to be the aggregate

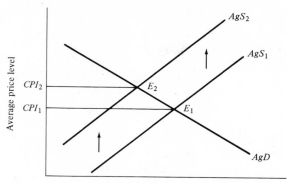

Figure 18.6 Cost-Push Inflation As the cost of producing goods and services increases, we can expect aggregate supply to shift upward, such as from AgS_1 to AgS_2. Increased labor cost, rising energy costs, and the increasing cost imposed by government regulations are examples of causal factors. The result is an increase in the price level, such as from CPI_1 to CPI_2, which is referred to as cost-push inflation.

supply function at some initial point in time. The equilibrium is at E_1, with CPI_1 being the general level of prices.

If the cost of things used in the production of goods and services goes up, we can expect that firms would only be willing and able to produce and sell a given quantity at a higher price. Thus we can expect the aggregate supply relationship to shift upward such as to the curve AgS_2. This would cause a rise in the general level of prices to CPI_2. This shift from AgS_1 to AgS_2 could be stimulated by any or all of the causes suggested above: increased fuel or other resource costs, higher labor costs due to higher wages and fringe benefits, or increases in the cost of capital (such as shown by the increases in the prime interest rate). In addition, reduced productivity of labor will increase costs, as shown in Chapter 8. This, in turn, will cause a reduction in supply. As mentioned earlier, productivity in the United States economy has not been keeping up with the historic trend, or with other major industrialized economies. In fact the good news about productivity reported in the February 28, 1980 *Wall Street Journal* (p. 3) was that "productivity fell less in the 4th quarter (of 1979) than posted earlier." The rate of change in productivity was different in various sectors but in the important manufacturing sector it was reported that "productivity fell at a 1.3% rate in the revised data, compared with the 1.5% reported earlier." If we find ways to increase productivity, such as through more capital expansion, and/or improved worker skills we may find a reduction in the rate of inflation and greater increases in real output.

It should also be noted before leaving this section that government plays an important part in contributing to cost-push inflation as well as to demand-pull inflation. In the case of the latter, deficit spending and continued expansion of the public sector puts pressure on prices from the demand side. From the supply side (cost-push inflation), government regulations are responsible for significant increases in the cost of making goods and services available in our economy. These regulations generally have benefits as well as costs, but in terms of inflation, it is the costs that must be considered. The cost of building a new coal-fired electric generating plant is increased because of the major environmental impact studies that must be conducted for national, state, and local agencies (frequently the requirements of each are sufficiently different that three almost completely different studies must be done). The costs of completing paperwork for IRS, OASHA, EPA, CPSC (Consumer Product Safety Commission), and others are becoming increasingly burdensome, especially for smaller firms. The total of these costs are difficult to estimate, but we know that they will be passed on, at least in part, to consumers in the form of higher prices and thus will contribute to inflation in our economy.

TRADITIONAL UNEMPLOYMENT AND INFLATION POLICIES

We have traditionally relied upon the macroeconomic tools of monetary and fiscal policy to deal with the problems of unemployment and inflation in the economy. These worked reasonably well when the problems stemmed almost solely from demand-side forces. As long as unemployment was predominantly of the demand-deficiency type, an expansionary monetary and/or fiscal policy could correct the problem by increasing aggregate demand. When inflation was principally of a demand-pull nature, contractionary monetary and/or fiscal policy could effectively reduce the demand pressure and stabilize prices. These policies do not work as effectively when the problems are more related to supply-side phenomena, however. In fact, they may even be counterproductive.

Consider, for example, the Federal Reserve's dramatic policy moves of October 6, 1979, in which the discount rate was increased by 2 percent. The Fed's principal concern was to attempt to curtail the rapidly building inflationary pressures in the economy by restricting the money supply and thus slowing the growth in aggregate demand. However, with strong *inflationary expectations* in the economy, firms continued to show strong demand for money even at the high nominal interest rates. Real interest rates, after adjusting for inflation, were really not very high and firms knew that, with the inflationary psychology in the economy, consumers would accept (and even expected) higher prices. It would be easy, therefore, to pass on the higher cost in higher prices. Higher interest rates show up fairly quickly in the *CPI* as the home ownership component jumps sharply with the increased cost of financing a new home. On a 30-year mortgage for $50,000 (e.g., the financing of a $62,500 home with 20% down), the increase in mortgage rates from about 11.5 percent in the summer of 1979 to about 14.5 percent in February of 1980 would have meant an *increase of $117.13 per month* in the family's mortgage payment. That would have represented about a 24 percent increase in the monthly cost of home ownership, without considering such things as heating costs, which were also rising rapidly. As this cost increase is incorporated into the *CPI*, the reported rate of inflation is higher.

At the same time Congress was becoming concerned about the rate of unemployment and was actively considering proposals to cut income and/or social security taxes to stimulate aggregate demand and increase production and thus employment. Clearly such a fiscal policy measure would run exactly counter to the Federal Reserve's monetary policy, which was increasingly contractionary in the early part of 1980.

If trying to deal with these problems from the demand side is not successful, perhaps we should look more closely at supply-side factors. This would involve more microeconomic analysis of unemployment and inflation. It may well be that the best place to start is with the issue of productivity. We know that productivity in the United States has not been growing at the rate we have historically come to expect and that it has not been keeping pace with our international competitors in the world economy.

What would microeconomic theory suggest could be done to increase productivity? Programs that raise the human capital of the labor force would increase the marginal productivity of labor. This would have two important consequences. First, the cost of production would be reduced, which would in turn reduce inflationary pressure. It is too much to hope that prices would actually fall significantly across broad sectors of the economy because prices tend to be inflexible downward, as we noted earlier was true of wages (although prices are probably not nearly as rigid as wages in a downward direction). Second, increasing the marginal productivity of labor would shift the demand for labor curve to the right and reduce unemployment (see Figure 18.4).

Programs to encourage greater saving and more investment would have similar results. If interest on personal savings were at least in part exempt from income taxes, there would be some additional incentive to save and make more money available for investment. As we saw in Chapter 16, a tax policy of providing greater investment tax credits would also stimulate investment in the private sector. Investment in new and better plant and equipment would provide labor with more efficient productive facilities and would increase the marginal productivity of labor. Once again there would be the dual result of lowering the cost of production and increasing the demand for labor resources. The result would be desirable both in terms of reduced inflationary pressure and in terms of increased employment.

Unfortunately when politicians recognize the difficulties of controlling inflation and unemployment with the traditional demand-side macroeconomic policies, they tend to think first of using some form of wage and price controls. There have been various forms of wage and price controls attempted in the past, including wage-price freezes, wage-price guideposts or voluntary controls, and mandatory wage-price guidelines that include penalties for violations. Wage and price controls are a direct attempt to stop an inflationary wage and price spiral, and as C. Jackson Grayson points out, the idea of such controls is not new.[1] There were wage and price freezes as early as 1800 B.C. in Babylonia. Anyone caught in violation was drowned. In A.D. 301 the Roman Emperor Diocletian set schedules for 76 wage categories and for 890 price categories. Again the penalty for violation was death. In our early history the Puritans had a code that limited wages and prices. The Continental Congress enacted price ceilings before the Declaration of Independence. Most modern nations have used some form of wage and price controls in wartime, and in Europe they were used in peacetime after World War II. In general these controls were not very effective and were dropped fairly quickly. Those instituted by Diocletian lasted only 13 years, and our early colonial attempts were dropped by 1780. However, in Babylonia price controls did last for over 1000 years (perhaps drowning is a sufficient penalty to enforce such controls).

In the United States wage and price controls were used extensively during World War II. As the economy expanded in war-related production during 1940 and 1941, inflation also increased. President Roosevelt attempted to deal with the problem through voluntary controls and established the Office of Price Administration (OPA). These voluntary controls did not work and on January 30, 1942, the Emergency Price Control Act gave the OPA legal authority to control prices. There were gaps in this authority, and some prices continued to rise rapidly. In October 1942 the Stabilization Act was passed, which put prices and wages under the control of the National War Labor Board. Even so, prices increased nearly 4 percent between October 1942 and April 1943. In that April President Roosevelt ordered more strict enforcement by the War Labor Board and OPA. From April 1943 to September 1945 (20 months), the price level rose just 4.2 percent.

However, rationing had to be enforced to help the controls to be effective. Shortages of many goods (such as gasoline, cigarettes, nylons, meat, and sugar) developed. A vast system of coupon rationing had to be developed (5 billion ration coupons per month were processed) and en-

---

[1] C. Jackson Grayson, "Controls Are Not the Answer," *Challenge* (November-December 1974), 9.

forced. The number of people necessary to handle the program was phenomenal—50,000 paid workers and over 200,000 volunteers (it would be very difficult to get such volunteers without a national commitment to a cause such as during World War II). At the end of the war, consumer support for and cooperation with the wage-price control policies declined. On June 30, 1946, the control laws expired, and in the next *month* wholesale prices rose 10 percent and some retail prices increased by as much as 25 percent.

Perhaps the most recent attempt at controls was the system announced by President Nixon on August 15, 1971, which froze wages, prices, rents, and salaries for 90 days. Between August 15 and November 15, 1971, prices rose at an annual rate of only 1.9 percent. During the next phase (Phase II), a Pay Board and Price Commission controlled wages and prices. Price increases were limited to 2.5 percent per year, while wage and salary increases were limited to 5.5 percent yearly. During this period (November 1971 to January 1973) inflation was held to 3.6 percent. Phase II consisted of voluntary guidelines, with the 2.5 and 5.5 percent figures the official guides. During this phase, from January 1973 to June 1973, prices rose quite rapidly. The *CPI* rose at a 10 percent annual rate, the Wholesale Price Index rose at a 20 percent rate, and some items such as food and fuel rose at a rate of 30 percent. On June 13, 1973, Phase IV began. Prices were again frozen, this time for 60 days, to try to cool off the inflationary expectations in the economy. Even so, from June 1973 to March 1974 prices rose at a 9.6 percent annual rate.

There is a clear pattern to wage and price controls. They work fairly well in the very short run, but in the long run people find ways around the controls. When the controls collapse, inflation surges ahead faster than before. Wage and price controls distort the functioning of a market economy and lead to shortages, "black markets," and general economic imbalances. Consumers, labor leaders, and businesses tend to allocate time and efforts to unproductive activities related to dealing with and trying to influence the controlling agencies.

But most important, controls treat symptoms rather than the causes of inflation. In fact they draw attention away from the causes (such as low productivity). If we are to maintain a predominantly free enterprise system, we must deal with the basic causes of these (and other) problems rather than impose artificial controls that further distort the system. A knowledge and appreciation of the fundamentals of microeconomic theory should help in this regard.

Selected Readings

Finegan, T. Aldrich. "Should Discouraged Workers Be Counted as Unemployed?" *Challenge* (November–December 1978), 20–25.

Houthakker, Hendrik S. "Growth and Inflation: Analysis by Industry." *Brookings Papers on Economic Activity* 1 (1979), 241–256.

Lerner, Abba P. "Stagflation—Its Cause and Cure." *Challenge* (September–October 1977), 14–19.

Nulty, Leslie Ellen. "How Inflation Hits the Majority." *Challenge* (January–February 1979), 32–38.

Robinson, Joan. "Solving the Stagflation Puzzle." *Challenge* (November–December 1979), 40–46.

QUESTIONS

1. Write a short explanation of the following terms or concepts that were used in this chapter:

   (a) consumer price index
   (b) cost-push inflation
   (c) demand-deficiency unemployment
   (d) demand for labor
   (e) demand-pull inflation
   (f) frictional unemployment
   (g) inflation
   (h) seasonal unemployment
   (i) stagflation
   (j) structural unemployment
   (k) supply of labor
   (l) unemployment rate
   (m) wage and price controls

2. Explain each of the four types of unemployment discussed in this chapter. Which are the more important in terms of policy considerations? Suggest some economic policies that would be potentially useful for reducing each type of unemployment.

3. Use the three graphs shown to explain (a) cost-push inflation, (b) demand-pull inflation, and (c) a combination of cost-push and demand-pull inflation, where Q represents real output for the entire economy (i.e., output in constant dollars).

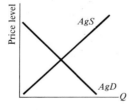 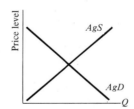 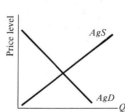

4. "We must change our attitude toward unemployment. Since the economy is not likely to be able to provide jobs for all that want one, we must stop measuring people's worth by their work." Do you agree or disagree? Why?

5. Why does inflation cause both uncertainty and distortions in the economy? Question 3 in Chapter 17 involved a benefit/cost comparison. Would the rate of inflation have any impact on your analysis of that problem? Explain.

6. In Table 18.1 we saw that there is considerable variation in the unemployment rate among different subsets of the population. Some of that may be due to discrimination of one form or another, but some also has an economic basis. Use your knowledge of production theory and of the demand for various factor inputs to explain why such differences might exist.

7. How does the relationship between productivity, cost, and price help to explain cost-push inflation? If productivity is related to technological advancement, how can we expect increased technology to reduce inflationary pressure in the economy?

8. In Chapter 16 tax policies that influence investment by business firms were discussed. Explain how these policies may be related to both unemployment and inflation.

9. Write an essay describing the economic, personal, and social costs of unemployment. Which of these costs do you consider to be most severe? Which is the most difficult to deal with?

10. List and discuss several characteristics that would increase the likelihood of your being unemployed, and explain why these characteristics would have such an effect. What, if anything, can be done to counteract these effects?

INDEX